'TEARS ON MY PILLOW'

(BOOK TWO of 'DARE YOU RIPPLE MY POND')

THE ADVENTURES OF AN IRISH SCHOOL BOY.

AGAIN TO MY WIFE BRIDGET.

BY

LOUIE BYRNE

Published By Premier Books
Unit R, Cradock Road,
Luton, Beds. LU4 0JF

Tel: 01582 572727
Fax: 01582 585868

British Library Cataloguing in Publication Data.
A Catalogue record for this book is available from the British Library.

Copyright © 1998 by Louie Byrne
All Rights Reserved
ISBN # 0 9524278 6 9

'Give me a friend who will love me for what I am,
And keep ever burning before my vagrant steps
The kindly light of hope and thought.
I come not within sight of the castle of my dreams.
Touch me and be thankful for life and for times'
Olden memories that are good and sweet,
And may the evenings twilight find me gentler still.'

CONTENTS

INTRODUCTION

'Tears on my Pillow' part two of 'Dare you Ripple my Pond' is no simple nostalgic glance back at an idyllic childhood, nor is it a figment of ones' imagination. It is a factual historical account of a new Ireland. An infant state born out of centuries of brutality, oppression and hardship. A nation left impoverished by her oppressors, her wealth and culture plundered. There was no time to sit by the ashes bewailing poverty, nor was there time to sit in the ashes waiting for someone to give a handout; there were no handouts.

It was not easy recalling the atrocities of the 'Army from Hell', the notorious 'Black and Tans.' It was they who beat and blinded my father, an innocent citizen. Nor was it easy to relive the pain and humiliation I suffered at the hands of Some of the Christian brothers. Not alone do I carry the Scars of the brutality inflicted by them on my body, but worst of all I also carry the scars on my mind. I was a child without a father; my mother, found it hard to feed her growing family. Alone and with very little help she struggled on. My frail body, without enough clothing and with boots that retained more water than the gutters, had to withstand the rigours of a damp climate. My feet, my hands, my ears and yes, my very soul, were broken raw with chilblains that refused to heal.

I prayed to my God for a little relief, just one night free from pain was all I asked. "Why me God? What did I do to deserve such pain and suffering?" I cried my pitiful tears onto my pillow. He did not answer my pleading prayers. Why was he never around when I needed him? Why me! In my frustration and pain I cursed my God. I often wonder if I was doing my penance on earth.

I coveted learning. I wanted to make something of my future. I did not deserve to be brutally assaulted. Not only was my body crying out for nourishment but so was my mind. The state provided me with a little nourishment; in the guise of a half- Pint of Milk and a Bun, five days a week, excluding holidays. This meagre sustenance may not seem a lot to some but to me it was Manna from Heaven. Yet it was denied to me time and time again on the whim of my teachers, the Christian Brothers. This was the unkindest and most calculated act of callous punishment that they could inflict on me. They knew that I waited in anticipation for the hour when I could leave the classroom and relieve the pangs of hunger. The humble bun and bottle of milk, that was my salvation. When they took that away from me, they took away my soul. I continue telling the story of my life, warts and all ....

These then are the stories of a thousand, thousand children, as told through the eyes, alas now dimmed with age, of a simple boy/girl who only wanted to play beside his/her pond. I tell the stories as they happened and dedicate them to the children of the 30's and 40's. Through all the adversaries of Church and State and with a Great War denying them a reasonable childhood, most survived. The stories are not told to castigate the Church, the Christian Brothers, the Nuns nor the State. The State was as impoverished as we were and were it not for the education that I received from it and the brothers, then this book and my other books may never have been written. Others have written claiming the state owed them a living, I do not believe this. The state is only as rich as her people and to sit in the angry ashes waiting for a handout reminds me of the dog sitting on the thorn. Some it would seem are never grateful. Limerick people are known throughout the world for their charity towards the stranger and I feel angry when I read books written by foreigners unfairly castigating my people and my city who when their own country turned their backs on them, Limerick welcomed them with open arms.

However the writing of my autobiography will not wipe away 'The tears that I shed on my pillow'.

RIPPLES IN THE SAND

As we tread the golden
Sands of life,
We often encounter
A ripple here and there.

Some are trodden underfoot,
Others become engulfed
In the fierce-raging
Billowy waves of Time.

But, for everyone,
Within those sands of life,
At least one ripple remains
Leaving an indelible mark

A special person, who-
Encircles all your apprehensions
Within the safe, secure fold
Of a strong protective wing.

Such a one, as casts a blind eye
To your faults and idiosyncrasies,
Who does not smother,
But allows you freedom to yourself.

Selected by the author from Ripples in the Sand.
A collection of poems composed by my good friend Maureen Sparling
Kings Island, Limerick 1997.

THE STRAND BARRACKS.

I have referred to the Strand Barracks throughout my books. Many readers are of the opinion that this was built as a military establishment. This is not so. The correct name for the building was ....'The House Of Industry.'

It was built in 1775 by the then Mayor Joseph Johns. Following legislation in 1772 to establish Poor Houses throughout Ireland, The idea was that the poor beggars should be taken off the streets and byways. The land belonged to Bishop Gore and he leased it to the Corporation on payment of one peppercorn annually in perpetuity. The terms being that a building to house the poor would be built on the site. The Grand Juries of the city and county of Limerick each donated the sum of £500 towards the erection of the home. The building, designed by The Reverend Dean Hoare and the construction supervised by Lancelot Hill. The building was in the form of a large square with a dressed stone façade. At a later date it was decided to build an asylum for lunatics at the rear of the building where the gardens stood. Doctor Edward Smythe of Dublin, being a charitable man, gave £200 for the building of the cells to house these wretches. By the year 1827 the building, which had been built to house 200 inmates, now contained in excess of 450 and growing. There were many plans and schemes to move the inmates out but nothing was done until 1838. When the 'Irish Poor Relief Act' brought about the building of the Union Workhouse now known as 'Saint Camillus Hospital'. The inmates were moved to this new home and 'The House of Industry' was left vacant for some time until it became a cavalry barracks; Thus the corrupt name. Then it was again left empty until they became a barracks for the Irish Republican Army during the Civil war. (See 'Dare You Ripple My Pond'). The Republican were driven out by the Free Staters and once again the building was left to the ghosts of ages past. The barracks were used as offices during the building of the Shannon Scheme.

In the 30's many buildings collapsed in the old city and others were in imminent danger of disintegration, including our house in Francis Street. The corporation had no funds to rehouse the homeless and again the gates of the barracks were thrown open to the destitute of Limerick- Us!

Each family was given One Room which was fitted out with a free standing stove with a flue stuck up the existing chimney. There was no sanitation and no water until a communal tap was erected near to the building which had in the past been used as a morgue and which we used as our club. When the housing estate was built in the haunted glens of 'Killeely' the families were moved to the new houses and the barracks used as a storage depot and offices by the corporation. In the 1980's the 'U' shaped block inside the gates was demolished and houses erected on the site. The front of the façade is retained.

I'm pleased to see, if only to satisfy my own nostalgic memories of the place. If one looks up at the first floor nearest to 'Sarsfield' bridge they will see three windows. This was one room known as the Infirmary, where countless victims of the Great Hunger died that was our final home in the barracks. It was this room that my mother converted into three small rooms. We moved from a little, to a small, to a not so small room within its confines.

THE TELEGRAM BOY DID NOT CALL THAT CHRISTMAS

Mother continued to cling to her memories of better times. Although we were now living in abject poverty, she still maintained her dignity. She would sweep through the streets of the city with that elegant gait that said it all. "Here comes the breed seed and soil of Daniel O'Connell, touch me not." It would appear that we were in some way related to the great emancipator himself. There was plenty of help for those in need and more so for our family for we had many rich relatives in the city. Mother would not be beholding to them and her stubborn pride did nothing to relieve our hunger.

We were not encouraged to bring friends to our home and I could appreciate this under the circumstances. The only room with any semblance of decency was our sitting room and that was not a lot. We still retained the heavy old oak sideboard, the round table and a few butter boxes converted into chairs. We also had mother's armchair made from a tea chest or two. There was no shame in this, although mother thought so. In every house I visited the modified tea chests took the place of chairs.

On the wall hung the portrait of our mysterious relative in her large gilded frame. The times I stood before her and tried to unravel the mystery remain countless. There she sat with her rows of pearls on her well proportioned breast looking for all the world like the *Mona Lisa*. A Clandestine smile on her face. The floorboards were bare of any covering yet they were kept immaculately clean by constant scrubbing carried out by my sisters. We may have been poor but we were kept clean.

"Cleanliness is next to Godliness," Mother would remind us. We fared no better nor worse than the other families, yet there was one difference: Mother could never accept that we lost all during the occupation by the *Black and Tans, the army from Hell*. Although mother was a most charitable woman when it came to praying, she never forgave *Sergeant Horan of the Royal Irish Constabulary*. (See book one)

Christmas had come to our house and we had tried to instil some semblance of the festive season by decorating the few pictures with holly. There were only three persons in the house that Christmas, my mother, my brother Brendan and myself. Mother instructed me to go out the Ennis Road and collect good berried holly that was growing in abundance in Cardavon. There was also a great tree in the graveyard covered in fine berries. Mother insisted that we had enough dead people buried in our garden without taking holly from the graveyard. She warned us that the dead would take umbrage at us taking their holly.

In the meantime she took herself off to the market hoping to secure a hen or a goose on credit to be paid for when the telegram boy called. I decorated the American cloth on the mantle piece with berried holly and ivy. The shining toffee wrappers that I had collected over the year for such an occasion we made into chains and strung across the room. We saw no reason to whiten the window to simulate frost. Our room was so cold that it generated its own. I finished the decorating with a large branch on top of the *Mona Lisa* and around the edges I placed a garland of ivy. Mother would be pleased when she came back from the city, or so I thought.

The evening drew to a close as long lingering shadows crossed the room. The clinging cold bit deeper into my body. A tree peeping over the graveyard wall shuddered as the wind whistled monotonously and melancholy through its skeleton branches. I intended to cut that tree as soon as the weather mended for it reminded me of the cry of the *Bean-Ó- Sidhe.*

"Did the telegram boy call yet?" Mother entered the room and removed her favourite hat with the berries on top.

"Not yet Ma. Look I decorated the room for Christmas." I encouraged her to admire my handiwork.

"Good God! Is that ivy you brought into the house?" She collapsed into her chair and blessed herself.

"It's not from the graveyard Ma. I got a fine lot out in Cardavon." The way she looked with her mouth open I was sure she was about to have a fit.

"Ivy! Good God don't you know what this means? Get it out of the house at once?" Disappointed that my efforts were thwarted I began collecting the ivy and opening the cover on the range I began putting it in the grate.

"Stop that! What do you think you are doing?"

"I'm taking down the ivy as you told me. What's wrong now?"

"Don't you know that to bring ivy into a house denotes a death in the family? Take it out of my sight and as far away as possible from my door." Collecting the ivy I packed it into a bag and calling my dog Bruno to my side left the house and dumped it over the graveyard wall.

It was the Christmas Eve. Mother, Brendan and I sat looking into the dead grate. The rest of the family had flown the nest and mother was waiting to hear the familiar sound of the telegram boys whistle as he approached our door.

"We'll have nothing for Christmas if he doesn't hurry up." Mother called on us to say a silent prayer to hurry him to our door. There was to be no knock and no telegram that evening, no more than there had been the day before. Mother told us to stop praying. The money order we so desperately waited for from my sisters Mary and Phyllis, who were working in a car factory in Oxford was delayed. She told us the delay was caused, by the bombing of the factory by the German Air force. How she came by this information was a mystery to us. Why was she not showing concern for her daughters? This was of little consequence to us as we looked into the empty grate.

"It will come to morrow after the Germans leave." She enlightened us.

Why we sat looking into an empty grate was hard to understand. My cat as usual sat in the oven with the door open. Bruno, my dog, was rolled up in a ball under my feet keeping them warm. Our stomachs were as empty as our larder. Every time mother's stomach rumbled she said *pardon* and we laughed. Outside the snow continued to fall. We heard the neighbours pass along the road and wish each other a Holy Christmas and a happy New Year.

'Another year of this and school and I'll wind up in the nut house.' I thought to myself.

"It looks like it's going to be a white Christmas after all." Mother rose from her chair and opened the curtain, breaking the silence of the room. Bruno cocked his ear but soon returned to his dreaming.

"One snowflake doesn't make a snowstorm." Mother was like that forever making her own predictions. Not that we ever understood any of their meanings. She returned to her chair and sat down for a moment or two. Rising wearily from her chair, which she occupied like a queen, she left the room and walked slowly up the stairs.

We heard the door of her room open and we heard her footsteps cross the floor. After a short time we heard the door close, mother was coming back down the stairs. We knew that she would have her well worn beads in her hands. No doubt she was muttering a few extra prayers on her way as was her custom.

"We will kneel now and say our rosary. As we pray perhaps divine intervention would intercede for us. If not then we will offer it all up for Christ's sufferings for us." Looking up at the shining pendulum of our eight day clock she blessed herself. There was no need for her to ask us to kneel for no sooner had she entered the cold room than we were on our knees. Seeing that all was now prepared she sank to her knees with her beads at the ready.

"In the name of the Father and of the Son and of the Holy Ghost." Again she blessed herself and kissed the black and silver crucifix reverently. The cross contained a relic of the true cross on which Christ had been crucified. The beads were sent to her by her daughter Delia. Who was a nun of the Franciscan Order. Again she looked around at us to ensure that we were following her diligently. 'Amen.' We answered. Prayers had begun.

Cibby Eye Lashes stretched himself and came out of his home in the oven and crossed the floor. I saw his tail wagging as he sunk deeper and deeper into the floor. I knew that he was ready to attack and I smiled as I looked towards my brother. I encouraged him by trailing my beads along the floor. Then as mother was about to get into the prayers he pounced. Grabbing her rosary he began to swing on it much to our amusement. Mother shooed him away with a swipe of her hand. Turning he looked at her in that sarcastic manner that only a cat is capable of.

"Control that cat of yours or I'll do it for you." Mother warned me.

"Yes, you! Who else causes trouble but you and your menagerie." Brendan delighted that I was being chastised looked at me with that smug smile of his. I was again swimming in troubled waters. Raising his tail in the air the cat sauntered off towards the oven. Taking a sniff of the interior he turned his back and retreated to join 'Bruno' under the stairs where it was warm.

"You! Stop that at once. Move over there out of troubles way." Mother chastised me as I began to nudge Brendan. When order was again restored she once again began to pray. Slowly, thoughtfully and reverently she led us through the five sorrowful mysteries. With the rosary finished much to my relief I began to rise to my feet. By now my legs were stiff and numb and I had *Pins and Needles.*

"Blessed be Jesus." Mother opened the prayers into a long litany of the saints. I painfully returned to my knees. If ever anyone deserved a place in heaven then I did for my sufferings, I thought. These prayers were known as *The trimmin's of the Rosary.* Slowly the oil lamp lost its glow. What oil there had been in it was now consumed and the room slowly plunged into darkness. Ignoring the darkness, she continued praying until all the prayers were said. With the supplications completed for that evening, she rose to her feet much to my relief.

"There's a frost in the air, that will make the snow settle." She opened the door and looked up and down the street.

"The Telegram boy will not be calling this evening, perhaps to-morrow, God willing." She sighed as she closed the door. As I climbed the stairs and passed her room, I heard her crying and praying for the telegram boy to call. Although she knew that the next day was Christmas day, she somehow believed that divine intervention would make an exception for her.

Mother's faith was as unquenchable as were the proverbial flames of Hell. She firmly believed that through prayer, which she maintained was all powerful. Some money, no matter how small would come to our door before the night had passed and if not that night then next morning. I knew that it would not happen and resigned myself to the fact. This was the eve of Christmas. The country had closed down for the holiday. I, for one, had no illusions of a gargantuan feast or a meal of any sorts that night nor for the next few days. That night cold and hungry and deserted by my God and the telegram boy I turned to the wall. I adjusted my sparse pillow and burying by head within its confines I silently cried myself to sleep. On the eve of *Saint Stephen's* day she told us that the waiting was over. To morrow the post office would open and our telegram would be delivered. As he was the first martyr we should say a prayer to him for good luck.

"Ma! To morrow is the *Wren's Day.* Only the public houses will be open." I informed her. The shadows lengthened, the winds continued to moan. One by one the birds retired to their roosting places. All was now quiet as the stars in their myriad colours took their places in the frosty sky. Some unable to cling to her mantle cascaded down to earth leaving a silent streaming tail behind them. The graveyard never too far away reflected the serenity of the solemnity and seriousness of life. Mother maintained a silence that was broken only now and then as she let out a sigh of resignation. The frost continued to obliterate the window panes. I knew that *Jack Frost* was busy creating intricate designs on the glass when I heard him making sharp crackling noises in the process.

"So it is, I'm sorry I nearly forgot." With a sigh she sat down in her chair with her hands in her lap. She knew her God would not provide, but then mother was the eternal optimist.

I adjusted my sparse pillow and burying my head within its confines I waited. I knew that like the predictable *'Old faithful'* geyser in *'Yellowstone Park'* my chilblains would return. Silently I cried into my pillow and prayed that I might be asleep in my tears before they erupted.

THE SHANNON VIEW HOTEL MURDER

Mother was making one of her special novenas to one of her favourite saints when an inspiration struck me like a bolt of lightening from the Heavens. Could it be I wondered, that Saint Jude to whom mother was now praying earnestly was giving me a divine message? I would like to have thought so but I fear my mother would not agree.

I looked across at her, she looked so timid, so vulnerable. The feeling was indescribable. She did not pray aloud; her gentle lips trembled ... I knew that she was praying. I wanted to assure her .....I really did. I didn't know what to do or say. How could I intrude on such an intimate conversation. She turned and looked straight into my eyes and smiled. I wanted to stretch out my arms and tell her ... . What would or could I tell her?

"I don't deserve your love and gratitude." I felt like telling her. I should have stretched out my arms there and then and told her how much I loved her and cared for her. I wonder did she understand how I felt about her?

"Don't worry Ma, all will be well; God will provide." These sentiments would be the thoughts of a fool and superfluous. An obscenity and a charade considering I didn't believe he would. Were these not her own thoughts and prayers that I so often silently chided her for believing in? God will provide; A God that was never about when we needed him. It doesn't matter now, it's far too late for she is long gone to her reward.

For some reason unknown to me, she was of the opinion that I was forever swimming in troubled waters. Where there was trouble she would always find Louie and his dog, she claimed.

The next day was the day of the *Wren* when the public houses would open their welcoming doors to the parched men of the city after the long Christmas closure. The only way to get a drink on Christmas day was through the back door and that was restricted to regulars.

'Wren's day' was the day when men and boys dressed up in carnival costumes and begged money from the gullible citizens. In bygone days it was the custom for the wren boys to find a poor starving wrens in the hedgerow. They would chase them over stiles and ditches until the birds were exhausted. Catching the poor birds they were then executed in the most barbaric manner and placed in a makeshift coffin and paraded throughout the city in triumphant ceremony.

A tune would be sung over and over again in praise of the poor dead wren, as they rattled their collecting tin cans under the noses of the citizens. Such a barbaric custom has long since died a natural death I am glad to relate, but the tune remained throughout my youth. There are several versions of this tune but let me tell you the version I knew.

'The wren, the wren, the king of all birds
On St Stephen's day was caught in the bush.
Up with the kettle and down with the pans
Please give us a penny and let us be gone.
If you haven't a penny a halfpenny will do
If you haven't a halfpenny, then God bless you.'

"Are you asleep?" I gave a kick at my brother who shared our bed.

"How could I sleep with a jackass at the head of the bed. Now stop kicking me, will you?"

"I have a great plan for to morrow." I rose from the bed and sat beside him.

"O God! Spare me from his ingenious plans." Brendan threw his hands into the air in despair before I could tell him. That brother of mine had little faith in me.

"This is a gander of a plan. Now listen carefully?" I could hardly wait to disclose the plan.

"Go on I'm all ears. This should be a hum dinger." He sarcastically remarked.

"To-morrow we will get up early and dress up as Wren Boys and make lots of money for mother. We will have a dinner fit for the King of England and a bottle of *'Sandiman's'* port for her. She would like a drop of port during the Christmas festivities, don't you think?" I looked into his face and I could see that he was sceptical, so I pressed the point.

"Why we may stretch it to a Christmas cake and plum pudding with custard. They will be cheap now that Christmas has passed." By now my imagination was running wild and I had in all the excitement forgotten to thank Saint Jude.

"Christmas festivities! That's a good one coming from you. You will let me know all about them. Still I suppose there's no harm in it." I was surprised when Brendan began to see the merit of my idea. Perhaps Saint Jude had given him the message too. We heard the knob turn on the door and looking up saw mother enter the room. She came and hugged us both. I found this peculiar as she was not one to show affection.

"It's a sad day that it has come to this. Not alone are there no toys for you, but bitter still that there is no food in the house. I thought God would have heard our prayers, perhaps it is for the best. I really am sorry." She would never challenge the will of her God and her apologies were for her failure to provide she claimed. Placing her hands over her eyes she cried silently.

"We're far too big for toys, and not in the least bit hungry." I lied.

"Well I am, I've had nothing to eat all day." Brendan grumbled.

Wiping her eyes she rose to her feet and went across to the window. The light was slowly being obliterated by *Jack Frost*. As he continued making his cold and intricate patterns on the panes.

"Don't upset yourself Ma. The money will come, you'll see." I was now crying myself. I had tried to cheer her up and only made matters worse. Then that was me, forever swimming in troubled waters. I knew in my heart that there was as much hope of the money coming as there was for a snowball to pass through Hell.

We seemed to have an obsession with religion. No matter what the privations or adversities, religion was always there to offer some hope. Not that religion ever put a crust of bread into our mouths, or a coat on our backs to keep out the cold biting winds coming off the hills of Clare. I suppose truthfully I could say we saw more dinner times than dinners.

"It's the Army from Hell, the 'Black and Tans' who caused us all this misery. May they and Sergeant Horan rot in Hell, God forgive me." Mother intoned more or less to herself. This outburst shocked me. Whatever else, mother was a most charitable woman and would never say a bad word about anyone. But then who would or could judge her? Considering what she suffered and was still suffering as a result of their barbaric conduct As if reading my mind, she recanted.

"May God and his Blessed Mother forgive me for wishing them ill. I just cannot find it in my heart to forgive them. You wouldn't understand." Whatever happened all those long years ago must have been horrendous to have left a permanent scar on her.

"Did I ever tell you of the murder at the *Shannon View Hotel out at Castleconnell?*" She tucked her thread bare coat around her as the cold wind howled through the trees in the old graveyard outside. The snow began to fall thick and fast and grew into a long hillock on the outside window ledge. Black slush fell down the chimney and formed a frozen mound on the slate bed. Mother's predictions of a white Christmas were coming true although a few days late, just like our telegram.

Did she tell us this story? She told us this story and a thousand more of the atrocities committed by the notorious *Black and Tans, the army from Hell,* against the Irish nation. We heard the stories so often from her, Uncle Gerald and Joe, not discounting the neighbours that their conduct was indelibly imprinted on our young minds. (*Most I have told in Dare You Ripple my Pond.*) Forgetting our hunger and the cold, we settled down to listen once again to the incidents that brought about this night. We did not interrupt her train of thoughts as yet again she began another story of the atrocities committed by the *Black and Tans.* Perhaps there was some therapeutic value in her telling us the stories.

(The Black and Tans, the army from hell, that name synonymous with brutal terror was, and still is held in contempt by the people of Ireland. This barbaric

force was sent to Ireland by England to subjugate the people following the unsuccessful rebellion of 1916.

The British cabinet adopted a proposal made by Winston Churchill that a special force of 8,000 soldiers be raised to reinforce the Royal Irish Constabulary. By the summer of 1922 there were in excess of 12,000 auxiliaries. They served in two categories: The Royal Irish Constabulary Auxiliaries Division and the Auxiliary Cadets. The auxiliaries were kited out in Khaki with black leather belts and dark green caps. They were christened 'The Black and Tans', by the Mayor of Limerick. This because their uniform resembled that worn by a hunting fraternity in Scarteen County Limerick. (The Mayor was subsequently murdered in his bed by the Black and Tans.)

The cadets were regular officers dedicated to the Empire, their King and England.

Sir Harmar Greenwood made the following observation at the time:

'The vital point is to deal with the thugs, a number of whom are going about shooting in Dublin, Cork and Limerick. We are sure and certain that they are handsomely paid. The money coming from the United States of America. It is passed through Bishop Fogarty a prominent Sinn Fein supporter and Arthur Griffiths on cheques issued by Michael Collins. He is the adjutant general of the Irish Republican Army.

A time when the Irish nation rose not for the last time to break the fetters that held her unwilling to the British Empire. Britain had fought a bitter and bloody war on the pretext of freedom for smaller nations, excluding those held in bondage to her Empire.

The Black and Tans established such a reign of terror in Ireland that day or night innocent citizens lived in fear and panic. Even in the confines of their own homes they were not safe as the screech of the lorries and the knocking on the door resulted in another beating or a murder. They were, or so it seemed establishing a permanent dominance over my city as they imposed a curfew starting sometimes as early as two o'clock in the afternoon.

The old Irish Republican Army were taking stock of all the terror and were waiting to retaliate. A draconian curfew was extended to certain parts of the city of Limerick in the spring of 1921. The only purpose was to intimidate the innocent citizens further and in the hope that they would turn on the republicans.

This brought matters to a head. IRA headquarters southern command gave the companies in the city permission to wage war on the tans. C. Company were only too willing and anxious to answer the challenge.

Their opportunity came as they went looking for Tans in the Irish town. Several tans armed to the teeth came out from a public house at the junction of John Street, Broad Street and Mungret Street. They swaggered down the street *challenging all before them. 'C'. Company under the command of Commandant Dundon, were coming up White's laneway when they heard the raucous challenges. Meeting the challenge face on he approached them and under covering fire from his men threw a grenade into their midst. The Tans, no longer the bully boys retreated to the safety of their barracks near by. They left two of their comrades lying wounded behind them as they retreated firing indiscriminately. One civilian died and two others were wounded.*

The Tans would seek cowardly revenge as the following incident recalls.

Mother continued her story.......

In the spring of 1921 all was quiet as the guests took a respite in the lounge of the *Shannon View Hotel in Castleconnell* after a day's fishing on the falls. They spoke of the fishing and the fine weather as they mulled their drinks. The guests from Britain and other parts of Ireland were in good spirits as they exaggerated about the huge fish that got away.

"Yes, I would have got that one only my line got snagged in the falls. Had him within inches of my keep net." One mourned the loss of his fish.

A generous but sceptical sympathy was extended to one and all. After all they were fishermen and prone to boast. One of the honoured guests was William Harrison Cripps and his wife. Unknown to them a column of Tans were moving cautiously between the tall hedgerows. It was evening when there came a knocking on the door. The landlord, Dennis O'Donovan, looked out the window to see three civilians parking their bicycles against the wall. They rubbed their hands together as they waited for the door to be opened.

"Good evening gentlemen, come in there's a good fire in the grate." Dennis welcomed his guests. Ignoring the welcoming fire they retreated to the bar and stood close together. They were strangers who spoke little but when they did, they spoke to each other in whispers avoiding the other guests. These were troubled times in Ireland and the landlord was apprehensive of the strangers who refused to mix and stood alone by the bar drinking.

The night wore on and the conversation became more jovial. Dennis set aside his fears and joined in the bantering and conversation. The strangers continued to ignore the many invitations to join in the company, preferring to keep to themselves. The guests were startled when the door was thrown open and two civilians came charging in brandishing hand guns.

"Put up your hands and line up against the wall." Came the challenge from the intruders. The three strangers immediately opened their coats and drawing revolvers opened fire on the two intruders. The guests were now fully aware that the three were *'Black and Tan'* spies. Their purpose in going to the hotel was to gain what information they could from any loose talk. The names of two were,

Sergeant Hughes and Constable Morrison and the other who had travelled from Dublin was not named.

The two that burst into the bar were unknown to the other *'Black and Tans'*. As the two made a dash to escape one was shot and fell before he reached the door. The unknown Tan rushed over and secured the door before retreating to safety. Outside the other Tans were convinced that something was amiss. The officer in command ordered that a *Lewis Machine Gun* be brought forward and mounted on its tripod in front of the hotel. Without any caution or calling on the occupants to surrender, the machine gunners opened fire. Sergeant Hughes fell under a hail of bullets from his own men and Constable Morrison was wounded. The guests fled behind what protection they could find. The undercover Tan now realised the mistake and shouted as loud as he could above the rattle of machine gun fire coming in from outside.

"Stop firing, Cease firing. There are no 'Shinners (Sinn Fein Members) in here."

After several more appeals the murderers stopped firing and all was calm. The unknown Tan and the wounded Morrison suggested that the landlord should open the door and surrender. Dennis O'Donovan came from under an upturned table and opened the door.

"I'm the landlord, I'm unarmed. Please don't shoot."

Raising his hands he approached the machine gunners. Reaching a wall the landlord and Morrison were ordered to face it with their hands in the air. A servant girl watched from an upstairs window as they walked past the yard. She was warned to keep clear of the window or be shot. Ignoring the threat she continued looking.

She heard gunfire coming from the direction of the yard. Realising that something terrible had happened the girl ran down the stairs and rushed on into the yard. She saw two bodies faced down riddled with bullets lying in the yard. Blood was flowing down the channel and into the drain.

"Where is Mr O'Donovan? Where have you taken him?" She challenged one of the Tans.

"There's Mr O'Donovan. He pointed with his gun to one of the bodies.

"Good God! Do you know what you done? You murdered an innocent man." She cried.

There was to be no remorse as he grinned. "Serves him right for harbouring *Shinners."*

Mr O'Donnell was not a member of Sinn Fein nor did he ever harbour any of them. His body was examined by Dr McConnell. Who counted six separate bullet wounds.

The Auxiliaries (*Black and Tans)* sent a copy of the findings of the military inquest to Mrs O'Donnell, regretting their tragic mistake. These inquires were known in Ireland as *Courts of Military acquittal.* The witnesses on the British side always had a lapse of memory when questioned. Or else they could not disclose details for security reasons.

There was an old saying in Ireland at the time ... .

'Beware the horns of the bull;
The puck of the goat
The heel of the horse
The smile of the English'.

Mother concluded telling yet another incident of past years.

This brutal murder might never have come to light had it not been for the presence of William-Harrison Cripps and his wife who reported the incident in detail to his brother Lord Parmoor. Their account of what took place that bloody night was strongly rejected by the military court.

I have no doubt but that there are several versions of this bloody mass murder. That it took place and went unpunished is an indisputable fact of history. It is also a fact that the British people were outraged by the conduct of this so called Police force appointed in their names.

It could be argued that this was not a suitable story to tell children during the spirit of Christmas. I understood why she told the story and that satisfied me.

I wrapped my share of the blanket round my shoulders and slowly succumbed to sleep. Yet it was little consolation to me as I shed silent tears on my pillow that night.

My feet were icy cold as I waited for my chilblains, *Old Faithful,* to again erupt in fury. As God was always out whenever I needed him, who was there left to turn to?

It was cold, Bitterly cold as a butterfly with transparent delicate wings came into the room. What is a butterfly doing out this cold night I thought? She did not wish to be seen, but I saw her as she landed by the cold black iron fireplace. Shaking her myriad coloured wings she rattled the grate with a golden wand.

"I am the spirit of *Myosotis* (Forget-me-not) sent by the Gods who have witnessed your suffering. I travelled here from *'Tir-na-nÓg'* seeking out children in solitude. I know only happiness and can grant your every wish. Cry no more! Allanah, dry your tears. I will care for you as I do for the delicate flowers of spring." She gently spoke to me, her lilting musical song soothing away all my sorrow.

All at once glowing logs sent sparks of pure gold up the chimney, some escaped and landed on the bed with a musical sound. She wafting heat towards my bed with her delicate wings. I wanted to call out and tell mother that the fire was alight and that the bed was being showered with pure gold. She should hurry in and collect it before it vanished.

I wanted my mother to know that all would be well. Yet for some unknown reason I could not leave the enchanted bed and although I tried to call out loud and clear my voice was muted. I was under the enchanted spell of the fairy butterfly.

She looked across at me and continued fanning the flames with her delicate wings. I snuggled deeper into the huge scented floral bed.

"Remember I am Myosotis, call my name whenever you are lonely or in sorrow. I will come and dry the tears on your pillow." Her lilting voice lulled me into a deep restful sleep.

It was morning, I awakened to find myself back in my cold bed. The goddess Myosotis had departed with the night. I rose and looked out upon the bleak landscape and the lopsided tombstones in the graveyard beyond my bedroom window. Nothing had changed or so I thought. But last night matters took a turn for the better, my chilblains had remained dormant and the tears on my pillow had dried.

Did God finally find time to answer the prayers of a child? Was it he who sent an angel in the disguise of the Goddess Myosotis to comfort me last night.? Would he now remember me and send her every night to comfort me? Was it the telling of the *Sean Sceals* that resurrected the *Goddess Myosotis?*

I'll not forget the old stories and the memories of my youth around the old turf fire. I'll try to remember the good times and mitigate my sorrows. From six years to sixty years is a long monogram. Can the candle burn as brightly at sixty as it did at six?

Will the Goddess Myosotis come and wrap me in her wings when life dreams are no more?

Will she, when love and caring turns to bitterness and hatred and becomes once again an obscenity return and enfold me in her delicate wings, or will she come for one last time as the log sends out its dying spark and bid me, *Slan Leat.*?

Dream! Dream on for who knows what to-morrow might bring.

WREN DAY ENCOUNTER

Next morning I rose early determined to make an early start to the day.

"God, it's freezing! The garden is covered in ice and the road looks like a sheet of glass." I ran my hand around the frosted glass. My brother, on hearing the state of the weather pulled the blanket over his head. He had no intention of facing the elements. Hunger was better than facing the cold outside, not that it was any warmer inside.

"Come on you loser, you promised, remember? The earlier we start the more money we will make." I pulled the blanket off the bed. After a lot of persuasion on my part and by dragging the blanket off the bed he finally got to his feet. Breakfast, such as it was consisted of a thin slice of dry bread and a mug of *Cocoa Shells*. Without milk and sugar, Mother would always keep some food back for breakfast.

"Never go to work without your shovel." Was one of her sayings. I presumed what she meant was that one should always start the day with a meal inside them. At least it was hot and we tried unsuccessfully to eat the shells afterwards. Although we were ravenous with the hunger it was impossible to digest them. As the war was still raging in Europe, Africa and the Far East there was little if any cocoa available to the general public. The factories sold the shells from the cocoa beans and these became our breakfast drink. Tea was rationed to one half ounce per person per week and the bread was black or near to it. There was a satirical song of the time that went something like this........

> *'So we're saying good bye to them all,*
> *The long and the short and the tall.*
> *Bless DeValera and Sean McInteer*
> *For giving us the brown bread*
> *And the half ounce of tea.*
> *So we're saying 'Good Bye' to them all*
> *As off to our billets we crawl.*
> *There's nothing in Eire, with blind DeValera*
> *So cheer up me lads bless them all.'*

Having finished breakfast, such as it was, I thanked God and calling Bruno I made for the front door.

"And where do you think you are off to?" Mother came from the scullery and stopped me in my tracks. Bruno my hero, on hearing her ran between my legs for safety.

"I'm off to see the Wren Boys. Why?" This was a questionable remark to make to my mother.

"Don't you dare question me. I'll be the one to ask questions in this house. Do you hear me?"

"Yes ma, sorry." I replied full of contrition.

"Up to no good no doubt and taking that thing with you." She pointed to Bruno who crouched down on all fours and looked up at her with sorrowful eyes.

"Not you, you mongrel. God! You have that dog as bad as yourself." Bruno again took refuge behind my back. It was always me, now she was comparing the dog to me.

"I mean him, not you. Heaven help me, you are driving me stone mad. I'm now talking to your dog. Go on get out of my sight." Mother stamped her foot and pointed to the door. I presumed that she was annoyed with herself for not having any food in the house. I understood that it was not her fault. Bruno was so glad when the door opened that he jumped over the gate without waiting for it to be opened. I left the house to be greeted by a freezing blast of cold air and sleet.

"Don't let him catch cold now, do you hear me? He's not as tough as you." Mother warned me as Brendan joined me. He was wrapped up like a dog's breakfast as he left the house. Mother sprinkled holy water over us and told us to bless ourselves. Bruno cocked his head to one side and looked up at me.

"Not you Bruno, you and me are dispensable. She means him." I nodded to Brendan who was skating down the road on the previous nights Skating rink. Seeing that there was only a year between us I could see no reason as to why I should be appointed my brother's keeper. On our way to the city we passed several *Wren Boys* dressed in elaborate costumes. Many were dressed up in fancy costumes, straw hats and bloomers. Some were leading donkeys, others goats.

"We don't stand a chance against that lot. We may as well pack it in now." Brendan, the proverbial pessimist forecast. I ignored his assessment of my brilliant plan.

We went out the dock road and entered the city dump at *Corcanree*. To Bruno this was manna from Heaven. With his hair standing on end he was off on the chase as rats of all shapes and sizes scattered before his onslaught.

"That bloody coss of yours, does he ever give up." Brendan watched as Bruno went off on the chase. I found an old pram sitting upside down on the tip. On turning it over a bundle of rags fell out. Cautiously I opened the bundle. As I did two or three rats jumped from it and made a hasty retreat, only to fall into the clutches of Bruno who tossed them one by one into the air. One was lucky in that he escaped into the Shannon. I didn't tell my brother about the rats. He was standing in comparative safety under a lone tree. He was rather squeamish about them and seemed to think that I set them on him.

"Come on, look what I found." I pushed the Pram that had a rickety wheel on to the roadway. I returned to the dump and found a glass baby's feeding bottle that was broken on one end. (The baby bottles in those days had openings each end.) Attached to the good end was a rubber teat that was clogged with muck. In the clothing I found a bonnet in fairly good condition. I also found a dress and a lot of red wrapping paper. God I thought, St Jude must be watching over me. This was what I needed. I pushed the pram out to the dock road where the fountain with the lion's head and the big iron cup on a chain quenched the thirst of the citizens on their outings. This was supplied with the compliments of Limerick Corporation. I washed and rinsed the bottle and having cleaned the muck from it I replaced it on the bottle.

"Now put on this bonnet and stick the teat in your gob. That should keep you quiet for a time." I handed him the broken bottle and the bonnet.

"There might be poison in that bottle and that bonnet could be full of fleas. What if mother saw me? She'll kill you, you know. I'm not getting in there either it's soaking wet." That brother of mine always had one excuse or another.

"Is that to your liking, your Lordship?" I dried the inside of the pram with my dress and sarcastically bowed before him. Ignoring me he began to examine the interior of the pram. With his nose stuck in the air he sniffed the interior.

"Ok. If that's the way you feel. I'll get in the pram and you can push it around the city." I volunteered. He paused to deliberate the proposal for a few moments. Then he considered that he would be better off in the pram with me doing the pushing. To him circumspection was the better part of valour.

"You don't need to get inside yet. I'm not pushing a big lump like you along the cobbled street. Wait until we get into the town centre." I stopped him as he was about to settled down in the pram. He put the bonnet on his head and began to suck on the teat like a baby. God but he looked a proper Amadan. (Fool). I didn't tell him. That would only make matters worse.

"By the way, where did you get this from? Has it been cleaned?" He squeezed the teat and held up the bottle for inspection.

"It's well clean now, that's for sure." I dare not tell him that I found it amongst the rags and rats. It would only upset his delicate stomach. What he did not know would not hurt him. I put on the red dress and tied it at the waist with a rope. Making a halo of the red paper I placed it on my head. For good measure I returned to the tip and blackened my face with ashes. I looked grand or so I thought.

I pushed that stubborn pram along the road and was relieved when we entered the city proper. Slipping and sliding I pushed the rickety pram all the way until we reached O'Connell Street and paused at the corner. I anticipated we would collect a lot of money here as it was an ideal position. I was to be disappointed for it seemed that half the Wren Boys of the city had the same idea.

"Here take this and don't forget to rattle it and pretend to cry." I handed him a cocoa tin with a slit cut across it to receive any donations. Shaking the tin he was more than surprised when it rattled.

"Listen! There's money in here already." He shook the tin trying to dislodge the contents.

"Leave it alone. It's only a few medals that I put in to make it appear that we got some money." I could see by the look on his face that he was disappointed.

Slipping and sliding I continued pushing that rickety pram along O'Connell Street and at Burton's corner I stopped and told Brendan to get inside. Once again it was slip and slide as I pushed the stubborn pram with the heavy lump of a brother lodged inside. Up William Street I struggled and had to contend with Brendan shouting orders from the confines of the pram.

"Mind the channel. Can't you push it proper?" The repartee continued. Had I been on the docks, I'm sure I would have pushed him and the pram into the Shannon.

"Go up this way will you." He shouted from the comparative comfortable confines of the pram.

"What do you mean, go up there? That's *Foxes Bow*. There's nothing up that way but 'Matterson's bacon factory."

"I'm dying for a pee. Hurry up will you." He called in desperation.

"If you're all that desperate, then get out and run up yourself. I'm not your nanny if you must know." Leaving the pram beside the wall we both ran up the alleyway to relieve ourselves. On our return we were annoyed that some thieving *Git* had stolen our pram and its contents.

"I told you before that if it was not nailed down, it would be stolen. Why they would steal a red hot stove would some people." There was nothing for it we would have to abandon our mission. By now the weather had deteriorated and a misty sleet began to fall.

"They'll be in for a nasty shock when they open the tin and find a few medals," I consoled myself. Lifting up the hem of my dress I tucked it into my rope belt. Making our way back into William Street we continued to accost the beleaguered citizens who by now had more than enough of begging Wren Boys. It was at this point that I noticed two inebriated soldiers approaching us. Brendan was about to run down the road and accost them. I stopped him and pulled him back into Foxes Bow.

"What the Hell is the matter with you?" Shaking himself free he scolded.

"Are you blind or something, can't you see who they are?" He looked around at the two soldiers who were singing and taking both sides of the footpath in their stride.

"Oh God, It's uncle Gerald. Do you think he saw us? If he tells mother she will be the death of us and it will be all your fault."

"Don't worry, look at the state of them. They are two sheets before the wind. They can hardly see the road before them. Quick as you can take your rags off." I pulled my dress off and the paper from my head.

"Hallo Uncle Ger. You never called this Christmas to our house." I greeted innocently.

"Is that yourself, Louie? You don't look well. Wh whr where is the other goat?" He spluttered as he tried to focus his bleary eyes on me.

"I'm here uncle Ger. I see you are enjoying Christmas." Brendan came out from the shadows and approached him.

"Is there sominn wrong, some kind of an epiderr, an epiderri, a plague in the town?" He spluttered as he pointed to me.

"We are O.K, why do you ask?" I found it best to humour him. He could be in the rats.

"You look queer. Kind of, of you know sick, pecku, pekoo, peculiar." He pointed at me and let out a series of farts as he staggered to the wall for support. Then he smiled, no doubt happy to be relieved of the discomfort.

"These are my nephews, John. A right pair of scalli, scallig. Whner whe where the hell have you got to John. Come here?"

"I'm here Ger, over here." He waved with one hand and tried to pick up his peaked cap from the footpath with the other. His hob nailed military boots slipped along the path.

"These two are my sister's children and a right pair of scall, scalligs, scallywags, they are. They are both orphans, all of them." He placed his hand on my shoulder and nearly brought us both crashing to the ground.

"Sorry! It's the Lee boots you know." Lifting up his foot to show the shamrock studs only to slip and fall to the ground, from where he again broke wind.

"Who pushed me? Give me a hand up someone." Brendan and I came forward and got him back on his feet. Somehow or other his companion retrieved his cap and was holding on desperately to the grill on the window of the public house. His cap sat at an angle on his head.

"Here son, go and get yourself something for Christmas." Gerald's friend reached out and gave us a sixpenny piece (two and a half new pence) each.

"Oh thank you very much Sir. A happy New Year to you." I looked down at the sixpence. Gerald stood in the middle of the footpath with his feet apart trying desperately to stand upright as the city spun around him. He looked like a Giraff trying to get at a clump of grass. Looking up with a grimance on his face he again let off a long series of farts. Relieved of the wind he gave a beguiling smile.

"Tell Kate (My Mother) that I'll call down to see her as soon as I can. John and myself are on spec speci, God that Guinness is full of wind, duty guarding

Ardnac, Ardnachru, Ardnacrusha. You know the power station against saboo, sababoos, saboteurs. It's all very hus, hus, secret. Don't go telling anyone will you." He staggered to the nearest shop door and propped himself against it.

"Here, don't go away yet, I'm talking to you. I got something for you." This piece of sensitive information was followed by a further series of farts. Reaching into the pocket of his army great coat he removed some coins and gave me one. Then he passed wind in a bellicose manner much to the disgust of two women passing by.

"Happy Nooo year. So Sor soree. Very sorry missus. Plees please ac acep. Oh shit forget it. A happy Newwwww Year to one and all." He smiled like the proverbial Cheshire cat as he again let off a prolonged series of farts.

"Is this what the Free State Army has come to? He's lucky my Tom is not with me. He'd punch him so hard that he would knock him into next week." She looked with disgust at Gerald as he lifted his cap and bowed before them.

"What do you expect from Dev's army? All wind and piss as you can hear, disgusting whelps. Not like my Tom. Now he's a real soldier fighting the Japs."

"I thought that your Tommy was working in Fords in Dagenham, with what's his name?" Her friend questioned.

"He was, so he was. That was until John Bull served the papers on him." The two women continued on down the road.

"Sorry about that, happy Christmas." Again he farted as he gripped my hand for support.

"Where is the other one? There were two of you." He asked as he moved along the street and staggered into the railings of the Munster and Leinster bank. Holding on to the railings for dear life he began to sing.

LITTLE OULD TOWN IN THE OULD COUNTY DOWN

"Shure, if I had the wings of a swallow,
I would travel far over the sea;
Then a rocky ould road I would follow,
To a spot that is Heaven to me.
When the Sun goes to rest,
'way down in the West–
Then I'll build such a nest,
In the place I love best.

In that dear little town,
In the ould county Down
It will linger way down in my heart–
Though it never was grand,
Sure it's my Fairy land,
Just a wonderful world set apart

'Oh! My Ireland of dreams,
You are with me it seems,
And I care not for fame or renown
Like the black sheep of old,
I'll return to the fold,
Little town in the ould county Down'.

In the evening when shadows are falling,
Round the doorway without any key
There's a voice in my dreams ever calling–
There are eyes ever watching for me.
There is someone I bless
With true tenderness,
And her lips I'll caress,
When I bring happiness.

In that dear little town
In the ould County Down
It will linger way down in my heart
Though it never was grand,
Shure it's my Fairyland,
Just a wonderful world set apart.
Oh! My Ireland of dreams,

You are with me it seems,
And I care not for fame or renown,
Like the black sheep of old,
I'll return to the fold,
Little town in the ould county Down.

On finishing the song he again let out a series of farts that could be heard half way to Park. Bruno went to the edge of the pavement and began to howl.

"Will you shit shu shut up tha that skutt skuttering mongrel he sounds like the Bean-Ó- Sidhe. Bad cess to him I can't hear myself singing. Sorry about that, it's the cabbage and turnips." Sitting on the pavement he hugged my dog to him.

"That was my mother's song you know. God be good to her soul." He told the dog as again he farted. Bruno took one look at him and ran away. Where is that other one? I'm shure I saw two of you." He again added as an afterthought. Once again he began singing .....

"High upon the gallows tree, swung the noble hearted three
By the vengeful tyrant stricken in their bloom;
But they met him to face with the courage of their race,
And they went with souls undaunted to their doom."

"Hold on for me Ger, I'll join in the verse." His companion staggered across the road and held on to the grill beside him. With one hand held tightly on the grill, he helped uncle Ger to his feet. Removing their caps they held them high. Then they began to sing ....

"God save Ireland! Said the heroes;
God save Ireland! Said they all.
Whether on the scaffold high
Or the battle field we die.
O, what matter when for Erin dear we fall".

"GOD SAVE IRELAND" They shouted as an encore.

Punching the air they embracing each other and simultaneously broke into raucous laughter. Again both let off a series of farts that turned the air blue.

"I'm here Uncle Ger." Brendan came forward and pulled at his arm.

"Oh, so you are. Now where did you come from? Let me see." Gerald swung on the grill like a monkey with one hand as he searched in his pocket with the other and retrieved a coin. As Brendan reached out for the coin, Ger let off another long series of farts and dropped it. Down the footpath rolled the elusive coin with Brendan in hot pursuit. Finally a passer by put his foot on it and flattened it.

"Thank you very much." Brendan retrieved the coin from the outstretched hand of the stranger. Uncle Ger and his friend John staggered arm and arm round the corner and into the Round House.

> *'Fill up once more, we'll drink a toast,*
> *To comrades far away;*
> *No nation on this earth can boast*
> *Of braver men than they.*
> *And though they sleep in dungeons deep,*
> *Or flee outlawed and banned,*
> *We love them yet, we can't forget*
> *The Felons of our land'.*
> *In boyhood bloom and manhood's pride..........'*

We could hear the whole pub singing as we passed Feathery Burke's on our way home. Gerald who was a fine tenor leading them along.

Brendan stopped at Saint Michael's old cemetery near to the milk market and reached into his pocket.

"How much did you get?" He asked holding his money close to his chest.

"I never looked, hold on." I rooted in my pocket and produced a shilling.

"I got one too." Opening his fist he showed me the coin.

"With my sixpence, I'll have one and sixpence." He gloated. I was about to shatter his dreams.

"Oh no you won't! Don't forget that mother is at home waiting for a few bob. You know as well as I do that there is no food and no turf (Fuel) in the house." I reminded him as if he needed reminding.

"Just because you are older than me doesn't mean that you can bully me, you know. Half of it is mine and I want it." He had little sympathy for mother's predicament.

"You can bawl and shout as much as you like. This money is for Ma, so there!" I strolled down the street ignoring his protests.

"Oh my God, whatever happened to you son?" Two women in shawls approached me and stroked my face. Then they began looking through my hair.

"You poor child and it Christmas too. What a shame! Whoever done this to you should be thoroughly ashamed of themselves." Were these two the worst for drink or had they escaped from the nut house I thought?

"Someone stole our pram in Foxes Bow and we are going home to Killeely." I informed them. I was trying to humour them.

"They didn't take the baby as well. Where is the creatur? Do the guards know?" One of the women exclaimed as she held her fingers to her lips.

"There's no baby, why?" I looked at them puzzled.

"Thank God for that. Here take this and get the bus home. There aren't too many running, it being the holiday. God love you, get your father to look at that." She handed me a penny.

"I don't have a father, he died a long time ago and is buried up in Saint Lawerence's." I told them keeping my distance.

"Sure, don't God love the poor orphans, here take this for a few sweets and say a prayer for me and Molly," her companion handed me a sixpence. I could not understand why these women were being so kind to me. Limerick was full of orphans, perhaps it was because it was Christmas.

"What was all that about?" Brendan came up the road and joined me.

"I don't know. They felt sorry for me and gave me a sixpence and my bus fare home. Is there something the matter with my head?"

"Are you joking? Your face is covered in red dye from your paper hat and it's running down your face. You look as if you were in the wars, what with your black face and all." I realised then that the women got the impression that someone beat me up and stole our pram.

We did not take the bus home but went up to the Horses trough at the top of George's Quay and washed our faces. On we went to a turf store in Watchouse cross and after a lot of hard bargaining I got a part sack of broken turf for the princely sum of sixpence. I had to promise to return the sack next day. Brendan reluctantly helped me to carry it home. Mother to say the least was over the moon when we entered the house carrying our precious gift.

"God bless you, you little angels," she even patted 'Bruno' on the head much to my surprise. I liked that gesture.

"We got more than that ma, here." I handed her the shilling and looked to Brendan for his contribution but without success.

"God and his blessed mother bless and protect you. I told you that our prayers would be answered," she held the coin to her breast as if it were a fortune.

"Where did you get all this money and turf?" She hesitated and questioned me.

"We met Uncle Ger and a friend. They were both as drunk as coots. They were on guard duty at the power station all week and that is why they could not come to see us."

"Thank God that he did not call, and me without a bite to eat in the house. I wouldn't want him to see us like this. I'd die of shame." She looked across at the empty grate.

"The money is better spent on food here than in the publican's pocket. You get the fire going and I'll go and get us something to eat." Mother put on her coat and left for the nearest shop. We did not get a lot for the few shillings. We could have got more if Brendan was not so greedy. We did however have a meal, which Brendan shared and Cibby Eye Lashes returned to his bed in the oven.

Mother sat by the fire dreaming, separated from reality by the long interwoven cobwebs of time. Perhaps in her dreams she was entreating the ghost of her long dead Joe to return and share the burden that was now a heavy cross on her back. Perhaps she may have been born under an unlucky star or Heaven forbid, her God had really deserted her and her children.

Perhaps mother, God rest her, was right after all. *God does move in mysterious ways.* We did have a late Christmas but a merry one that year. Who are we to doubt the faith and prayers of a widowed mother?

It was a New Year, a new beginning what would it bring with it? Would I continue to be the flotsam of society? Would I be punched and kicked at the whim of others. Would the brother's have a change of heart and stop deprieving me of the bun and bottle of milk? Would *Old Faithful,* my chilblains finally become extinct. I could forsee very little change, the war still raged and a few more neighbours died. Others unable to cope packed their belongings and handed in their keys and took the boat to England.

The telegram finally arrived next day just enough to pay off the huxter shop down the road. Mother would get her pension of fourteen shillings on Thursday. Would she finally forgive and forget the *Black and Tans and Sergeant Horan?*

Ger and other old soldiers would still stagger up the road fighting John Bull's war in their drink sodden minds. They would grow old but their memories would stay young ......

> '*Few and short were the prayers that they said*
> *And they spoke no words of sorrow*
> *As they steadfastly gazed on the faces*
> *Of their dead comrades on the battle fields .*
> *They now had plenty of time to remember them*
> *Perhaps too much. perhaps..................'*

Mother would still dream of what had been, the family would be dispersed to the four corners of the world. My *Mona Lisa* would retain her mystic smile. Some of my friends would never return to their native shores. What would the New Year bring to me and my dog and cat? Would the tears dry on my pillow? What prospects were there? What hope?

HAPPY NEW YEAR

COWARDLY MURDER AT ROSMADDA MILL

Uncle Gerald and his comrades were forever telling stories about the atrocities committed by the notorious *Black and Tans* and the infamous Sergeant Horan of the Royal Irish Constabulary. One evening as we sat on the bank of the Blackwater River (An Dhub Uisge- The Black Water) looking into the stream that fed the now ruined Rosmadda Mill (Ros Madadh- The dog wood), he told us the following stories.

It all happened on a fine Sunday afternoon in the year 1921 when the three young brothers Cecil, Aidan and Thomas O'Donovan and their cousin Benjamin O'Donovan of Thomondgate decided to take a walk out to Corbally in the city suburbs. They were unaware that the area was well know to the devils from hell, *The Black and Tans.* It was in this area that the East Clare flying Columns, ably assisted by their Limerick counterparts, were most active.

Like most young boys they were all set for a days innocent adventure in the countryside. Little did they know that the *Hyenas*, the *Black and Tans* would be out in packs looking for easy prey to murder. Reaching the fork near *Larkin's Cross.* They decided to retrace their steps and take the back road to the old ruined mills. Sitting on the river wall they spoke of this and that. One brother suggested that they should take a ramble across the Lax (Salmon) weir. The others were determined to explore the ruins of the old mills.

They watched the Mill Stream form a whirlpool and vanish beneath the otherwise still waters. One threw a stick into the pool and watched as it was vomited out into the river Blackwater. They continued their childish game for some time. Tiring they sat on the bank and watched the majestic and curious swans come from *Swan Island* begging for food. Proudly they displayed their cygnets to the boys. From an ash tree overhanging the stream a Kingfisher was stalking a fat trout. Swallows flew high in the sky and a Corncrake called to her mate. God had indeed been kind to their country. Curiosity attracted them back to the old mill. They were warned of the dangers lurking within its crumbling walls. The old devastated mill beckoned and called to them to come and have a last look before it finally vanished beneath the old Mill Stream. They spent some time scrambling over the old machinery and searching in every nook and cranny. What fantasies, what adventures filled their young minds as they peeped cautiously into the dark rooms we will never know.

Time was moving on their parents would be waiting anxiously for their return. This was no time to be out in the countryside. They did not wish to be on the road at dusk for it was nearing curfew time. It was then under the cover of darkness that the Jackals, *The Black and Tans,* would be out looking for blood. They were unaware that the area was under surveillance from the *Black and Tans.* It was unfortunate for them that the tans decided to raid the mill and surrounding countryside that afternoon. Two brothers, Cecil who was seventeen years old and Aidan who was fourteen years of age left the mill and began to climb the stone steps leading to the *Pike* bridge unaware of the two *Crossly Tenders* coming from the direction of Limerick.

The Tans hearing the laughter coming from the direction of the old mill stopped their vehicles and jumped off their tenders. Pulling their caps deep over their faces and placing their goggles over their eyes they lay in ambush. This was the code of the beasts, *The Black and Tans*. The two innocent boys unaware that death was staring them in the face continued on towards the bridge. The officer gave the signal. The murders cocked their rifles and without a word of warning, mortally wounded both boys.

Thomas and Benjamin, left the riverside and came along the bank to rejoin the others. They heard the shooting and ran to see what was taking place. Seeing the carnage they retreated towards Corbally seeking help. Their parents were not connected with old I.R.A nor were the boys members of any organisation that could be construed as illegal or subversive.

These were not martyrs for old Ireland, they were two innocent youths. No longer would they play in the haunted fields of Monabraher. Their parents would wait in vain for their account of their adventures that day. They were the flowers of Limerick plucked before they could show their true beauty.

No more would they crave to their parents with tenderness and gratitude. The family chain of gentleness had been severed, their voices muted. Who could explain their sudden departure. Their sophistry of love, fondness and affection severed in the most brutal and obscene manner. The neighbours looked at the bloodied bodies and asked. "Is there anything that we can do?" Do! Do what? Could they perform a miracle? The flowers were now but a distant memory.

The day was nearing its end, the trees began to respond as a gentle zephyr shook them. Had the *Bean-Ó-Sidhe* arrived for the final wake of our *Fenian* dead? The church bell rang calling the faithful to come and pray for the souls of the two children. Without hesitation the people gathered, the ringing bell called louder. Then all was silent before the air was rent asunder as the choir and congregation joined in the hymn of sorrow. The stifling heat of the church and the smoke from the candles added to the atmosphere of despair.

"Into thy hands O Lord... ...." The Priest held his hands open wide and cried aloud.

A lone voice in the congregation cried out "Jesus mercy, Mary help." The astounded congregation was struck silent. Many began to openly cry.

'You can pluck every rose, except those that are already plucked.'

The *Bean-Ó-Sidhe* would again return to Limerick's silent waters. She would look with horror at the butchers armed with their weapons of slaughter. The master and the beast had claimed two more scalps to add to their murderous shield.

He also told us that near to the same place in the Fairy Fields a running battle took place near to the Clare railway crossing near Woodcock hill. From the story he told it would appear that the intention was to capture an ammunition train that was bringing supplies to Ennis. What they did not know was that the British had advance knowledge of the plan and reinforced the train with extra troops. Two volunteers named Gleeson and McCarthy kept up a long running battle against overwhelming odds through the bracken and rushes.

With their ammunition exhausted they tried to escape back to Limerick. Both were seen and as volley upon volley of Fire power was directed at them they fell wounded. They were captured and taken to Ennis barracks where they were brutally assaulted and where they subsequently died. He was not too sure if they died before they were taken to the barracks or if they died in the barracks.

He told us of the rescue of Bobby Byrne from the city home and the sorrow when he died the same night from his wounds.

Of the time when short of money to buy supplies, the Clare brigade made a daring raid on the general Post Office in Limerick and got away with about £2,000. He was forever reminding us of the fight for Ireland's freedom and the gallant volunteers.

Further tales of the brutality of Sergeant Horan and the blowing up of the houses in Lock Quay. Convoys of lorries, Crossly tenders and Lancia staff cars cleared the streets as British engineers in white overalls and guarded by *Black and Tans* with rifles and fixed bayonets herded the men, women and children out of their homes. Those reluctant to leave their meagre personal possessions behind were mercilessly horse whipped out by Sergeant Horan. Then they placed explosives in the houses. When all was ready a signal was given and the homes complete with furniture and belongings were blown up. The convoy not satisfied and still out for savage revenge, packed up their war machine and drove into John Street where they continued with their terror campaign. Once again evicting the citizens from their homes before blowing them up.

The women and girls returned to the scene hoping to salvage some of their possessions. The men dare not return, for if they had then they would be brutally beaten or shot. This was not to be, for no sooner had they scrambled into the tottering buildings than Sergeant Horan and his butchers returned to the scene. Once again he took a sadistic pleasure in beating them out of the street with his Horse Whip. His pack of murdering tans took delight in sniping at the unfortunate women and girls trapped in the wreckage. In order to prevent them salvaging any of their property, he ordered the Tans to pour petrol on what remained of the wrecked buildings and set them alight. Family photographs and memorabilia were lost forever in the inferno.

On other occasions he brought us to the many roadside graves and Republican burial plots.

"This is how we treat our Fenian dead." He would remind us as we looked at the badly neglected graves and memorials. Was it the loneliness of boundless anger and sorrow of a lost cause that brought about his sentimental memories? I knew from past experiences that the pivot of past events in his life rotated with the anxiety and trauma of uncertainties.

Like a gyroscope losing its momentum, yet it struggles against the losing odds so too did Uncle Gerald. He reminded me of the monks and nuns who having entered the religious orders at a tender age are now told, when it is too late of course, to do anything about it, that it was all unnecessary. The web of deceit and religious bigotry and craven idolatry finally conceded but alas for them to-to late. They too are frustrated and angry.

Beyond the bounds of consciousness a web woven within their conscious thoughts weaves a thread of bitterness. I knew Uncle Gerald and I also knew that the thread of hopelessness and despair had wound itself 'round his very soul. He had fought for King and Empire and returned to see his native land being raped and plundered. He joined in Ireland's fight for freedom only to find his land betrayed and divided in a bitter civil war.

He married and built up a beautiful home. Then one evening on returning from work he found a note on the table from his wife informing him that she had returned to her native Dublin with another man. Uncle Gerald was a loser, a champion of lost causes.

He seldom, if ever spoke to us directly, but then we did not want to listen. We were not willing to console him, we let him ramble on and on, he was a real philanthropist. We were happy to watch his every action and listen to his stories with the insatiable curiosity of children. Perhaps we should have been more understanding of what was taking place in our young lives. What took place then is now but a blurred memory. The indescribable curtain is only now lifting from the woven web.

UNCLE TOM AND AUNTY LIZ

I don't remember much about Uncle Tom and Auntie Liz. They were relics of the past and I mean that with all due respect. We would meet them casually in the city on the odd occasion. Mother never did disclose to me as to which side of the family they belonged. I suspected that it was my father's side. They were not really our uncle and aunt but relatives.

One could not help but notice the pair of them, as they strolled round the town looking for the best bargains. They appeared to lean on each other for support, like two book ends. We never thought that they could ever be separated. They had been together since time began, or so it seemed. They seldom left Limerick except for the occasional day trip to Kilkee for a therapeutic paddle in the sea. They were as snug together as two bugs in a rug. They were never in any hurry for as Liz would say......

"When the good Lord made time he made plenty of it." On a summer's day they would sit outside their cottage watching the world go by. Sometimes Uncle Tom would take it into his head to take a stroll down to the docks.

"Come on Liz alanna, let's stretch our bones." Without a word of protest she would rise from her stoleen and join him. Visitors seldom called into the cottage, they were content to hold their conversation at the half door. Not mind you if the rain was about, then the door was opened and without asking the tae pot would be rinsed out in warm water. Liz would place her well worn palm on the side of the pot and smile as she felt the warmth. The pot was now ready for the brewing of the tae.

Without asking or offering, her cake tin would be taken down and a few scones buttered. Each knew what was needed when they had company. Tom set the table as Liz went about her business wetting the tae. As a well oiled clock is dependant on its pendulum, so Liz and Tom were dependant on each other. Tom wore a heavy 'Cromby' coat come winter or summer with a long woollen scarf wound round and round his neck. On top of his head was perched a deer stalker cap with the flaps open , he looking for all the world like a daschound. Should the weather be unkind Liz would tie the flaps in a neat bow under his chin.

Auntie Liz, as I remember her wore the longest dress I ever laid eyes on. It covered her from head to toe. That is with the exception of her booties. These were the neatest pair of button boots, as mother called them, I ever saw. They had long since vanished from the shoe shops of the city. She too wore a heavy woollen coat and over her shoulders a plaid shawl. This she placed over her head and tucked under her chin in crabby weather. Apart from all these features there was one other outstanding attribute and that was their noses. Below their nostrils there was an indelible yellow stain caused by their constant snuffing. This they carried in a round silver box that they shared.

"Oh hallo there. God Bless you, aren't you both looking grand." Mother greeted them one afternoon.

"It's yourself is it now and I see you have him with you." I was used to being greeted as 'Him' or sometimes as 'It'. Even Bruno got more respect than I did.

"God bless you, are you a good boy then?" Auntie Liz poked her hand out from the protective warmth of her coat and patted me on the head like a dog.

"Tom, see to the child, will you?" She nudged her husband before returning her hand to its protective hiding place.

Uncle Tom procured a coin from a deep recess in his coat pocket and handed it to me.

"Will you not be wasting your few coppers on him. You're too good, if you must know." Mother chided them.

"Oh away with you Kate, weren't we all young once? He'll say a prayer for us in the Franciscans, won't you?" Again she patted me on the head.

"Will you be taking the snuff, Katie?" Uncle Tom again dug deep into his endless pocket and produced the obligatory silver box. It was a ritual that they went through whenever they met mother or any of their friends.

"No thanks, I'll not bother if you don't mind. We have a lot of messages to get. Sure I'll be up to see you both during the week if God spares me." Mother made her excuses and calling on me she made her way up the street.

"Why does he insist of calling me Katie, and that snuff, a filthy habit. It was brought here by Sir Francis Drake. Still England never gave anything good away."

They were never blessed with children. It was the will of God and they accepted it as such. They found comfort in each other's company like Derby and Joan. Wherever one was then the other was not that far behind. We were so used to seeing them around the city that we did not notice when they were missing.

One day a guard *(Policeman)* called to our home and told mother that uncle Tom had been taken to the city home in a critical condition. She should go there as soon as possible. Mother wasted little time in getting to the hospital, alas she was too late. Uncle Tom had passed away long before she got the length of the road. Mother came into the kitchen and grabbing me by the arm waltzed me out the door and on into the street.

"Oh no! Not you. That dog is like your shadow; where you are so is he. Oh come on then." Bruno delighted at being invited ran up the road barking.

"Oh God, on top of everything else, do I have to contend with him howling. Will you shut him up?"

"Bruno, cut it out. Come here. What's the matter Ma?" I knew by her agitated state that all was not well.

"It's Uncle Tom. How am I to break the news to Liz?"

"Break what news ma? Has something happened?"

"Sorry I should have told you, Uncle Tom has died, God be good to his soul. Now bless yourself and say a silent prayer for his soul." Why mother was in such a hurry to deliver such tragic news I could not understand.

"Come on. Let's get a move on. Poor Liz will be in a distressed state." She insisted.

"Ma, she does not know yet." I enlightened her.

"Will you shut up and get a move on," I never saw her so agitated.

We made all haste through the city and on into the suburbs to where they lived. I had never been to their house. Mother stopped outside the door of a neat cottage, one of two, and opened the door.

Auntie Liz was sitting beside the open grate smoking a clay pipe when we entered. There was no fire in the grate and the house seemed lacking in the usual welcoming warmth.

"It's yourself is it Kate, do come in! Come in and take a seat. She sat as if in a trance sucking on her cre dudeen.

"Why did you let the fire go out? You'll freeze to death," mother ran and collected some paper and sticks. These she placed into the fire basket and set them alight before setting handy pieces of turf on top.

"There now that's better, don't you think?" She rubbed her hands together.

"What do you make of my Tom?. Does he need anything? Whatever came over him? One minute he was as right as rain and the next he was flat on his back before me right here" She pointed to a spot on the floor.

"Oh Liz, I hate to be the conveyor of bad news, but Tom, God rest his soul, passed away peacefully a few hours ago." Mother went and placed her arms around Liz.

"He's dead, if you must know," I informed her. I felt sure that she would not understand the way mother was explaining it. Mother looked at me with daggers in her eyes.

"So my Tom has gone to his maker. I'll miss him Kate, so I will." Poor Liz seemed to be in shock.

"Who will make the fire now my Tom is no more?" Tears filled her eyes, mother started to cry and so did I. Bruno began to howl and had to be put out into the garden.

"I'll put the kettle on and make a sup of tae." Mother wiped her eyes and pulled the crook away from the fire and placed the iron kettle on it and pushed it over the turf.

"It will be an empty house without him and that's for sure Kate." I could see the deep furrows on her brow as the flames reflected on her face. To me, a child, she looked a hundred years of age. Why I thought to myself that she must have known 'Finn McCool'. (A legendary figure in Irish Folk lore).

There were no more tears in her sad eyes as she continued sucking on her Cré dudeen. (Clay pipe) She seemed to be in a trance as she rocked backwards and forwards. Perhaps she knew that she was now all alone. Can a bird fly on one wing I thought to myself.

There was a lot of toeing and froing between the two houses and the hospital for the next couple of days. There was no wake held in the house as mother had arranged for the corpse to be held in the morgue until the day of burial. I was looking forward to the wake but when I did not see Uncle Tom in the bed I knew that it was a foregone conclusion.

On the second day mother left the house to make arrangements with the priest about the burial. When she returned she was as angry as a bag of bees, I can tell you. She entered the house and banged the door.

"Whatever is the matter Ma?" My elder sister asked.

"You won't believe it, you just won't credit it. I thought my ears were deceiving me. Do you know that they have forbidden us from attending Tom's funeral. Can you beat that?"

"Don't be silly Ma, you got the information wrong. Nobody can stop us attending a funeral, least of all one of our own. Whatever brought this about?" She tried to comfort Mother.

"How little you know. I should have told you a long time ago. You see Uncle Tom was a Protestant." We looked at each other unable to comprehend what this had to do with his funeral.

"I went, as you know to see the Priest for permission to attend the funeral. He told me that we could go as far as the gate but that we could not attend the service nor could Liz under pain of mortal sin. He would not be buried in a Catholic cemetery, nor could any Catholic member of the family attend. I tell you I was fit to be tied. Had he had not been a priest I would have boxed his ears, God forgive me." Mother sat down in her armchair only to rise immediately and go to the window from where she faced us.

"I'll tell you this, not all the Priests and Bishops in Holy Ireland God bless and protect each and everyone of them, can stop me from attending Toms funeral and showing my respects." We could see she was looking for moral support and encouragement.

"Good for you Ma, you go to his funeral. What harm will it do? Who is to know but God himself. Uncle Tom never harmed a soul and should not be buried without his kith and kin present." My eldest sister encouraged mother.

"I will to be sure. I'll defy them just this once. May God forgive me. Hasn't poor Tom as much right to Heaven as anyone else? More so than some I could mention."

I wondered did she mean the priest or perhaps me? No, surely not mother.

Next morning mother donned her flowery hat and left the house without a word to any of us. She returned at midday and drawing her Hatpin from her hat she patted her hair and sat down in her chair.

"I went to his funeral, so I did and I don't regret it one little bit. Liz came with me. We said our own prayers in our own way and let the others to theirs. I saw no harm in that, so I didn't." She was more or less herself.

"You did the right thing Ma, so you did. Now stay there and I'll make you a nice cup of tea and you can tell us all about it." My sister opened the top cover from the range. Flames escaped but these she soon confined with the kettle."

"Ah well! What is done is done and cannot be undone. God rest his soul. Poor Liz insisted on going home alone in the carriage. All for the better, poor soul, she wants to be with her thoughts. She'll have to face it. I was in a worse boat when your father died, God be good to him." Mother removed her size four shoes and rubbed her feet together.

The kettle began to sing as steam belched out the spout and the lid began to hop up and down.

"It was a nice service, not unlike our own in many respects, if I say so. Don't any one of you mention to a soul what I done this day. Do you hear me?" She wagged a finger to emphasise her warning.

Auntie Liz sat by the fire when mother entered. Mother sat down beside her and started dreaming. I sat on the little stooleen. All was calm now as a gentle breeze wafted the lace curtains to and fro. A butterfly trapped between the curtain and the glass was making a vain effort to escape. Rising, Auntie Liz opened the sash allowing the butterfly to fly free.

Opening the curtains she looked out of the window hoping to see her Tom come up the old road to greet her. The solitude was soothing to her. Turning she looked up at the little altar that her Tom cared for so much. He took on the task to please her although he was not of her religion and to let her know that he understood. Her Tom was the most generous understanding husband and sweetheart that any woman could ever wish for. A bit old fashioned in his ways but then who was without a little fault.

Reaching up she removed the single rose from the vase and held it close to her breast. As she bent her head to smell it her tears fell gently on its petals. In her hand she held it tenderly still wet with her tears. Letting it fall to the floor she looked down at it, her mind became a blank. Closing her eyes she looked into her soul. Someone unkindly had cheated her and dealt her a losing hand. The bird could not fly on one wing. She stood as in a vacuum looking at nothing in particular.

Opening her eyes she looked across at the now vacant chair beside the fire, her Tom's chair. It stood where it always had in his enchanted place. Where throughout all their adversities he sat and consoled her. Within her he had left tender love and understanding.

"Tom will you ever pick up my rose." She called to the phantom sitting beside the fire. Then she smiled. A zephyr blew smoke from the old chimney wafting its scent throughout the old cottage.

Mother looked across at her and putting her fingers to her lips denoted that I should remain quiet. Bruno was sleeping beside the fire. All was still, was mother expecting the spectre of Uncle Tom to appear, I wondered?

How long she sat observing the rose lying on the kitchen floor she did not know. Her Tom would have loved to talk, he was a real chatter box. Yet the story was now told, the book closed and the cup was drained. It was now but a female secrecy, the window was open and her butterfly had flown.

'Perhaps I should have kept him a little longer,' she spoke breaking the silence. Again she smiled.

Uncle Tom was buried in his family plot in St Mary's Protestant graveyard.

END OF AN ERA

It was the coming of winter. A biting cold wind swept the squally snow across the city. Over the great river Shannon high in the sky hung a watery moon. It looked as if it were trying escape as far away as possible from the bleak weather. The streets and houses were covered in a blanket of snow that radiated a watery glow over the land.

The wind blew ripples of snow into the air from the sleeping snow. These formed long mounds which grew higher and higher. Then they calmly waited until the stronger wind returned and turned them into small clouds and carried them off to pastures new. Mother was worried about Auntie Liz and went daily, come rain or snow to attend to her needs to tidy the cottage.

"We'll have to do something about Auntie. She mopes around the cottage at all clocks. She cannot be left on her own to cope." Mother warned us time and time again. Matters were brought to a head when a neighbour sent for the doctor to see to Auntie Liz. She had taken to sitting outside the cottage come rain or snow and talking to her Tom as if he were still beside her. She became agitated when the *Blue Nuns* started to visit her and fuss about her cottage. Her mind began to wander, she began to live in an enchanted world within her own soul. A tranquil home, where her Tom was always present. This was where she wished to remain away from the uncalled for intrusion of others. Her Tom would see to her needs, had he not always done so? By what right were these busy bodies taking that responsibility away from him?

"Will you get out of my house please? My Tom will see to that if you don't mind." She would reprimand the nuns and replace an ornament moved for dusting back to where it originally came from. She was finally diagnosed as suffering from senile dementia and unable to cope on her own. The shock came for mother when plans were made to remove Liz to the City Home.

"They'll remove her to the City Home over my dead body. They have the cheek of the devil, so they have." She paced the kitchen floor. We knew that she intended to bring Auntie Liz to stay with us and was trying to make the task all that easier. Then it happened, one day as I returned from school there she was as large as life sitting by the fire, Auntie Liz herself. Although I did not see her face I knew at once that it was her, for round her neck was her old plaid shawl.

"Hallo Auntie Liz. Come to visit us, have you?" I greeted her. She made no response as she sat looking at the range. Coming closer I noticed her well worn beads in her hands and she numbering her prayers.

"Sorry Auntie, I didn't notice." I called out louder thinking that she was a bit deaf. She jumped up in her chair, which was mother's chair, and looked at me with scorn.

"What's wrong with you, you brat, shouting like that? I'm not deaf if you must know. I heard you the first time." She scolded me.

"Sorry Auntie, I didn't think." I placed my school bag over the nearest chair. I wondered how she made it to our house. Perhaps mother had fetched her.

My cat, Cibby Eye Lashes was in his usual place in the oven looking out at me. Normally he would come out to greet me on my arrival home. This time his escape was blocked by the feet of Auntie Liz. She had her booties off and was toasting her feet in the oven. Removing her feet she searched in her clothing and retrieved her clay pipe. Taking down the tongs from the nail on the wall she raked from the fire a glowing ember of turf and gripping it in the jaws of the tongs she lit her pipe. Blue smoke filled the room as she puffed and sucked her pipe into life. Cibby Eye Lashes just managed to escape from the oven before she again placed her feet inside and sat back comfortable puffing on her pipe.

Her button booties lay neatly by her side as slowly she sank deeper and deeper into the old sugan chair. Mother came back from doing the messages sometime later and informed us that auntie was unable to look after herself. She would now live with us for her own safety. Telling us did not really matter. Mother ruled the roost. What did concern us was, where was she going to sleep.

This was soon resolved as a horse and cart stopped outside our door and the driver dismounted and came to our door.

"Where do you want it?" He asked me as I opened the door.

"Where do we want what?" I asked.

"The bed of course, what else?" He pointed to a brass bedstead with a rolled up feather mattress on top. In a separate pile were pillows, blankets and sheets.

"Ma! There's a man at the door with a bed, he says it is for us." I called.

"Will you stop shouting. Do you want half of the neighbours to know our business? Get in." Grabbing me by the ear she despatched me back inside the house and out of harms way.

"Will you bring them in here please, the boys will help you." The bed was unloaded and deposited on the floor of the parlour. The man stood leaning on the jamb of the door when all was unloaded.

"Is there something else that you want?" My sister asked.

"I'm waiting to see the Missus, if you don't mind."

"Ma, the driver wants you." I called out.

"Will someone take him away, for God's sake?" Mother entered the parlour and shooed me away like a wayward chicken.

"I completely forgot all about you. How much is the damage then?"

"A shilling ma'am as agreed." He lifted his cap out of respect.

Mother went across to the sideboard and reached inside the china black swan and took out a coin and gave it to the driver.

"God bless you ma'am." Again he removed his cap looked at the coin and spat on it before putting it in his pocket. Mother thought this a filthy habit.

"Good luck to you now." He closed the door behind him and I listened to the clip clop of the horse's hooves as they left the street. Auntie Liz had come to stay.

"Where would you like it put Liz?" Mother called.

"I'd like it under the window, If It's not too much trouble." Liz interrupted her beads.

Mother instructed the eldest boys to assemble the bed under the window in the parlour. The mattress was unrolled and the bed made ready. Mother went to the cupboard under the stairs and began searching.

"Now where is that blessed thing? I'm sure that we had one. Oh! There you are." She came out backwards from the cupboard carrying an enamel 'Poe' (*Chamber Pot'*) and placed it discreetly under the bed.

"That's your old Piss pot." I nudged Brendan and began to laugh. Mother looked at me with that look that said more than words.

"Listen to me you and listen good, do you hear? Go over to Lena Carr's and get me a Sacred heart lamp with a clear globe and a heavy base. Now make sure the globe is clear and don't you dare break it, or else ...." A sixpenny piece was wrapped in tissue and tied with a safety pin inside my pocket.

"Now hurry on and don't lose it, do you hear?" Bruno was up and out the door before me. As there was no electric lighting in our house, the lamp was for Auntie Liz to see with. Should she awaken in the night.

Auntie Liz hogged the fire day and night. Even Cibby Eye Lashes who was always first to the fire had to watch out for an opportunity. It was only when she removed her feet from the oven that he could make a dash for his place inside. Poor Bruno saw little of the fire and would spend his time looking out from the cupboard under the stairs at the distant warmth. Although we saw little or nothing of the fire, surely a small dog could be found a spot. I told mother of my feelings and for my pains got a box on the side of the head for my cheek.

"With all the praying she is doing for the like of you, you should not deny her a little comfort. Now stop moaning about your animals. God, where did I get you from?" She added as an afterthought. I often wondered that with all her praying for the foreign missions who were converting heathens, why her husband was never converted? I thought of asking mother but she would only belt me for being cheeky, so I kept my feelings on the subject to myself.

Uncle Tom was scarcely mentioned unless his name cropped up for a prayer or two during the family rosary.

Days became weeks and weeks months. Liz was now spending more and more time in her bed holding long conversations with her Tom. It was frightening and morbid to say the least to hear her talking to a ghost. I told mother that I was of the opinion that Auntie Liz was stark raving mad and for my pains was given a good thrashing. Now that she had vacated the fireside this left room for my animals and us. Whenever she wanted to use the poe we had to leave the room and wait outside until she finished. Sometimes she would spend a long time on the poe, grunting and groaning. This sounded hilarious to me and I could not help laughing and giggling. This in turn brought the usual slap across the backside or the nearest part of my anatomy. Sometimes mother would open the front door after auntie had used the poe and waft it to and fro.

"She cannot help it, if you must know." Mother would apologise.

Mother was worried for her wellbeing and suggested she send for the doctor and priest in that order.

"A doctor and a priest, fed up with me are you Kate? Can't go too soon for you? Never mind, I'll soon be no trouble at all to you." Liz would indulge in self sympathetic rhetoric.

"Now don't be so morbid. Of course we don't want rid of you. Stay as long as you like. Only please let the doctor give you the once over." Mother more or less apologised.

Within a matter of weeks she was confined to her bed and we were barred from the sitting room. Despite her protestations mother did send for the doctor and the news was not good. Poor Auntie Liz had but little time left on this earth.

No more would Auntie Liz look out the window expressing her weary thoughts. The pivot on which all her emotions turned had now come full circle. The fading light of the autumn day spread over the glen of Killeely. An indescribable melancholy overtook her rational reasoning. "My Tom! My Poor Tom." She cried incessantly as she numbered her beads.

The anguish of sorrow and boundless loneliness was more than she could bear alone. She persistently looked out of the window without seeing. She knew how miserable she was, she was tired of life and anxious to be with her Tom. She cried constantly, the thread of love and hope that had been so carefully entwined round her heart was now broken. Who would she tell of her sorrow, who indeed was there to listen? Most certainly not me! Sorrow days had once again awakened within her.

"Oh God! Why, why did you do this to me? Why did you take my Tom away from me?" Sorrowful depression had once again awakened within her. Despondency now took a hold of her dreams. There was no doubt but that she craved to be released from the world, her prison. Her Tom was waiting for her to break free from the fetters of bondage and join him. How often I prayed that God would grant her request if only to give us a little peace.

It was a gloomy night so it was that February. One of those sad nights when you'd expect the spirits and ghosts to be abroad. The ever moaning wind was showing no sign of abating if nothing else it was increasing. It made sinister chilling moans as it moved through the open tombs in the old graveyard behind the house. It seemed to single out our house as it lashed our windows and doors with its pent-up fury. This was the night of the dead, a night of the *callings*. Yes! It was on such a night that we could expect the *Bean-Ó-Sidhe*.

Hearing a lot of movement downstairs, I listened for some time before getting out of bed. I put on my trousers and went to the window. Snowflakes caught up in the fury of the night landed and clung in desperation to our window panes only to be brutally snatched off by the cruel wind. Confused thoughts crept through my adolescent mind as I crept down the stairs. Someone or something had disturbed my sleep. Perhaps Liz needed help.

On tenterhooks I opened the parlour door slowly and was surprised to see the big lamp in its brass cradle lit. The sacred heart lamp now had a red globe and the Connail Mór (Big Candle) with its message of death was sitting on the table. I knew that Auntie Liz had gone to join her Tom. God must have heard my prayers at last, pity he was not about when *Old Faithful* attacked my feet and hands. Why else would the Connail Mór be lit? Why would Bruno be so quiet? Mother was kneeling beside the bed with her rosary in her hands. On hearing me she looked up and rose to her feet.

"So you heard her too, did you?" she whispered.

"Heard what Ma? I heard the storm and a noise and came down to see if auntie needed any help?"

"No! Not that kind of noise. Did you not hear her, the *'Bean-ó-Sidhe'*? She looked from the window to the door. She never mentioned that Auntie Liz had passed away but I knew something was wrong. The howling wind seemed to increase in intensity.

Her talking of the *'Bean-ó-Sidhe'* in the middle of the night did not help my ego and sent shivers down my spine. I looked across at the bed. Mother firmly believed that fairy woman came to escort the spirit of the dead from this life to the next. Bean meaning woman and Sidhe meaning fairy, although often heard has never been seen. She comes at the time of death crying and seeking the metempsychosis of the soul of the dead. Some believe that she transports the souls to those of the fairies.

(The fairies being the angels who were cast down from heaven during the battle between Saint Michael and Saint Lucifer. They were deprived of their immortal souls when they were driven from Heaven as a punishment and would steal the souls of mortals who died in order to gain readmission back into Heaven.

This belief is not new for it was handed down long before Christianity came to our shores. In some countries they are known as 'Pixies' and others as 'Hob Goblins'. The names may differ but the belief remains more or less the same. There are those who will swear that she has called on them and told of an impending death within the family. I too can name people who received the news of a death long before it was officially known. Some may scoff and deride these beliefs but who can argue with the facts. Did not Christ appear to the apostles as they hid in their room? See 'Ancient Stories of Ireland')

"Listen! Listen carefully and you might hear her." Mother put her fingers to her lips. For my part I had no intention of waiting to hear her. A chill filled the room although there was a good fire in the grate. I moved closer to mother seeking protection from the spectre of doom. It was not considered lucky to hear her calling, for if she could not take the soul of the dead then she would seek yours. I wonder did mother want her to take me out of her sight? This it would seem to be as good a time as any.

All I could hear was the mournful cry of the wind as it whistled through the trees in the graveyard behind our house. Then I heard the usual noises of the night, a tom Cat calling, a dog barking in the distance. But the cry of the Bean-ó-Sidhe I did not hear, thank God.

Mother crossed the room and reaching over the bed opened the curtains. Then she opened the top sash of the window. The cold early dawn filled the room chasing the darkness away in its wake. The Connail Mór waved its beckoning light to and fro. Blessing herself she stood to one side of the room. The soul of Aunty Liz was now free from its earthly bondage and free to go and join her Tom.

"Sure it's little wonder that you did not hear her, she has long gone by now. Whatever was I thinking of?" She looked at me and smiled." Yes! She has returned to her lair." I often wondered what happened when people died during the hours of daylight? I did not question as to why she opened the curtains so early. Surely she did not intend to disturb Auntie Liz who seemed to be sleeping peacefully.

Then looking down at Liz she smiled and drew the sheet over her face. Crossing the floor she opened the door of the eight day clock and stopped the pendulum. Taking a bottle of holy water she blessed the four corners of the room. I knew then that Liz had really died.

"Let us kneel down and say a prayer for her soul. She has joined her Tom." We knelt by her bedside and began to pray. Other members of the family came and joined us. It seemed strange that she never told us outright that Auntie had died. In the middle of the praying she rose to her feet and entered the kitchen to prepare breakfast leaving the rest of us praying.

After breakfast my eldest sister was sent down the road to fetch the nurse. In the meantime mother brought down a large tablecloth and covered the big mirror on the sideboard. This was done to release the soul of the dead from the house and to prevent it losing its way to the other world. Again she sprinkled the four corners of the room with holy water, the chimney, the threshold and all present. Finally she blessed herself and called on us to do likewise.

"You can all leave the room now and don't return until I send for you." Drawing the curtains she shepherded us out of the room and closed the door behind us. In the meantime Aunty Liz would be prepared for her final journey to her last resting place on earth.

It was some time before I returned home and found the parlour door open. The curtains were now open and the window closed, the soul of auntie Liz had finally left the house. Mother was sitting at the table chatting to the nurse over a cup of tea.

"You can come in now. We have done all that needs to be done, haven't we Maisie?"

As I entered the room my attention was immediately drawn to the bed. Auntie Liz was no longer inside the bed. She lay on top as if she were asleep, dressed in a long white dress. Her smart button boots that had been highly polished were on her feet and buttoned up. A white ribbon of cloth had been placed around her face and tucked under her chin in a neat bow. Her grey locks had been combed and neatly parted in the middle. Her hands rested on her chest and were entwined with her rosary as if in prayer. Two pennies rested on her closed eyes. I thought she looked better in death than when she was alive. The poe was no longer under the bed.

"Doesn't she look grand? Your mother and me done her proud." The nurse smiled.

"Would you like a cup of tea and a bun?" Mother lifted up the pot and shook it.

"If the pot stretches to it, then I'll have another." The nurse pushed her cup and saucer towards mother.

"I may as well make a fresh brew. There will be others calling, I'm sure." Mother took the pot to the range.

"Kate, I was telling you just now, it's a crime shame to let that gold ring go down with her. Won't you let me take it off?" How often had I heard that before.

"No! I couldn't live with myself if I done that. Her Tom put that ring on her finger the day they wed and only he should take it off."

"Will you talk sense Kate? Tom is dead and gone, there's only you now and Liz would be proud to let you have it."

"I've made up my mind, the matter is a closed book."

"The decision is yours to make Kate, but for what it's worth I think you are making one big mistake. Liz would not be too happy if she knew you had refused to take the ring and you with no husband and a house full of children." She lifted the cup to her lips and looked over the rim at mother.

The ring would be discreetly removed before the corpse was put in the coffin.

"Looking at you drinking that tea reminds me of poor Liz and her tea leaves." Mother changed the subject.

"She was one for 'Tossing the Cup.' The best fortune teller this side of the river Shannon. Whatever is the right time Kate?" She looked up at the eight day clock, its pendulum now silent.

"You'll be back to morrow, won't you, Maisie?" Mother reminded her.

"Don't fret, should the good Lord save me then I'll see you about eleven. You go and see the priest and the undertaker."

I was glad when the nurse called next day, for mother was in a foul mood. She had been to see the priest and whatever transpired between them was not for children's ears.

"Maisie, I'm glad it's yourself, I'm bursting to tell you about that priest again." Mother began to walk briskly around the room.

"Would you ever let me take the weight off my feet, before you start. That walk from St John's will be the death of me." She flopped into the nearest chair.

"You won't say no to a cup of tea before I start." Mother was already pouring the tea.

"Tell you nothing but the honest truth Kate, I'd commit murder for a cup right now. Do you mind if I slip my shoes off." Before mother could reply she had put one foot behind the other and pushed one shoe off, then the other.

"Thanks Kate. Go on tell me the news before you burst." She took the cup from mother's hand.

"It's that parish priest again. He's as thick as two planks of wood, so he is. May God forgive me my sins."

"Whatever is the matter? It's not like you to behave in such a manner. It can't be all that serious, now can it?" She laid her cup to one side and looked at mother intently.

"I went to see him about the funeral arrangements and he was all nice and full of sympathy. That was until I told him that I wanted her buried in the same grave as her Tom. It was then that he turned on me like a Jekyll and Hyde. He was all high and mighty sitting on his high horse, so he was."

"Whatever for Kate? Sure he should have taken it as granted." The nurse looked puzzled.

"Know about it? Sure he nearly had a fit there and then."

"Bury her where, in a Protestant grave? Are you mad woman?" He screamed at me. "As true as God he did, so he did."

"She cannot be buried with him, not in a Protestant graveyard. I won't allow it. Do you hear me? I had all this out with you before woman." He shouted loud enough for half Limerick to hear him.

"Did you not tell him that Tom was her husband? If I'm not too mistaken there are Catholics buried in part of that cemetery too."

"Are listening to me at all, Tom was a Protestant and Liz a Catholic. It was not a matter of the graveyard it was the grave."

"You should have told him to go to blazes, so you should, God forgive me.

"He is adamant that she be buried in her family plot. He will not allow any of his clergy to attend a service in a Protestant graveyard."

"What does he mean by the family plot. Do you know where it is? There is no time to wait."

"Now how would I know that? It is somewhere in Mount St Lawrence. Poor Liz, thank God she is not alive to witness this sad day."

"Whatever are you going to do Kate? Are you going to let her be separated from her Tom? Oh Kate! I really am sorry." The nurse put her hands over her face.

"What can I do about it? I can only do as he says. How else can we have her buried? We can't leave her lying there, we need the bed." Mother looked across at Auntie Liz lying peacefully on the bed.

"That's one for the books no doubt, if ever I heard one. Still Kate I'm sure that God in his infinite mercy will unite them in Heaven, in spite of the Parish Priest." The nurse tried to calm the situation.

"Amen to that Maisie, I hope that he does. That priest is determined to do in death what he failed to achieve when they were alive. Liz will be buried with her father and mother and there is nothing I can do about it."

"For God's sake don't condemn your soul to Hell by talking like that, it's not worth it. Leave it in the hands of Almighty God."

"You're right. I only hope that the parish priest is not officiating at the service. I just might be tempted to do something I'd regret later."

"You'll need to send one of the boys to the gatehouse at the cemetery at once. The grave has to be opened today. Here you, whatever your name is take this and catch the bus to Mount St Lawrence and tell the gatekeeper that we want the grave opened at once. Tell him I said so." She handed me a penny for the bus fare.

That afternoon the undertaker came with the coffin and placed Auntie Liz inside and closed the lid.

A sweet odour permeated from the coffin and filled the whole house. I was glad that mother was not going to keep her in the bed any longer.

The whole family attended the requiem mass, which was conducted by one of the curates and not by the parish priest as mother feared. Four brown lighted candles in brass candlesticks stood guard at the four corners of her coffin resting on the catafalque.

After the service the sad cortège set out on its journey to the Catholic cemetery at Mount St Lawrence. The church bell tolled the death Knell calling on the faithful to say a prayer for the departed. Two peals and then a pause continued as the funeral procession crossed the Shannon. This to denote that it was a female funeral. (Three peals and a pause for a male funeral and two and a pause for a female) It sent its message across the river Shannon past the grim towers of King John's castle and on into the graveyard at St Mary's Cathedral. Liz was going home but not to her Tom.

Mother took hold of the leather strap holding the window of the carriage closed and released it. The cool sweet air from the Clare hills brought a refreshing breeze. The muffled tone of the bell echoed across the still waters.

As the cortège passed along the banks of the river Shannon we could see the squat towers of St Mary's. The branches of the trees in the old graveyard waved and murmured in sorrow. As the cortege came nearer the trees discharged yellow and green leaves on the hearse. The falls at Curragower, not that far away, shed extra watery tears as it lamented the parting. Mother sat staring out of the carriage window slowly sucking her knuckles as she listened to the gurgling waters and watched the myriad cascade of coloured leaves gently fall to earth. We knew what mother was thinking as she turned her gaze towards the old cathedral.

"I expect Liz has her face turned in sorrow towards there. Sorry she cannot be with her Tom." She took out her handkerchief and wept uncontrollably.

"Oh Blessed Jesus, forgive me for what I done this day." She rested back on the Leather head rest and wept. I felt sorry for mother. What kind of a God would do such a thing? I thought. Why send poor Uncle Tom to Hell just because he was a Protestant?

The graves of Liz and Tom have long since been obliterated but I would like to think that they found each other in the other world. Let's hope that they did. I'm sure they will understand as to why I told this story. This was the way it was, Catholics were buried in Catholic graveyards and Protestant in Protestant graveyards. Unbaptised children and suicides were not buried in consecrated ground but in fields. They did not go to Heaven we were told. The children went to Limbo. Those who committed suicide and all those who were not of the true faith went to Hell, or so we were taught.

I always found it sad when I discovered the body of an infant wrapped in a cloth inside a butter box in the old vaults of the Protestant graveyards. I used to say a little prayer for them. (*See Dare you ripple my Pond book one*)

BIGOTRY

Our gang gathered in The Peoples Park one fine Sunday evening. We lay on the green sward under the imposing granite Doric column dedicated to Thomas Spring Rice of Mount Trenchard. We knew that he owned a huge estate down at Foynes and that he was chancellor of the Exchequer. He also sent the starving people of Limerick to Australia during the great famine. He was a very rich planter. Oh yes! I nearly forgot he was also the 1st Baron Monteagle of Brandon. Why this huge column was erected to his memory we could never understand? Why are there no monuments to our own famous citizens?

We should have known the answer. The city fathers much to their shame to this day have never given any recognition to her citizens. It freely gives accolades and honours to strangers who dishonour and castigate the city. Her own writers, engineers and scholars are ignored. They have to leave Limerick to gain recognition. Perhaps it is the curse of Saint Munchin.

It was the month of June and a hazy heat permeated from the sun soaked ground. Hawthorn bushes, of which there were a profusion, sent out their intoxicating message to every passing bee to come and join the feast. High in the blue sky, swallows chased hoards of flying insects. Fluffy clouds raced across the blue horizon and obliterated the sun for a fleecing moment. We had nothing better to do than to rest our weary bones and while away the afternoon.

Slowly the setting sun sent a fading beam of light down on the sinking Protestant church of Saint Michael in Pery Square. It is a handsome Tudor-Gothic church and was erected in 1824. It is often referred to as 'The Sinking Church' as the foundations of the chancel were found to be insecure during construction.

Seeing that the sun was now but a fading light, we rose as one and sat looking at nothing in particular.

"They all go to Hell, you know." Came an abstract remark.

"Who go to hell?" Lazily I looked up from my bed in the green sward.

"The Protestants, who else?" The debate opened with the fate of the Protestants and their life in the here after.

"God help them," Josie, my second in command looked across at the church and graveyard.

"They all go to hell and that's that. What kind of a gob shite are you?" I was annoyed as I thought of my Protestant relatives.

"It's a known fact. Ask any Christian Brother or priest, they'll tell you." Another bright spark put his penny worth in.

Our philosophical debate opened with the total damnation of all that were not Roman Catholics.

"You believe then that Roman Catholics have a monopoly on heaven. Is this what you really think? What of the other religions around the world"?

As on both my mother's side and my father's side there were both Catholics and Protestants I secretly wondered if they were correct.

Would I ever see Auntie Liz or Uncle Tom in the here after? I'd see Auntie Liz, for she was a Catholic. Poor old Uncle Tom would he rot in Hell?

Would God make an exception of them and let them both into paradise? After all they were husband and wife. It did not bear thinking about.

I always had an insatiable appetite to find out what went on at a Protestant service. Yet we were forbidden under the pain of damnation to our immortal souls to enter their places of worship. We were even prohibited from entering their graveyards. I was now, by my thinking of entering their place of worship endangering my immortal soul.

"What if one of us entered their church just to see what goes on in there?" I suggested.

None would hear of it, enter a Protestant church indeed. The very thought of it sent shivers down their yellow spines. They moved to a safe distance from me. Was I their leader, to be ostracised by my faithful compatriots?

"The Holy Catholic Church is the true Church and was more than good enough for our parents, and their parents before them. They suffered and died for it if you must know." They vindicated any counter charges I might make.

"If we just took a peep inside, we might learn something of what they get up to. We could then make comparisons with the Catholic Church." They would have none of it.

"Look here Louie, we are all good Catholics. At least most of us are. The English along with everything else tried unsuccessfully to take our religion from us too. Our ancestors fought and died to keep the torch alive. We owe it to them to keep our faith."

"Good God! I only suggested that we take a peep inside not convert as a body to the Protestant faith. Sorry I mentioned it now." I began to sulk.

"Remember the hymn lads.........."

> ' Faith of our Fathers living still
> In spite of Dungeon, fire and sword'
> Oh! How our hearts rejoice with joy
> When'er we hear those glorious words.'

Brendan, as if to add fuel to the situation opened his gob and began to sing............

> 'Faith of our Fathers, Holy faith,
> We will be true to thee "till death.

Soon every head in the park and beyond was turned in disbelief at the profanity of the young louts.

"Will you stop. You're making a show of us all." I chided them.

"It was you who started it, wanting to attend a Protestant service."

"I said no such a thing, all I said was........" Here I was interrupted.

"If you are all that concerned then go inside by all means. We will wait outside for you. Go on then." It was now time for me to pick up or shut up.

"Ok. I'll go, but you lot wait for me and promise you will never tell anyone about it." My gangs promises were like the Treaty of Limerick, not worth a tosser (crown cap of a bottle). We rose as one and left the park, much I might add to the delight and relief of elders of the city. We passed *Carnegie Library* and approached the open gates of the church. Here the procession halted and took their places along the wall like a row of crows watching the carcass of a dead cat- Me! I looked back towards them. Would they encourage me to abandon my plan? It was all too late. They were all for damning the soul of their leader. I felt slightly apprehensive as I entered the gate and approached the front door. I looked back, they were gloating and watching me, I saw them sneer and nudge each other. I knew what they were thinking. 'Would Louie have the guts to go inside'.

There was a notice pinned to the door. I wondered if it said...*No Catholics allowed.* I studied the notice and was more than surprised by its message...........

> *'Pause traveller ere thou enterest and bethink thee;*
> *How Holy and how wholesome is this place;*
> *Time that thou spendest here will link thee*
> *With men who once were of thy race....'*

My thoughts drifted back to the works of John Bunyan and his story of The Pilgrim's Progress which he wrote in Bedford jail in 1678...........I read on.

> *'This is thy Father's house, to him address thee;*
> *Herein his children worship face to face,*
> *Who at the coming in, with peace will bless thee,*
> *And going out make joyful with his grace.*

I grabbed the brass latch of the inner door and with sweating palm opened it. I was now a captive inside a Protestant Church for the first time in my young life; The door swung closed behind me, I was now trapped. The church had a strange eerie silence about it or was it me?

There was no Holy water font, no confessionals, no burning candles, no stations no statues. Two large candles were ablaze on the high altar and apart from a brass crucifix the altar was bare. Then I noticed the sparse congregation occupying a few seats to the front of the centre aisle. Nobody noticed me, I felt like a foreigner in a new land. I tried to make myself as inconspicuous as possible. I wanted to get out of this place, I did not belong here.

Then I felt a premonition or was it guilt? These were not my people although they too were Irish, of that I had little doubt. Then an inner voice spoke.

'Look at yourself', it derided. 'You stick out like a sore thumb. Why don't you turn around and leave this Sacred place. Why do you mock your God?' I felt ashamed, for I was not mocking anyone. My mates could laugh and scorn but this was God's house just as much as our own. I could feel it.

I would and could take part in this learning experience. Having come so far it would be folly to leave now.

'Look about you' the inner voice again prompted. 'There is nothing to fear within these walls. You wanted to know what took place at a Protestant service. Come! Come inside, listen and learn.'

Slowly I crept deeper into the church, my heart pounding like that of a cornered hare. I felt that I was making myself more and more conspicuous by the minute. If only I could turn and run away from the place.

The decision to stay or run was no longer mine to decide as a young man approached me and smiled. He handed me a black book with gold edging and a red cloth bookmark hanging from the centre pages. Still smiling he gestured to a vacant seat and returned to his pew. There were cushions to kneel on unlike the hard boards in our Churches.

I was in a quandary. I did not know how to behave. I knew that I must not genuflect nor must I make the sign of the cross. To do any of these things would be to recognise their religion and this I was forbidden to do.

I was aware that they were badly misled people and if they did not return to the true faith then they would surely rot in Hell. I felt sorry for them and put all the blame for their misfortune on Henry the Eighth of England.

Frightened to look at their altar, I wondered if the Greek words *Agnosta Theo* (to an unknown God) that Saint Peter found inscribed on a high altar in Athens was also inscribed on their altar.

I cast my eyes on the cushion. The cushion was embroidered with the words *To the Glory of God* and something about a Women's league.

There were three aisles in the church, one central and one to the east and west. Although the church lacked all the trappings of the Catholic Church, I was more than surprised that I missed none of them. Perhaps the quotation I read on the door was responsible or maybe it was the delusive seduction of the quiet music being played on the church organ.

Unlike my first apprehension I was now sensitive of the oak panelling and the shadowy aisles. Long seats with brass Candleholders took pride of place each side of the altar.

I was brought back to reality by the Choir Master blasting out some chords on the organ. Then there was a moments silence before the air was rent by a second cord. This one was full, bold and demanding. It was magnificent in its rendering and sustained itself in suspended animation. It poured forth from the long cylindrical tubes high up in the organ loft like cascading stars in an infinite Heaven. It seemed to be inexhaustible in majestic and sonorous harmony.

That one cord alone caressed the ears for a fleeting moment and brought one nearer to the mystical surroundings.

Boys in frilled surplices, carrying candles in brass holders came from the vestry and took their places in the seats. The service began with a celestial hymn that called on the congregation to cleanse their souls. I had heard it before but I stubbornly refused to join in singing a song of praise to their God. Although the melody embraced me and overtook me like the gentle breeze I stubbornly resisted and remembered my schooling. When tempted return to your own prayers for God sees and knows your every thought

I sat in my seat far from the sparse congregation and said a few prayers of my own. When the minister called the congregation to rise for the blessing I ignored him. Why should I rise? I was not one of them.

My conscience kept telling me over and over again, "Shame on you. Are you not aware that you are upsetting your Catholic dead?" Then the same voice would say 'Thank you for remembering your Protestant deceased in your prayers'. Perhaps they too needed a hungry prayer. My mind was in an impasse, for there were now more questions than answers. The service continued with the minister entering the pulpit from where he read his chosen text....

"What came ye into the wilderness to see, a reed shaking in the wind?"

I was sure that he meant this chastisement for me, for he was looking directly in my direction. The preacher drooled on. His sermon seemed as barren and the superfluity of the words failed to impress the congregation or me.

Finally he concluded........

> 'And now unto God's gracious keeping I commend thee;
> The Lord bless thee and keep thee.
> The Lord make his face to shine on thee;
> The Lord lift up his countenance upon thee
> And give thee peace'.

Then he called down God's blessing on the King and Queen of England and the royal family and their heirs and successors.

The setting sun, now a crimson ball slowly sinking in the evening sky, had descended until its rays shone obliquely into the church without intruding on the solemnity of the congregation. It added to the spiritual bounty of which I was already conscious.

I left the church before the others for I did not wish to commit a sacrilege by intruding on their sincere faith. Although I had been present at their evening service I did not participate, nor could I.

I joined my companions on the wall outside and acknowledged the nod and smile from the sparse congregation as they left their church. Did they know that I was a Catholic and had violated their church or did they try to understand? I'll never know.

As we returned to our parish we burst into song as was our custom. Ours were the songs of sentiment. We poured out our hearts to whoever was the current mystical beauty in our adolescent heads. We had just finished 'My happiness' when I told them that the Protestants prayed for the King and Queen of England.

One member of the gang took umbrage at this and started to get on his high horse. I soon shot him down.

"I don't know why you are getting so upset. Let me enlighten you, me old China." I felt that now was the time to divulge a few hidden facts.

"The Free State government declared full allegiance to the crown and started a civil war. They forbid any member refusing to take the oath of allegiance to the King from taking his/her seat in the Dail. Did you know that?" He looked at me with his mouth open. Then for good measure I added.

"When the bodies of the Irish Republicans, shot by the Free Staters fighting for a free and United Ireland were released to their families, do you know what happened?"

"I'm sure you will tell me." He groaned.

"The Catholic Churches in Dublin closed their doors on them and forbid the clergy to offer a mass for the repose of their souls, much to their shame."

I could see that this line of conversation was getting out of hand and walked away singing.... The Mountains of Mourne.

The others joined in ....

> ' We've seen England's King from the top of a bus
> But the silly old bugger he never saw us,
> And though by the Saxon we once were oppressed
> Still I cheered, God forgive me,
> I cheered with the rest. '

> 'I asked the Valley of Echoes if she Loved me, Loved me'.

Another song, Another raucous chorus.

"Will you shut your Gobs, in God's name or I'll send himself down to you." A window opened in Watergate and a basin of slops missed us by inches. A baby started to yell as we stood in the centre of the street. We began singing...

> *'A baby was sleeping*
> *It's mother was weeping*
> *For her husband was far*
> *On the wild raging sea'.*

Our singing echoed into the walls of the old city where I expect the songs are still trapped to this day within some hallowed crevice.

That night I recalled my visit to the church. Somehow I felt that God understood me; nobody else seemed to. I envied those who had access to such beautiful spiritual bounties. I thought too of the bigotry, ignorance and intolerance that surrounded me. One day I would sail away from Ireland and find a Utopia where people would accept each other. I was young and naïve to believe that such a place existed. Perhaps I was dreaming of Heaven. In all my travels World wide I failed to find my paradise until I returned to my pond, my Shannon. This is my paradise, where I usually sit alone and relive the days of my youth.

THE NIGHT THE FIRE DID NOT CATCH

Brazen clouds began to take possession of the watery blue sky. These were vulgar, dense Storm clouds. I saw them far off peeping over the Clare Hills not too far away. I knew that soon they would darken the city. I heard the moaning of the wind as it hurried the storm on. I was conscious of its formidable power. The darkness grew darker and darker if that were possible. I prayed for the storm to break before it left the hills. I was worried for mother. Would she make it home before the storm broke? Suddenly and without any warning a flash of lightening rent the clouds apart. I waited and counted... One, two, three, I continued to count. On reaching the count of eight I smiled for I now knew that the storm was still some distance from the city. Then as if in mocking defiance reverberating thunder crashed from the skies. Above the roar of the thunder the heavens opened and discharged piercing icicles that hopped along the road. I heard urgent knocking at the door. Mother dashed into the house and removing her flowery hat she blessed herself. As she prayed there was a sudden almighty flash of lightning followed by a crash of thunder. Crash after crash rendered the skies apart. Why, I thought in my fear was my God sending such demoniac fear upon us? Again the thunder roared and the lightening flashed. I made for safety under the table and prayed my repentance for doubting God. Mother sat in her chair with her messages by her side.

"We'll light the fire when the storm passes, please God." She told us between her prayers. We were warned never to go near open doors, Fireplaces or under trees during an electrical storm.

As we could not afford the luxury of keeping a fire in the grate all day. It was only lit in the evenings. Mother called it being prudent. It was of little comfort to us as we sat in an Ice cold room trying to concentrate on our homework.

When convinced that the storm had passed she produced an old copy of the 'Limerick Leader' and tearing each page in half she twisted these into thin strips. These she placed in the fire basket of the range. On top she placed pieces from an old orange box she procured in the city. The fire was now set. Having lit the fire she opened the oven door and removed a sod of turf. She had placed it in the oven the previous day hoping that it would dry out.

"Those turf merchants have a lot to answer for before God. Fancy selling a bag of sodden turf to a poor widow woman." She more or less spoke to herself as she placed sizeable pieces of turf on the kindling. Yes! We heard this remark a thousand times.

The fire sparked and sizzled as boiling water was excreted from the wet turf. Consequently it was not long before the fire was quenched. Nothing daunted, she raked out the fire and started again. As there was no longer a supply of paper so she looked around for an alternative.

When I saw *Cibby Eye Lashes* make a dash for the oven and knew that mother had succeeded in lighting the fire. When the fire took hold mother added the usual combustible materials, old boots, vegetable peelings and bones.

Most nights the room would smell like a crematorium. We burnt any old rags we could find and these smelt worse than the bones. If the cat or dog had fallen in the fire we would not have noticed.

Next morning I set out for school in the full knowledge that I had completed my homework to my satisfaction. Following the usual morning prayers we were called forward to present our homework to the good brother for examination and correction.

I opened my satchel, confident that I had for once mastered the task set before me in the form of homework. Where, oh where was my homework? I was sure that I had put it in my satchel the night before. There was no need to search further. It was not in my desk nor was it in my satchel. I had inadvertently left it at home or worse still lost it. I looked in fear as the crocodile file of boys placed their homework on the desk. I knew that I would have to face the brother eventually. How could I persuade him that I had done my homework and unintentionally left it at home? He had heard this excuse a hundred times and more.

"Oh dear God help me." I prayed as I never prayed before. I searched into the deepest recesses of my mind for a plausible excuse. Each one I thought of he had no doubt heard a thousand times before in his long teaching career. I knew what the outcome would be and braced myself.

'Here was another little caffler, a smart arse, trying to pull the wool over the good brother's eyes.' I knew that for a good Christian Brother he had a warped sense of humour. The line of boys dwindled faster than I had anticipated. My mind was in a quandary, not that it mattered. I rose from my seat and joined the dwindling queue. I felt like the condemned man entering the gas chamber. All eyes seemed to be watching me. What was I thinking about? I shook my head hoping to find an answer. I managed a half smile or was it a nervous twitch as I caught his eye. We looked Eyeball to Eyeball. I gave up first and looked away. My tormented mind raced through a meeting between Doc Holliday and the Clay brothers on Boot Hill. Who would wind up dead with their boots on? The outcome was a foregone conclusion- Me! He was faster on the draw and anyhow he had all the cards in his favour. I saw the doc draw his gun. It was the brother drawing the dreaded black strap from deep inside the recesses of his cassock. Was I going mad or worse? Again I cleared my mind. Think! Think! Then I thought of a great plan, I would put on my sorrowful face. My mother called it my St. Anthony face. As he had so much faith, hope and charity within him, I hoped that a little might in all probability rub off on to me. There was no harm in trying. What alternative was there?

"Well, where's yours?" I heard him ask as I came out of my day dreaming.

"Where's what, Sir? I wrung my hands and deepened my sorrowful looks.

"Your home work of course, you Amadan." He bent his whole frame into my face. I could sense that he was in no mood for my theatricals. He set the challenge, would I back off or face him.

"Oh that, Sir. Well! It happened like this." Now was my chance to practice a few speeches from Shakespeare.

"This is how it is Sir. I done my home work, but as you can see I have not got it here." I put my thumbs in my braces, a bad habit of mine. I was now getting carried away with my own importance. This was a very dangerous thing to do before the good brother.

"Never mind the excuses, where is your homework?" He lifted me by the sideburns off the floor. Tears filled my eyes as he dropped me.

"Well Sir!" I wiped a snot forming on my nose with the sleeve of my ganzie. He looked at me in disgust.

"Haven't you got a handkerchief?" Handkerchief! Such luxuries were beyond our means.

"Come on then let's hear your excuse." He began tapping the leather strap on the desk.

"It was like this, Sir. At the last moment the lamp went out for want of oil and the room was plunged into darkness. Mother sent me to the shop, which is some distance away to buy some. What with a war on their meagre ration was exhausted. When I returned home it was late and I forgot to put my homework in my satchel. That Sir, is the honest truth. Would I lie to you?" Not a bad excuse and a plausible one at so short a notice or so I thought. Not so the good Brother.

"So you became one of the *Vestal Virgins* then, did you?" He again pulled me by my sideburns and twisted them. I wished that he would refrain from this brutal form of punishment. Again the intense pain brought tears to my eyes.

"*Vestal Virgin* Sir, what are they?" I looked at him with the innocence of a child.

"You are so thick that you don't even know your bible. You're nothing but a little runt. No oil for the lamp indeed! I heard most excuses over my long teaching career. It is my punishment on God's earth to be sent to Limerick to hear the *Hum Dingier* of them all."

"I'll run home at break time and fetch it Sir, honest I will, I promise." Ignoring his sarcastic remark about Limerick I continued to plead my case.

"Go home! Are my ears deceiving me? Just who do you think you are fooling? Most certainly not me." He looked around at the other pupils in disbelief. Then I saw the dreaded leather strap at the ready. Craftily I reached into my pocket and withdrew the Horsehair and placed it in my palm. We believed that a Horsehair placed across the palm would absorb the pain of the leather strap. We knew that some of the brothers had lead stitched into the strap to for obvious reasons.

"Put out your hand before you lie your way into the jaws of Hell." I heard the Australian stockman's leather whip crack in the air. I Heard his leather chaps rub against his thighs as he dismounted from his horse. I pictured the cattle stampeding before the merciless onslaught of the vicious sting from the whip, then he was upon me. Flexing his muscles in preparation for my punishment.

"I did it Sir, honest I did." The dramatics were over. I half held out my hand hoping for a last minute reprieve. There was to be none.

"Your grammar is worse than your excuses. You are nothing. Do you hear me? Nothing but a waste of time, the runt of the litter! What your parents were thinking of when they brought you into the world, I don't know. There's far better flotsam in the Shannon river that you." So much for my ego!

He grabbed the tips of my fingers and pulled my hand forward on to the hard desk. This to inflict the maximum pain.

Crash! The first landed on the tips of my fingers and removed a large portion of flesh. A sharp stinging pain like a bolt of lightening ran up through my arm. Crash! Another followed and then two more in quick succession. Then the order came to change hands. The brutal punishment continued as my bloodied wounds were ignored.

There was nothing new in this form of punishment with the exception that in this case my fingertips were bleeding. I held out my bleeding hand to show him what he had done but he ignored me.

"In addition to your homework, you will this evening write out grammatically correct in the context of a composition the correct meaning of, *To do* and *done*. Do you understand?" He tapped me under the chin with the leather that again brought tears to my eyes. My bloodied hands he ignored.

"Yes Sir, I will Sir. I promise." I shook before him like a read in the wind.

"Don't you be smart with me. I can read you like a book. This is more than I can say for you." Again he lifted me up by the sideburns and dropped me.

"Now hold out your hand." For my so called dumb insolence the good brother gave me an extra two slaps on each hand once again ignoring the blood in the process.

"There will be no bun and bottle of milk for you to day as an extra punishment." Hearing this was to me far greater punishment than the bloodied strap. I was looking forward to the bun and bottle of milk. It was not a lot but it would be the only sustenance I would get that day.

That afternoon I sat under the overpowering portcullis of the castle of King John listening to the majestic Shannon demanding entrance into the vast and overbearing Atlantic ocean. She would not be denied her goal, why then should I be the exception?

I listened to the rustle of the leaves in the Cemetery of Saint Michael as they kissed and caressed each other. I thought of how *Drunken Tady* battled with the *Bishop's Lady* on the old bridge of Thomond not that far away. This was my city, my heritage why was I being denied? I heard the song of the blackbird. I watched the dandelions shoot their seeds from their pods like flights of arrows into the sky. I thought of the year 1690 when bloodied arrows cascaded over the walls of the castle. I held my hands out and looked at my bloodied fingertips. They quivered and to me looked like the bloodied arrows of William's men. It was not William's men who were inflicting this punishment on me. My temper rose-it was my own people who were punishing me. I saw my city as I never saw it before. The leaping salmon fighting their way to the spawning grounds far up river in County Cavan. The cormorant sitting on the *Curragower Falls* watching and waiting. The butterflies with their long proboscises gratefully accepting the nectar offered by the wallflowers that grew in profusion on the castle walls. A gift in return for transporting their pollen. I went down the steps to the waters edge and washed my bloodied hands in the soothing waters of my river. I heard the beautiful chimes of the Bells of Saint Mary's, I looked down the river Shannon, The *Ladies lake* situated opposite the Strand barracks where I learnt to swim was looking enchanting. Perhaps the princess *Myosotis* was sitting in the pool watching and waiting for me to come and seek refuge in her wings. Yes! It this was indeed a lovely land.

I watched as my watery blood flowed down the river and wondered as to where it might land. Perhaps on some Tropical Island where the fairies reigned. With their power of metempsychosis they may turn it into a clone of me. Perhaps! What would mother think?

"What another Louie," the shock would surely be the death of her.

As the mantle of evening slowly enveloped the city I emerged from my Utopia and entered the world of reality.

When I returned home that evening I searched unsuccessfully for my copybook. Mother came into the room and asked me what I was searching for.

"I'm looking for my homework from last night. Did you see it?"

"No! All I found was an old copybook that was full. Now don't tell me that it was yours?"

"That's it. What did you do with it Ma?" I could now prove to the brother that I was telling the truth.

"Sure I lit the fire with it. Did you want it, I'm sorry. Was it very important?"

"No Ma, it does not matter, it's too late anyway." What use would it be in me bringing in my homework a day late. He would only accuse me of cheating and lying , resulting in another beating and perhaps the loss of my bun and bottle of milk."

Lying in my share of the bed in the dark of that night my temper seethed like a bubbling cauldron. The blood soaked through the bandages that mother had covered my fingers with. I thought not of praying but of a curse, a horrible curse a deadly curse.

"May the curse of... ..." As I evoked the wrath of the Devil lightening lit up the room. Thunder crashed and rattled the panes in the windows. I looked over the blanket then fearful of the consequences of my evil thoughts I covered my head. I joined my hands under the blanket and prayed to my God to forgive me for such bad thoughts.

'*Old faithful*' started itching my feet, my hands and my ears. I knew that I was in for another restless night. I would dearly have loved to rub my feet together to ease the itching. I knew from past experiences what the outcome would be, the tender hot flesh would peel away causing further pain.

'Ah yes! Those that God loves he punishes most'. That night I cried tears of self pity into my sparse pillow.

CHILDREN OF THE 'GOOD SHEPHERD'

Of all the grim portentous buildings I have ever cast my eyes on or that I ever had the misfortune to visit, there is one that will live forever in my memory. That is apart from the *House Of Industry* where I spent part of my youth. It is the *Penitentiary, Orphanage* and so called *Magdalene Asylum* of the Sisters of the Good Shepherd. Owned and controlled by that order and is situated on the Dublin Road, Limerick. Looking at the high stone walls surrounding it was enough to put the fear of Christ into any girl who was unfortunate enough to find herself incarcerated or threatened with incarceration behind its grim walls.

A home for girls had been established in Limerick long before the Good Shepherd nuns arrived in 1848. Ireland and especially the west was in the grip of the great hunger when the nuns came to Limerick. This home was established by the Rev. James Houlihan of Saint John's Parish. He removed the girls from the unsanitary and congested building that had been established some years previously in Newgate Lane by Fr. Fitzgibbon.

This home was controlled by a charitable woman, Miss Reddan. When members of the Good Shepherd nuns came to Limerick from the mother house at Angers in France, she was obliged to hand her small institution over to them lot stock and barrel. In deep depression and dispirited she left Limerick and joined the Sisters of Mercy in Cork. A cruel barbaric system of discipline took the place of the more liberal reign of Miss Reddan.

The nuns were ready to expand and with the blessing of Dr. Ryan and the clergy they opened a convent in Clare Street at the back of the brewery. This they subsequently purchased. As their income increased they firstly bought the lace factory of Messrs Walker and with the cheap labour of their captives they turned a loss making lace factory into a profitable enterprise. Soon more sites were purchased including the Christian Brother's School. This was followed in quick succession by the purchase of a large number of houses and lands in Magdalene Lane and Pennywell Road. The nuns were on their way to building their huge penitentiary and laundry. As there was still a lot of surplus labour within the girls they also purchased in excess of twenty acres of Pasture land and trained the girls as cowherds and milkmaids. They now had a profit making complex, thanks to the wayward and orphan girls of Limerick and Ireland.

It was to the order of the Good Shepherd that young girls were brought when it was claimed that they had disgraced their families. Had their parents, clergy and teachers spent a fraction of their time teaching them the facts of life, they may not have found themselves confined behind the bleak bastion. Many were sent there for staying out after hours or being what we called *Tom Boys*. These innocent victims of a bigoted system, some not yet in their teens, were forced to undergo the rigours of a very harsh disciplinary regime of a closed order of nuns.

Some of the girls were sent there because they became pregnant and were ostracized by their families for bringing shame on them. The majority were sent there by their parents or the courts as being out of control. Parents unable to feed their growing families and believing that their children would be well treated sent their daughters into the care of the good sisters. For use of a better word these girls were disestablished.

On one occasion a young girl, the eldest of a large family whose mother had died disobeyed her father and found herself dumped on their doorstep. Her crime was that she was determined to go to the circus in the city. Her father forbid her and confined her to the house. That night as her father enjoyed himself in the local public house she crept from the house and spent the evening enjoying the circus entertainment. She returned home at about 10 o'clock, long before her father and thought that she was safe. Next day her father was told of his Daughters evening at the circus.

"This is the last time you will disobey my instructions, my girl." He predicted. Next morning he told her to say goodbye to her brothers and sisters.

"Whatever for Da." She laughed unaware of what he had in mind.

"Just do as I tell you, you'll laugh on the other side of your face." Taking her by the hand he dragged her to the convent gates and rang the bell. The girl now fearing the worst and with terror in her young eyes pleaded with him.

"Oh Da! Not in there please, I'll never disobey you again, I promise. I love you and I want to go home to my brothers and sisters. Please Da! In God's name I beg of you." She cried through her tears.

This was to be the last time that she would ever again walk freely through the streets of her native city. There was to be no reprieve for as the door was opened he handed his daughter over to the sisters as one would a stray dog. There would be no second chance, the good nuns never refused an offering. She became what was known as a 'Magdalene' a derogatory name after Mary Magdalene, the prostitute who washed the feet of Jesus. These girls were not prostitutes nor were they criminals. In most cases they were young virgins caught up in a vicious web of barbaric, bigoted unchristian behaviour. (*See Dare You Ripple my Pond*)

Another complained to her parents when she was beaten time and time again by her teacher. The reason given was that she considered herself pretty and vain. Such conduct, Would not be tolerated by the good nuns. Vanity was one of the seven deadly sins and would have to be beaten out of her. Her parents refused to accept her complaints that the nun would beat a student without a good cause and dismissed her complaints. In desperation the girl refused to attend the school. She was warned that should she refuse to obey her parents she would be sent to the 'Good Shepherds'. Fearing the worst she attempted suicide which only exasperated the situation. To atone for the mortal sin she committed, she was sent to the Good Shepherd Convent to become a *Magdalene* and to slave without pay in the notorious laundry.

On one occasion she let some wet laundry slip from her grasp at the feet of the nun in charge. Firstly she had to kneel on the wet floor with her head touching it and beg the nun in charge for forgiveness. She continued to protest her innocence, and explaining as best she could, that it was an accident and that she could not help it. This was construed as insolence and disobedience. She was taken to a side room where her dress was lifted from her. She was made to stand in the cold awaiting the arrival of the Mother Superior. After a long period of time the mother superior arrived, she was carrying what the girl described as a long rubber truncheon. If she was shivering from the intense cold before hand, she was now trembling in dread. She was trounced severely with the truncheon. When the mother superior tired of beating her left, two other nuns entered the shed one was carrying a shearing scissors. She was held down and had what hair she had left on her head cut off. Then one of the nuns removed the long black leather strap that they wore around their waist and trashed her within an inch of her life. She was left in the shed overnight as a further punishment. She claimed that she was left with the stripes of a Zebra and the face of a Panda for weeks after. That girl spent most of her life behind the grim walls. She never saw her family again, nor did she want to.

It must be stated that the windows were barred and all gates locked. The whole complex was surrounded by a stone wall, ten feet in height, some walls had spikes on the insides and were topped with barbed wire and broken glass bottles. Escape was virtually impossible. Should a girl manage to escape and some did during the milking, then all hell would be let loose. The convent bells would be rung incessantly, this would bring the guards on the scene and all roads leading out of the city would be watched. It was said that it was easier to escape from Limerick jail than from the Good Shepherds. When the girl was captured she was returned and punished severely as an example to the others.

Magdalene's were considered as sinners and were segregated from the orphanage and condemned to work in the in the laundry from dawn to dusk six days a week. Sundays were spent on their knees in prayer and hymn singing atoning for their sins. They were seldom allowed to speak, nor were they allowed any recreation periods. Should one of the nuns cross their paths then they were obliged to stand to one side with their heads bowed in submission.

Many of the babies in the orphanage were the children of the Magdalene's. They were segregated from them. Mothers denied access to their babies, babies denied the comfort of their mothers. Their Mother were in the eyes of the nuns sinners and had, like Mary Magdalene to be punished for their sins. As the children grew up they were reminded constantly by the Nuns that they carried the mark of 'Cain'.

It is not for me to tell the stories of the inmates of the Good Shepherd or other institutions, I am not qualified to do so. I can only relate the stories that were told to me.

Girls that were sent into the convents of the Sisters of Mercy in Ballinacurra considered themselves lucky, I use this word with my tongue in my cheek. They did not have to work in the laundry. The very mention of the Good Shepherd convent sent shivers down the spine of many a girl.

Babies born within its confines were found new homes in Canada, America, Rhodesia and elsewhere. No parent in Ireland wanted an illegitimate offspring in the family. Such was the bigotry in Holy Ireland in my young days. Born the wrong side of the blanket brought shame and ridicule on the family.

"The Holy nuns will soon knock some discipline into you, my girl." This was a threat that soon brought most girls back into line.

For the boys it was the threat of Glin, Arthane, Danagan etc, run by the Christian brothers.

Discipline was strict and any misdeamour was immediately stamped upon by additional punishment. It was said that the soldiers in the military detention camp on *Spike Island* off the coast of Cork were better treated than were the boys and girls in the orphanages. They were shunned by the community and were seldom visited.

Why this barbaric and cruel institution was ever allowed to operate in the twentieth century now defies the imagination. Why charitable nuns partook of such crass punishment is now beyond belief. Inside the fortress was housed the now infamous laundry.

Here I must pause for the laundry was built on the lands known as Farrancroghy. This was a notorious place known for public executions over two centuries. The area was considered to be haunted and unlucky. This did not deter the order of the Good Shepherd who purchased the lands for a pittance.

It was behind the closed doors of the laundry that the teenage *Magdalenes* slaved from early morning until dusk and beyond six days a week without respite. It was a sprawling complex operated entirely by the girls. The Heartbeat of the operation was three huge steam boilers fuelled by coke. The young girls fed the boilers as good as any navvies and maintained the pressure required. The convent found its customers in the city of Limerick, Clare, Tipperary and on into Cork. It had an insatiable appetite. The patrons, in their sympathy were of the opinion that they were helping the poor nuns and the orphans. Nothing could be further from the truth. The more workload the convent took in, so the girls had to work all the harder to keep pace with the demand. A private laundry was opened in later years behind the Franciscan Church but this was forced to close. It was claimed that the noise from it disturbed the good friars. The true fact was that it could not compete with the Nuns laundry.

Scores of people would queue outside the reception window with their bundles of laundry. More would come from hotels and institutions on foot and in carts. This would be taken in under the supervision of the nuns through a hatch and piled up on long drays. As the drays filled, the nun would call on two of the *Penitents* to wheel it into the Sweatbox. (The Laundry)

We often watched them as they stole a glance at an open hatch, no doubt contemplating their freedom. What was going through their tormented minds was another matter. There would be no freedom for them.

"The holy nuns will soon clip your flighty wings my girl." Was a warning given to young girls straying from the straight and narrow path and how true it was. They were treated no better than caged animals.

My wife and I were witnesses to an incident within the grim walls of the institution. It happened ... ...

In the summer of 1955 when I took my young bride to see how *Limerick Lace* was made in the convent.

We were ushered into a room in which was a large bench over which a large magnifying glass was set on a swivel. Above which a bare electric light bulb swung from the ceiling. The room was sparse of furniture and immaculately clean. At the bench sat an elderly nun and a young girl about ten years of age. We were in luck; If that is what I can call it. They were making robes for a newly ordained priest from some parish or other. The nun left us in the care of the elderly nun. There were silk and gold threads from around the world being entwined into intricate designs on robes of the finest silks and satins. There was Limerick Lace and baubles, all in all she told us that the cost of the completed vestments would be £7,000. A vast sum of money in those days, and I could well believe it. They were more in keeping with robes for a coronation than for a humble Parish Priest. We spent a long time studying the beautiful workmanship and expensive cloth. Then she sprung the most cruel surprise of all.

"Will you look real close at the work. Isn't it beautifully created and all to the glory of God?" We looked closely through the magnifying glass and indeed it was the workmanship of a gifted person. Some of the silk and golden threads were embroidered into the lace with the words; *'Sanctus! Sanctus! Sanctus!'*. This one robe alone would be worn around the shoulders of the priest during Benediction only. Others had hearts, crosses and shamrocks intertwined with the knot design. One piece had the *Monstrance* made of *Limerick Lace* with gold and silver thread. Words cannot describe the beauty of the robes and vestments. They were fit for a king and I must admit that whoever was paying for them was not short of money. Yet I have to say that they were, with all the poverty in Ireland at the time, an obscenity in my eyes. The money could have been put to better use.

The young girl took no part on the conversation nor was she given the accolade she rightly deserved. Speaking was strictly forbidden unless spoken to. The debasement of it all hit us like a bombshell when the old nun without any feeling told us.

"Do you know this work is so delicate that this young girl could go blind from the stitching? This work is offered up to the glory and honour of God." I could not believe that these words were being spoken by a Nun. We had little doubt but this had happened to others in the past. Why else would she say it? Still who would worry for these children were not penitents but orphans from another part of the convent. They too, though innocent children had to earn their keep.

As there were no nuns to guide us out of the convent we decided to make our own way. Inadvertently we got lost and found ourselves wandering into the laundry. If we had been shocked by what we witnessed in the lace room worse was yet to come. What we observed was like something from the pen of *Charles Dickens.*

We saw several young girls dressed in what I can only describe as sacks. Holes had been cut in the neck and arms to cover their bodies. It looked to us as if this was their only attire. I presumed that the purpose of this was to make then as contrite as possible. (Dressed in sack cloth) Some were stoking large boilers with coke; others were wheeling trucks of wet clothing out of the rooms. The heat was unbearable and there was little if any ventilation. The girls were sweating profusely. None of the girls spoke nor did they smile. They looked at us from under their eyes, wondering no doubt as to what we were doing there. We saw a nun sitting at a high desk that overlooked the room. Draconian methods it would appear were being used to keep the girls in order.

A girl entered carrying a bucket containing what we presumed was tea. Another followed carrying a basket in which were large chunks of bread. The nun rang a bell and the girls obediently collected a mug each. The nun began to pray as she prayed she looked up and saw us and immediately stopped praying. Hurriedly she ushered us out the door and called on another nun to escort us away.

"You had no right to be in there. Men are not allowed in here, nor you." She scolded as she looked angrily at my wife.

"Sorry sister, but we got lost." I apologised.

We were then escorted out of the laundry to the reception office.

At the reception desk we were sold a small handkerchief made of Limerick lace for the princely sum of ten shillings. That handkerchief we retain to this day.

In addition to the laundry, the orphanage and the Limerick lace making the nuns had further investments. Out in a place named *Monamuck* or better known to others as *The Nuns Fields* a they own some twenty plus acres of grazing land. This land ran close to the Grand Canal at *Plassey.*

Come hail, rain or sunshine we would see the girls marching like soldiers in two's with two nuns to the rear and two to the front. At seven o'clock in the morning and at four o' clock in the evening they would leave the convent to do the milking, mucking out and tending to the needs of the herds. The girls were compelled to walk with their heads bowed in atonement for their sins. Being allowed outside the walls to do the milking was considered a privilege that had to be earned.

Whatever happened within these grim walls remains a secret. One wonders if the whole story will ever be told. Much of what happened and as to where many of the babies went to remains a blot on the community. Some may argue that whatever punishment the girls suffered they deserved it. That is arguable.

What then of the Orphans inside the wall? They never harmed anyone. They too were branded *Children of the Good Shepherd.* Many of the nuns done wonderful work for the children but they are the forgotten ones. We tend to forget them and remember the bad ones. Perhaps many have good reason to.

The Good Shepherd Sisters are now all but gone from Limerick. The walls have been breached to allow a little fresh thinking to enter. New apartments have been built for the inmates that remain. They are so conditioned and institutionalised that they find it impossible to live outside its walls. All that remains now are the ghosts of those who died within its walls. Their last resting place, the neglected plot of *The Children of the Good Shepherd* in Mount St. Lawrence cemetery.

There are no names on the stone for they are the forgotten ones, perhaps the *Good Shepherd* has called them to his fold, I would like to think so.

THE COBBLER

Mother could not forget the good old days when things were so different. On the occasions when we had a stew, which was not too often, she would remind us of our table manners.

"You must not eat like that. Always take the spoon away from you. See that the table is laid out properly and start on the outside with the cutlery." I would look at the bent spoon that I had grabbed from the table before my brother could get it before me. This and the few bent forks and a knife were our sole canteen of cutlery. Her standards of ethics meant little to us; survival was more important. She knew where she belonged, that was now all but a spent dream.

"Oh go on. Take no notice of me. Eat it up; it will do you good." Throughout our adversities it was she alone who tried as best she could to alleviate, if not all our needs and wants, then the more important ones. When she could do no more for us. When she could no longer relieve the pangs of hunger gnawing within our slowly growing bodies, then she would go quietly to her chair and between her tears pray to her God for help. After a good cry in the privacy of her own world she would dry her tears and try to comfort us.

"Don't worry children. Matters are not that bad that they couldn't be worse." This philosophy was supposed to bring solace to us. We were not aware that every time we cried to her for food we were adding to her misery. What consolation were her empty words, *'God will provide'*, to us as our stomachs cried out for sustenance, he never did provide. I often wondered what it was that God had against us. Was there some reason as to why he ignored all our prayers.

"There are those in the world worse off than you, just you think of that." With a glance across the room she would let the message sink in.

As our boots became the worst for wear we would be sent out to find the strongest cardboard we could find. This she would cut into insoles and glue them to the uppers inside the boots. I hated the smell of that glue. It was made from Horses hooves and came in large slabs of a transparent colour. This she would break into pieces with a hammer and put in a tin and place over the fire. Slowly the glue would melt into a liquid and be poured along the edges of the home made sole or heel. Her efforts failed miserably when the rains came which was more often than not in Limerick.

Most times our stockings had no vamps but good tops for show. I would tie a string around the good top and place it over my big toe to keep it in place. Anyone looking at my feet would think that I had a fine warm pair of stockings on. Nothing could be further from the truth. Little did they know that my feet were scraping the cold wet streets of Limerick. In those days all young boys wore short trousers displaying their home spun socks. The boys from the *'Ranch'*

(Island Field) and elsewhere could show their poverty, but not us. We had imaginary refinements of grandeur that had to be shown.

When she had a few coppers to spare, which was not too often, she would weigh up her priorities. Our boots would be carefully examined and she would select the pair that were the worst for wear. In other words, the welts were falling off. Then it was off to *Carew's or O'Connell's* in William Street to barter for a suitable piece of leather. On the occasion I write about it was my turn.

"Come on you and leave that mutt (Dog) at home." I was summoned to the door. Bruno would not hear of being left in the house when I was going out. He made a dash between her legs and was on the street waiting, his stumpy tail wagging in excitement.

"Oh God! How I suffer with you two. Go on then put his lead on and don't let him search every bin in the city. He takes after you, if you must know; no shame." Sometimes I regretted getting the dog. People were always comparing us to each other.

'Carews' and 'O'Connell's are still in the same location in William Street. They are both harness and leather shops. In a tea chest outside the door were the bargain pieces of leather. These were off cuts and it was these that she and others would come to buy. Sometimes, if one were lucky they would find a piece that not only made a sole but a heel as well, but that was not too often. There were so many rooting in the chest that mother scarcely got a look in. The bigger and better pieces were inside the shop hanging from the ceiling. They cost a penny or two more. Unable to gain access to the tea chest mother decided to try her luck inside the shop.

She asked for each and every piece of leather to be taken down for careful scrutiny. Several pieces were selected and laid along the counter from these she would make her final selection. Having selected the piece she wanted, she twisted it, smoothed it, examined it carefully, held it aloft and finally smelt it.

Her action reminded me of the introit, followed by the Gospel and then the offertory. There the Priest consecrated the host and taking in his sacred hands and elevated it. Was this mother's acknowledgement or acceptance of the will of her God, I wondered?

"Smelling the leather reminds me of your father's shop. Sure it's only a bad habit. Take no notice of me." She held the humble piece of leather aloft. In some far recess of her mind for a few nostalgic moments she relived the happy days she spent with her Joe in the grandeur of their young married lives. Who would or could trespass on such fond and intimate memories? She stood holding the piece of leather to her breast with her eyes closed.

"How much is this piece?" After long deliberation she queried.

"The price is on it Ma'am and a bargain at that." The argument as to its value began.

"It states eight pence on it, a mistake I have no doubt that you will rectify." Mother took it out of the shop and held it up to the light.

"Here lift your foot." Returning to the shop she ordered me to lift my foot. Like a horse about to be shod I leaned on the counter and held up the sole of my worn boot.

It's not a bad fit, I suppose, well how much were you really asking"?

"If it states eight pence on it then that is the price. Is something the matter with it then?" The man continued with his task.

"It will hardly stretch to the sole of his boot and he's only a child. Not a member of the Franciscan brothers are you?"

"It's a fine piece of leather, came from a fine animal, got it from *Tinsley's*.

What do you mean am I a member of the Franciscan's?" The realisation of what she said suddenly dawned on him.

"I have a daughter in the Franciscan Nuns. If you saw your way to see me right I'd ask her to say a mass for you." There was a silence, no response. "You say It's first class leather. You go and tell that to the unfortunate animal who was slaughtered to get it. No! If I gave you sixpence it would be more than enough. Perhaps too much at that." Mother twisted and turned the piece of leather.

"Well Ma'am that's the price. Were it in my power I would let you have it for nothing, never mind a Mass, which I could dearly do with, thank you." He added as an afterthought.

"In your power and for nothing my foot. What hypocrisy, don't you own the shop and all the leather in it. To make matters worse there's a big hole in the top left hand corner." Mother stuck her little finger in the hole and held it up for the shopkeeper to see.

"Sure that's only a small eyehole to thread the string through. What do you expect for a few coppers, the whole hide?"

"There is no need to be sarcastic to a cash customer. I expect to buy a solid piece of leather. Not a sieve if you don't mind. It may be a small eye hole to you but to the rains of Limerick it could be as wide as the river Shannon." Came the counter attack from mother. Pausing for breath she again looked at the shopkeeper hoping he would relent.

"Will you look at the hole? I could sail a coal boat in it." Mother exaggerated for good measure. Ignoring her the shopkeeper continued to stitch the saddle that he was working on.

"No! Come to think of it, you really should accept my offer. Sure no sane person would buy a piece of leather full of holes. Do you think for one moment that I came down from Mulgrave Street?" (*It is here that the hospital for the mentally ill is situated*). Did mother really know what she was saying?

There was stalemate in the shop. I could see that mother wanted the piece of leather. She was reluctant to leave without it. The shopkeeper wanted to make a sale but not at a loss. He was holding out for what he could get, even if it meant a penny profit.

"Oh my God I knew it, get him out of here, now!" Mother whispered to me. Bruno had his leg cocked up against a saddle and was relieving himself.

"Did you say something, ma'am?" The harness maker continued with his task.

"No! Nothing, why?" Mother signalled to me to remove Bruno.

"Oh go on then, you've twisted my arm. I'm making a loss if you must know, but I'm a charitable man and I can see that you are in need." Give me seven pence and let's be done with it."

"Charity now is it? More like crocodile tears. You'd watch giving charity. No if I gave you seven pence for it then he would have to go without the Chester cake I promised him." Mother tapped me on the head; she should have tapped the dog too, only he was tied outside the shop scratching himself.

"Thanks anyway, I think I'll leave it and try O'Connell's. They might be better Christians." She fanned herself with the piece of leather and stood her ground. She had no intention of leaving without her precious piece of leather. If he could hold out a little longer he would have got his seven pence. On the other hand he would have been castigated and humiliated in no uncertain terms for taking the food out of the mouths of her children. Calling himself a Christian and a God fearing one at that held no water with mother.

"Oh very well then, let's see the colour of your money. Sixpence it is then. I'll say this for you, you strike a hard bargain so you do." Raising his hand he slapped it down on his leather apron and then extended it to her. She looked at his toil worn hand and then at him.

"This is not a horse fair, remember your place. You're in Limerick and not in Ballinasloe" (Famous for its horse fairs.)The harness maker quickly retrieved his hand. With the bargain struck, mother got her precious piece of leather and the shopkeeper his hard earned sixpence.

"You see! It was only worth sixpence from the beginning after all. You cannot be too careful with these people. How do you think they got that big shop?" Did she not consider that she had worn the poor man into the ground as she divulged these few words of wisdom to me.

"Good God, did you see what that dog of yours done? I could have died from shame back there." She scolded.

"I suppose I can have my 'Chester' cake now. The little shop in 'Foxes Bow' have fresh ones." I reminded her and changed the subject.

"Chester cakes indeed, sweepings of the loft. Don't you know that they make them from all the scraps of stale bread and cakes and God only knows what else. They add a few raisins and a dollop of sugar on top and sell them to the unwary. We'll try *Daly's* bakery or better still *Riordan's* on the way home. They're more upmarket you know. They might have some outside loaves and a damaged cake." We could also drop into the Franciscan's and say a little prayer or two of thanks." I knew that I would not get a Chester cake.

On returning home the precious piece of leather was placed in the wooden tub to soak overnight in order to make it more pliable.

Next day on return from school I was instructed to remove my boots and clean out the insoles. The leather was taken from the tub and the cobblers *Last* and the tools required for cobbling from their home under the stairs. These were some of my father's tools of his trade as a portmanteau maker. Mother donned her hessian apron and making herself comfortable sat down on the three legged stool. The last that was made of cast iron had three fittings, one for adult shoes, one for children's shoes and one for heels.

Mother was an experienced cobbler and why not? She was like the old woman that lived in a shoe. She had so many children and so many shoes to keep repaired. Firstly she placed the boot over the last. With a pinchers she removed what was left of the old sole and heel. These she put to one side for kindling. Nothing was wasted in our house. The new sole was marked out in the most economical position on the boot and marked out with a pencil. As deftly as any expert she tacked it to the sole with a few tacks. With her cobbler's knife she cut around the outside of the sole.

Again with the cobbles knife she removed a small strip of leather from where she intended to stitch the sole to the boot. She then made small holes about a quarter of an inch apart along the cut with her awl. In the meantime I was given the task of waxing and threading the strong thread through the eye of the heavy curved packing needles. The wax was used to strengthen the thread and make it watertight.

Mother stitched the sole to the uppers through the awl holes she had made previously. She had to pull the thread tightly through the sole and up through the uppers to make it as watertight as possible.

She never complained when the sharp thread cut into her hands and made them bleed. The fitted sole she then trimmed and any scraps of protruding leather she cut off. Finally 'Bees' wax was melted and run around the seams and over the stitching as a final waterproofing.

The heel was now cut and nailed in place. Shamrock studs and steel toe caps were fitted to the soles of the boots and steel shoes to the heels, This to prolong the life of the boots. The same operation was repeated on the second boot.

"There now, don't they look real grand? Try them on." She looked with pride at her workmanship. 1 too was proud of her efforts. I often stroll inside the shops now when I visit the old city and stand nostalgically smelling the aroma of the leather. Does the owner ever think as to who the strange man is who comes in every so often and stands looking around him?

Sometimes my old eyes cloud over and memories of mother and her hardships flood back. I remember the tears on my pillow and the prayers to a God that never seemed to be around when I needed him. I then have to leave before I become an embarrassment to myself and others. Nobody knows or cares what past memories are returning.

To day as I sit by my log fire after a hearty meal and not a care in the world my thoughts return to mother. I do not hear the crackling of the logs nor do I see the sparks race up the chimney. I hear the tick tack of the hammer and see the sparks as she nails the steel to the heels. I think that were she alive to day I could give her so much. Then I remember that look she used to give me that told more than a lengthy discourse.

My mother was one in a million, yet she was seldom appreciated.

ANGELENE AND THE FAIRY SNAILS

I was always a great believer in the ability of the fairies and their power over man and beast. One of these was the reading of the trails left by the snails from the fairy fort at Ballynanty Beag on the Cratlow Road.

One afternoon as I sat with Angelene on the pavement outside our house I told her that I had *The Gift*. This was given to me by none other than the Fairy King himself. I claimed, I could read the messages left behind in the Snails trail.

"You have no fairy gifts. I think you are making it all up," she laughed.

"No I'm not and I'll prove it to you."

"How? My mother says that I should watch you for you are always making up stories."

"Your mother never understood me nor the fairies. They can put a curse on her. She should watch out."

"Mother told me that I should go to church more often then nothing could happen to me."

"Your mother lives in God's pocket from what I see of her. Come with me I dare you." I reached out my hand and helped her to her feet.

"Where are we going? Mother said......"

"Come on. We are going to the fairy fort and I will prove to you that I am not making it up. You'll see." I was sick to my eye teeth of hearing about what her mother thought of me.

"I'm not going into the fort. The fairies might steal me. Then what would my mother say?"

"She would probably blame me. I thought you didn't believe in the fairies." I chided her.

That afternoon we went up the long drive of the old estate and on to the fort. As we reached the fort she stopped and sat on the grass refusing to enter. I went up to the circle of bushes and called to the Fairy King.

"I wish to enter the fort your majesty." I bowed and looking 'round at her smiled. At the same time my heart was in my mouth. I worshipped that girl so much that I was willing to sell myself to the fairies for her.

Slowly I entered the fort, well at least a few feet of it and began collecting snails in a cocoa tin. When I had collected sufficient I came out and joined her.

"See, I told you that I could speak to the fairies."

"God but you're strange, Mother was right. What have you got in the tin?"

"Fairy snails. Come on, you sit on the wall at *Hasset's Cross* and I'll go up the road and pull a few leaves of cabbage from a field."

"What do I do if they escape? I should never have come with you."

"They cannot get out. The lid is on tight, look." I pretended to try and open the tin.

"But they're fairy snails." She refused to hold the tin.

"Alright then. I'll leave them here beside you. Don't let anyone steal them."

"Steal them! Are you stark raving mad? Who would want to steal fairy snails?" Some moments later I returned with a head of cabbage roots and all.

"Here you carry that. I'll carry the snails." I handed her the head of cabbage.

"I'm not walking through Limerick carrying a head of cabbage with a field of earth and worms hanging off it. What if my mother saw us?"

"Your mother out here? Why the nearest church is in *Parteen*. If you don't want to carry the cabbage then you can carry the fairy snails." I knew that this would put her off.

"I'll carry the cabbage then. You didn't steal it, did you. I'd put nothing past you?"

"No I did not, I found it beside the hedge." I daren't tell her the truth.

'God help me,' I thought. She gets more like her mother every day.

On reaching her house I took the cabbage off her and told her to go and check if the mother hen was home.

She came back with the good news that the mother hen was absent.

"Good! Let's go into the house."

"What do you want in our house and by the way stop calling my mother a hen?" The alarm bells began sounding.

"We need two soup plates. Have you got any?"

"Of course we have plates. Don't you?" I ignored this cutting remark.

Angelene opened the front door and for the first time I was inside the inner sanctum. Just imagine it! Here was I within my destiny, it was all too much. I often think that if I had not been so busy with my spells then I could perhaps have stolen my first kiss. Would she have reciprocated or more likely knowing my luck screamed her head off. Ah well! I'll never know will I? It was as I imagined, a lovely house with shining brass ornaments and plates on the walls. It also had electric lights.

"How do the lights work?" I asked as I looked up at the bulb.

"From the switch on the wall of course, silly." She mocked me. I spent a few moments flicking the switch until the bulb blew.

"Good grief! Is nothing safe in your hands. What did you do that for?"

"Do what, I never touched it? It went pop on its own."

"You'll go pop if my mother finds out that it was you." She warned me.

"Where are the plates then?" I ignored her threat of setting her mother on to me.

"You want two, with flowers or plain?"

"Just two old soup plates. The snails are not too particular." She brought the two plates into the sitting room and laid them on the tablecloth. I laid my tin and head of cabbage beside them.

"Take that dirty thing off the table at once. You'll ruin the table cloth," she warned.

They say love is blind but I could see more and more of the mother hen in her the more we met. My love was beginning to falter. My charms would have to be carried out on the floor.

"Wait, pick them up at once." She returned with a batch of papers and placed them on the floor.

"Will you hurry up. If my mother finds you in our house she'll be the death of you."

"Have you got a candle?" I innocuously asked.

"A candle, what do you want a candle for?" She looked at me and I noticed an expression of incredulity on her face.

"It's all part of the charm, I need a candle." I tried to calm her fears.

"There's two on the altar over there, but they are blessed candles."

"Never mind that bring one over here."

"It's a sin to mock with holy candles, if you must know. You're not going to hold a *Black Mass* are you?"

A Black Mass! Where did she get that from I wondered? No doubt the mother hen was talking. Ignoring her remarks I placed a leaf of the cabbage on the plate. I opened the tin and took out a snail.....

'Shalley Muddy, Shalley Muddy
Stick out your Horns'
The Queen is going to
Marrrrrrrry you!

I held the snail by its shell and indoctrinated it with my spell.

"What are you doing talking to a stupid snail. They cannot understand you?"

"Of course they can. Don't be smart. If the snail does not respond then we will have to get a replacement. See."

"A replacement? Not on your Nelly, I'm not going back there."

However the three snails performed their task perfectly and I placed the second plate on top.

"Now take this and place it under your bed. To morrow........"

"In the name of God! Under my bed did you say? You are joking? No! You put them under your bed if you like but get them out of our house. I don't know how you talked me into this. What would my mother say?"

"There's no need to tell her. If you want to know your fortune then you must put them under your bed. In the morning let the snails go and bring the cabbage leaf to me and I'll read your fortune, simple. Here, you can keep the head of cabbage, it will go great with a pig's head."

"How disgusting. Don't tell me that you eat them." I declined to answer and decided to take the cabbage home to mother. She would appreciate it.

"Put the candle back on the altar and don't tell your mother." I blew the candle out and gave it to her.

After school next day I sauntered down her road and passed her house All was quiet.

I turned and began walking up the road when I saw Angelene coming towards me. I smiled for she brought a ray of sunshine into my life after a day of chastisement by the Christian brothers. She did not reciprocate but scowled enough to turn new milk sour.

"Well! Did you do as I told you?"

"My mother was nearly killed, thanks to you and your fairies." Was her abrupt reply.

"Whatever happened? Don't tell me you told her of all people."

"There was no need to tell her. She squashed one on the landing with her foot." She had to go to the doctor.

"She squashed one of my fairy snails and went to wh........." Before I could finish I heard the voice of her mother calling me.

"You! Yes, I mean you, just you wait there." She hobbled down the street. How I thought, could she suffer an injury from squashing a snail? It must have been a curse that the Fairy King put on her for murdering one of his subjects.

"Where were you yesterday with my daughter? Come on out with it." She interrogated me.

"Nowhere, just out to the cross and back. Did something happen to you?"

"I'll ask the questions if you don't mind. Were you inside my house?"

"Me! Inside your house! What would I be doing there?"

"Don't be impertinent to me. Your mother will hear of your conduct. Now! Were you inside my house?"

"Of course I wasn't. Why is something the matter?"

"Of course there's something the matter. Look at my foot? I went to the bathroom and in the dark trod on a snail and tumbled down the stairs. I could have been killed or worse."

Perhaps the Fairy King had called in answer to my request and taught her a lesson on my behalf. I half smiled to myself.

"What's so funny? She looked at me with daggers in her eyes.

"Nothing. Why?

"How could snails get into the house? That is unless someone brought them in?

"Her father went looking to see if there were any more. Then he found two plates under Angelene's bed with a cabbage leaf and two snails in the bottom trying to get out. He's wanting to have words with you, if you must know." I came back to reality to hear her continue with her tale of woe....."She would not tell us how the snails and plates got into her room, but I have my own suspicions. If I could prove it then you would by now be half way to Glin and chastisement by the Good Brothers. You mark my words, you'll come to a sticky end, so you will. Now get away from my street and away from my daughter. You're worse than the black men with your Voodoo."

I met Angelene a few days later when all had died down. She told me that her father gave her a thrashing and confined her to her room after school.

"Never mind Angelene. I'll go and see the fairies and tell them to put a curse on him." I tried to console her.

"You leave my father and mother alone. Why is it that whenever you and that dog of yours come next or near our house, something awful always happens? I never want to see or hear of you again, ever!"

"No! I didn't mean them to be harmed. Just a spell to make them leave you alone, that's all." I assured her.

"No harm! Is that what you call being thrown down the stairs? I told you stay away from me and my parents. Even the electric light blew when you looked at it. You could get us all killed, so you could. You should go to the priest and get exorcised, so you should."

"I had nothing to do with her falling down the stairs, now did I?"

"Of course you did, you and your fairies, why I have anything to do with you I don't know. Come to think of it have you put a spell on me?"

"I wouldn't do that to you."

"I wouldn't put it past you, now go away before my father catches you. You'll get fairies I can tell you."

I knew she didn't mean it and that she would relent. She really liked me. It was not her; it was that mother of hers. I would put a curse on her if I could, but she was protected by so many saints my spells would not work. I tried once to turn her into a hen.

THE CLAUGHAN PLAYING FIELDS

Most nights lying in our cold bed Brendan and myself would return to our world of mystics, fairies and ghosts or whatever came into our adolescent minds. Seldom did we relate to what was our present plight. Our world was one long adventure that had no ending. It was as if we feared reality would reach out its cold hungry hand and grasp away our Utopia. Yet there was always another day like Lent, spoiling the joys of Christmas and then giving it back in the form of Easter but not to us, alas!

When the room became silent I knew that Brendan had gone off to *Tir-na-nÓg*. I would lie awake looking into the dark corners. The whole world was now silent and then as I slowly succumbed to sleep they would start. *Old Faithful*, my chilblains! Like an angry volcano they would erupt into an uncontrollable red hot itching. I knew I dare not scratch them. I also knew that praying for relief was a foregone conclusion, God was always out when I called to him. I had put so much Holy water on my feet and fingers that I was in danger of getting foot rot. With smothered prolonged tears on my pillow I would try to sleep. I wanted to cry out for some relief. Perhaps if I called out or sobbed louder. What then? If God could not hear me then who could? What right had I to disturb the dreams of those around me?

By morning my tears and my chilblains would be resting. A new day but what would it bring... ....

Thursday afternoon was reserved for recreation on the playing fields at Singland. It was on these grounds that we trained and prepared for our annual sports day. On the day of the sports, those selected to participate in the various events, would assemble in their red and white strip. I always considered my skill with the hurley to be as good as the next, and made every effort to obtain one of the coveted places in the team.

The problem was that there were too many good players and not enough places, so I never did get the chance to play. I was however one of the best runners and presumed that I would be automatically selected. There too I was grounded, not because there were better that me. No! I was grounded because my mother could not afford the red and white strip. How could the brothers allow a boy into the team with a baggy short trousers and a shirt that, well to say the least had seen better days. I'd stand out like a sore thumb.

When the various teams and athletes had been selected, those not required were instructed to spend the afternoon on their knees in the monastery chapel or studying at their desks. That rule was changed at a later date to attending school on Saturday morning.

On one such Thursday afternoon, we were assembled in the monastery grounds. We lined up in column of two ready to tackle the challenges set before us. There we stood like Grecian Gods, Irish style, awaiting the call from *Caesar* and the chance to win the coveted laurel crown. It was then that I had this excellent idea. The problem was that most of my excellent ideas were a disaster.

Between the primary school and the secondary school was an Iron Gate. This Gate was used by the Brother's, to obtain access from the monastery to the primary school. Pupils were forbidden to use it at any time under pain of the dreaded black leather strap. As we lined up before our respective teachers for roll call I nudged my brother and whispered my excellent plan to him.

"I've got this great idea to get away this afternoon. Do you want to try it?"

"Of course I do, but it better be good." He whispered back from the corner of his mouth.

"Ok. This is it. After roll call we will go to the lavatories. There I will disclose my plan." I nudged him and giggled at my audacity.

"Quiet you two, no talking now." Bagsy came down the line of boys and stared at us both.

We looked sheepishly at him for a moment and then humbly at our feet. He returned to the front of the class and took up his position like the platoon leader that he was. Then the order came to march off. Left, right, left right the boys marched towards the exit gate. The classes marching in order of seniority.

As we came near to the toilets, Brendan and I slipped out of the ranks and disappeared inside. So far so good! We waited inside until the sound of marching feet died away in the distance, then crept out from the toilets. We looked all around the school enclosure. With our hearts pounding in our breasts we ran towards the gate. Slowly I opened the old gate on its rusty hinges. No matter how careful I opened it, it still made enough noise to awaken the dead.

As we entered the grounds of the primary school, I kept looking up at the many windows of the school, what if one of the brothers saw us? I wondered what happened to all the boys who were incarcerated within its walls when it was an orphanage.

"Will you come on and stop day dreaming." I heard my brother calling to me. We reached the main gate and like a pair of hairy men we were off into the freedom of the city, to be lost in its milling throngs.

We would have no need to fear the school guard. His only concern was the pupils from the primary school. My brother was so delighted with the success of my plan that he suggested that we should use it more often. I thought this a little bit premature. This was a commendation to me. Brendan was not one to offer compliments to anyone.

"Now whatever you do, don't tell anyone else. We must keep it secret." I looked at my brother and we both laughed at our audacity and the thought of fooling the teacher.

Next morning we returned to school believing that our prank had worked. The morning lessons went well indeed in more ways than one. Not alone was the black strap conspicuous by its absence, but we were not, so it appeared missed from the previous afternoon session. In my mind's eye I was by now planning how I would spend next Thursday afternoon. That afternoon our teacher was once again Bagsy. Did I mention that he was called Bagsy because he wore plus fours? A style of trouser, worn by golfers of the day. He was not the most understanding of the teachers and had no hesitation in punching a pupil in the face, as soon as he looked at them.

We were always cagey (careful) whenever he called us up to the front of his class. He was not prone to using the black strap. Rather he could and would aim a punch to the temple that would do justice to a professional boxer.

When we returned to the classroom that afternoon he was already in action at the large blackboard. He had drawn a large map of Ireland and her islands in green chalk on the blackboard. Turning he faced his captive pupils and removed the roll call from his desk. As he called out each name we answered *Annso* (present) in Irish. He always looked up to ensure that we were really present and not someone else trying it on. Having taken the roll call and accounted for his flock present and absent, he returned the book to his desk.

He picked up the long pointer that rested on the pegs holding up the blackboard. He tapped the map of Ireland that he had so skilfully drawn to attract our attention.

"Now I want you to take out your drawing books and draw this map and then fill in all the principal cities, towns and rivers of Ireland in their proper places." He walked with deliberate steps up and down in front of the class.

I opened my desktop and removed my drawing pad and turned to a blank page and began to draw.

"Before you start I want you and your brother out here. The rest of you carry on." He beckoned Brendan and I forward.

We went towards his desk and stopped a few feet from him for safety. A precautionary measure adopted by all the pupils, when confronted by him.

"How did you get on at the practice yesterday?" He asked. That teacher was as cunning as an old fox.

Like a fool I thought that he was going to put me forward for the big event, the annual sports day.

"Oh very good Sir, I managed to win most of the races I was in." I lied.

"I see, and how did you do?" He looked at Brendan who was hiding behind me for protection.

"I had nothing to do Sir." Brendan shuffled from one foot to the other on the bare boards.

"Do you know, I could have sworn that I saw the two of you in William Street yesterday. Were you?" He studied my expression as he sprung the trap.

I looked back at Brendan, then at Bagsy. I knew that he was playing a cat and mouse game with us. Bagsy moved forward towards me, I retreated and collided with my brother.

"You were never next or near the Claughan playing fields yesterday. Were you?" There was no need for either of us to answer. Now I was apprehensive of his next move. I kept my right hand across my chest. Ready to protect my face, should he throw one of his lightning punches.

On this occasion he did not throw his usual right punch. Instead he used the old trick of bringing both hands forward with the palms open and landing them swiftly on both ears simultaneously. What had happened to me? I was completely disorientated although I was used to such punishment. I staggered around the floor like a drunken man. A kaleidoscope of colours flashed before my eyes. The pain was intense. Then all went black. Next I knew was finding myself lying on the floor and Bagsy standing over me ordering me to my feet. The Room spun round and round as I rose unsteadily to my feet, then it stopped spinning.

He stood before me ranting and raving and calling me a caffler, liar, cur and every name under the sun that he could think of. I was the most evil wretch he had ever had the misfortune to teach.

Then he delivered a left punch or was it a right punch to my head. I saw his lips move and his hand pointing towards the blackboard but I did not hear him and instinctively went and stood where I believed he wanted me to stand. Sharp whistling sounds kept up a constant whining buzz as a drum beat a loud tattoo in my ears. I felt dizzy and nauseated.

As I stood beside the blackboard I looked across and saw him lashing Brendan with the pointer. He was then instructed to join me.

My ears kept ringing and popping and I put my fingers in them trying to stop the noises. Voices came and went as the other pupils answered questions. I could not comprehend just what they were saying. It was as if they were talking in whispers. My eyes hurt and felt as if that they had left their sockets. Finally much to my relief there was a popping sound in my ears and I could once again hear the chanting of my fellow students as they answered the many questions on the rivers and towns of old Ireland.

The pain however did not go away and that evening I related what happened to my mother.

"Don't worry, I'll soon have you right as rain." Mother told me. Mother had more cures for the ills of the world than the Mayo institute.

She went into the kitchen and returned with the Teapot. With a spoon she removed the Tealeaves from the pot and put them onto a piece of linen cloth and bathed both my eyes. Having bathed my eyes she again went to the sideboard and took out a bottle of olive oil and filled a large spoon from the contents. This she heated over the gas ring. Telling me to sit on a chair with my head to one side she poured some of the oil into my ear and sealed it with a cotton wick. She repeated the operation on my other ear.

"Rub the lobe of your ear until you feel it go inside your ear." She instructed me. I could feel the warm oil in my ear and its soothing effect. Perhaps it was psychological but it relieved the pain and eventually cured it.

Mother said no more to us about the incident in the school for the rest of that evening. Brendan and I left next morning for the long journey to Sexton Street secondary college. At school break we were more than surprised to see mother in the Schoolyard talking to our superior. We looked across at her, but we dared not approach. She was in deep discussion with the superior.

That afternoon we again had Bagsy teaching us geography. He asked various questions of the pupils but never asked Brendan nor I any. Each time he questioned the pupils in our row, he avoided questioning us. It did not take us too long to understand that we were being ostracised. We were more that happy to be left to our own devices. For days he did not check our work nor did he ask to see our homework. Mistakes were left uncorrected; our homework was left unattended on the top of his desk. We were abandoned like the plague. Ostracised!

We knew we were boycotted by our teacher and we related this to the day mother called to see the superior. Mother kept asking us if there were any more problems and as to how we were getting on at school, and we would tell her just great.

Whatever battering we got from the brothers at least *Bagsy* was leaving us alone. The days turned into weeks and we became the envy, not alone of the class but of the whole secondary college.

Our conceit and arrogance knew no bounds and we became more and more daring. Then one day Brendan took matters too far and began reading the Beano comic in the classroom. This was too much for Bagsy, who promptly confiscated his comic and despatched him to Brother Murrey, who gave him four of the best on each hand.

On his return to the classroom, he received a further four on each hand from Bagsy. He had decided that we were having it too good and should be returned to the fold.

THE FIDDLER AND HIS BOW BACKED MARE

The people of Park are proud hard working industrious and charitable folk. I remember well on one occasion when I stood looking over a wall at a field of cabbage that any farmer would be proud to own, the smallholder came from his cottage and approached me.

"Did you ever see a crop of cabbage like that son." He looked proudly at his neat weed free straight rows.

"No Sir I must say I have not, I was just admiring them." I nodded in agreement.

"Come in son, pick whichever one takes your fancy with my blessing." Opening the gate he invited me on to his allotment. Pulling up a giant of a head of cabbage he handed it to me roots and all.

"There son take that home and get your mother to boil it with a bit of Limerick bacon."

"I cannot take it, I have no money." I went to hand the cabbage back.

"Whoever mentioned money now? Say a prayer for me will you." These were true Limerick folk.

It was over by the Gallows Green near to Singland in the east of the city that the fiddler and his large family lived. I say his large family for when the count reached fourteen children, the Parish Priest himself lost count.

The Fiddler! Well he got his name from his mare more or less as you will learn. His mare was in foal as often as his wife was pregnant. Not mind you that he wanted his wife to be pregnant; the same could not be said for his mare. One could not really blame him, for he depended in part on the sale of the foals to supplement his meagre income. His only source of income came from the small sales he eked from his smallholding. The produce from which, he sold regularly in the milk market and on the streets of Limerick.

The Children, and I accept that I can include myself, were not too complimentary to the fiddler and spent a lot of energy trying to take a rise out of him. They would, and again I include myself, follow his cart and sing-:

> 'He comes from Park, the dirty Park,
> Full of dirty people,
> They throw their dung
> Outside their doors
> Not fit for the corporation.'

This did not apply to the fiddler, for every scrap of dung he could procure he lavished on his smallholding. It was a known fact that the people of Park used to collect the waste offal from animals and fish stores and bury them in their smallholdings. Consequently they produced the finest crops this side of Keeper Hill. It was said that they cut down their cabbages with a crosscut saw and used the legs for fencing posts. Perhaps a bit exaggerated but the quality of their produce was the envy of many. It was claimed that the fiddler's mare got its bowed back from all the foals she kept producing. It was some months after the birth of one of his many children that he decided enough was enough. He would go and have words with the parish Priest. He was finding that the house was no longer big enough to contain all their offspring.

Entering the presbytery, he was confronted by the parish Priest. He was by now a customary figure, coming to announce another birth and asking for a baptismal date. Whatever the priest expected on this occasion he was in for a shock.

"Father! I've come to ask a big favour of you, that is if you are not too busy." He looked out of the window at his beloved mare that was in foal as usual.

"What is it my son? I have a lot on today. Can you be brief?" The priest took his watch from his pocket and opening the dust cover looked at the time, before closing it and replacing it in his pocket. A hint that he had little, if any time for a lengthy conversation.

"I'll be brief indeed Father. It is like this, I'm sick and tired of my wife full of children and my mare foaling at the same time." He paused and waited for the learned cleric to reply. The Priest looked at him not believing all that he was hearing.

"Do my ears deceive me. You know what the marriage vows are all about, don't you?" The learned cleric looked disdainfully at the fiddler.

"You had best remind me again Father. It seems to have slipped my mind. I apologise but it was a long time ago, you know."

"The state of marriage is for the procurement of children. You know this better than anyone." The priest tapped his fingers together.

"Will you not be talking to me about the procurement of children Father? Sure me and Mary have done our share, not alone done, but done more." The fiddler nodded his head in agreement with himself.

"I know! I know and sure God knows that you speak the truth but such is his holy will." Here the priest raised his eyes to heaven and blessed himself before again taking out his watch and again looking at it.

"Now look here father, no disrespect to the cloth meant and none taken I hope. You are in better contact with the man above than I am or ever could be. So if you can spare the time, you tell him that my Mary, and come to think of it myself have enough children. If he don't be minding would he stop getting my Mary pregnant."

"Have you no thought as to what you are saying my man?" The Priest stuttered shocked at what he was hearing.

"Know what I'm saying! Of course I know what I'm saying and so should you, Father. Did you not tell me no more than two minutes ago on this very floor that it was the will of God that got my Mary pregnant. Well did you?"

"You don't seem to understand; Let me explain." The priest sat down on the seat in the hall.

"No need to Father; enough is enough and you tell him that from me, I'll not delay you any longer seeing as you are in a hurry. Good day to yourself."

The fiddler left the presbytery and the befuddled priest wondering just what he would say to his God that evening as he read his breviary.

As the fiddler had not got enough land to grow his few crops and graze his mare he was not adverse to putting her in someone else's meadow to eat her fill. Especially, if there happened to be a good stallion in the same field on heat. This to him would be a God send and a bonus.

On one such forage he was more than pleased to see a proud stallion grazing in a lush meadow divided by a make shift fence and gate. Leaving the mare in the field, he crossed to where the stallion was peacefully grazing. He opened the gate leading into the section where his mare was now trespassing. This God sent opportunity was not to be missed and he intended to take full advantage of the situation. He was sure that he saw his mare smile as she looked at the big stallion. Next evening he returned to the field hoping that the stallion had done his duty. He was more than surprised to find that his mare was not there. The stallion was standing alone in the centre of the field looking down at him.

"Have you seen my mare, here about?" He spoke aloud. The stallion pricked up his ears momentarily before returning to chewing the cud. He searched far and wide for her without success. Finally in desperation he was forced to go and ask the farmer in whose field he had left her and ask his help.

"Excuse me Sir; did you by any stretch of the imagination see a first class mare around here? I was told that some blackguards left her in your field." He lied to the farmer.

"Did you say a first class mare? No! Sorry, I never came across such an animal. Did you lose one?" The farmer scratched the stubble on his chin as he spoke.

"Are you sure now? It's a black mare with a white blaze on her forehead and a very slight curve to her back, if you know what I mean." He held out his palm and formed a curve.

"Come to think of it, there was such a mangy beast in my field. Was that your mare? Sure I was thinking that the tinkers had abandoned her. Do you know that she was pestering my stallion? I had to open the gate and chase her out."

This piece of news was both good and bad news for the fiddler. Firstly there was a good chance that the mare was now in foal. Where in the name of God had she gone? Perhaps the guards had picked her up. Should he go and ask them? He dismissed this notion from his mind. They would only summons him once again as they had done in the past for letting his mare wander on the roads. He dared not show his face inside the barracks.

He decided to pray to St Anthony; he would be his best bet in finding his lost mare. His humble praying brought little comfort. No matter how hard he prayed there was still no sign of his beloved mare. After a long search and questioning, he was finally directed to a field some miles away .

"There's an ould mare out in a field in Castleconnel. She fits your description to a tee. You couldn't miss her if you were blind. She's with several goats and a mule." He was informed

"Thank you, thank you very much, Sir. God bless your eye sight."

The fiddler returned home and wasted no time in getting his old rickety bicycle from the wall in the shed, then procuring a halter, he set out to collect his mare. When he came to the field, he dismounted from his bicycle. Putting the halter over his shoulder he entered the field.

There sure enough at the far end of the field was his beloved mare. He could not be mistaken, for he could see the setting sun over the curve in her back. Cupping his hands to his mouth he called to her. She, on hearing her master's voice cocked up her ears and trotted across the field to greet him.

"There you are ould girl, you're a sight for sore eyes so you are. Do you know that I searched the countryside for you? I thought that you were lost for good." He put his hands round the neck of his mare and stroked her nose. Then putting the halter round her neck, he led her to the roadway.

Removing his bicycle from the hedgerow he mounted it and peddled back to his home with his faithful mare trotting behind. The halter was securely tied to the carrier of his bicycle. He watched his mare over the following months as she grew fatter and fatter. He was delighted as he visualised the fine stallion in the field where he had left his mare that day. Surely his mare would give him a fine offspring from the stallion. The foal in time would bring him in a tidy sum. The time came for the mare to foal and the fiddler was like a hen on hot eggs, as he prepared a warm maternity bed for her in the stable. Nothing would be too good for her this time. He went so far as to purchase a bundle of fresh straw for her bed. Something he had never done before.

Like an anxious father, he spent most of his time between the stable and the house. Then it happened, the mare's water broke and the fiddler ran to the home of his best friend to seek his help with the birth. Lighting the hurricane lamp, they collected two buckets of soapy water and took them to the stable and sat down. In his pocket the fiddler had a flat bottle of whiskey to keep them warm as they awaited the birth. Together they sat on two upturned butter boxes and waited for nature to take its course.

"John, I'll not be forgetting your help this night, you can be assured of that." The fiddler reached into his hip pocket and removed the bottle of whiskey and handed it to his friend.

"That's more than generous of you. I'll take a drop now to ward off the chill of the night." Removing the cork from the bottle, he took a deep swill. The amber nectar flowed down his parched throat and warmed the cockles of his heart.

"Jesus! That's a drop of the good stuff." He pressed the cork back into the bottle and put it into his pocket.

"Would you mind giving me a drop, that is if you don't mind?" The fiddler stretched out his hand.

"Sorry Mick, sure I thought that you gave it to me." John removed the bottle from his pocket and handed it back to the fiddler. Taking a prolonged drink from the bottle, he replaced the cork and put it in his own back pocket. As he settled back down on his seat again, he noticed that the mare was showing signs of imminent birth.

"Jesus! It's happening." He jumped off the box like a frog off a log and nudged his friend John who was half asleep.

"Stand by John, she's bound to need our help after her experience with that stallion." He looked at the rear end of the mare as two small hooves appeared. John went and fetched the two buckets of warm water as the fiddler held the hurricane lamp nearer to the rear of his mare.

"Oh Jesus, Mary and Joseph, be good to my poor mare this night. He joined his hands in prayer. He made the sign of the cross over his mare and removing the whiskey bottle from his pocket he sprinkled some over her.

"What's the matter with you Mick? Wasting good whiskey on the mare. Have you gone mad?" Mick looked at the bottle and then at his friend John.

"May God forgive me, sure I thought that it was the holy water." He put the bottle to his lips and took another swig and replaced the cork.

"If you don't be minding Mick, I could do with a slug myself." John sarcastically remarked as he watched the bottle about to vanish into the back pocket of Mick.

"Sure didn't I forget John, sorry." He handed the bottle to his friend.

John being a life long friend of his had never seen him show any such concern when his wife was having a child.

"Will you not be so worried about your mare man. Don't you know by now that, 'Sweet bracken' grows on dark hills.

The mare's eyes danced in the glow of the lamplight as she tried to dislodge the foal. Finally with one last effort she disgorged the foal and turned her attention to cleaning it. The fiddler picked up a handful of clean straw and began to help the mare to clean the foal. Not that he was too interested in its welfare. What he wanted to know was what prize he had.

"Come here John and take a look. Are my eyes deceiving me or not?" He held the lamp high and looked down at the foal as John joined him.

There on the clean straw lay, not the fine foal that he had so dearly expected but a mule.

"Will you just look at that Fecking bastard? Who would give me the price of a pint for that?" He pointed to the mule trying to get to his feet with the help of the mare.

They both looked in utter amazement at the foal. The mother looked with pride at her off spring.

"Before you leave here this blessed night, swear John that you will never tell a living soul about this." The fiddler was so upset and ashamed that the fine foal he had boasted about was nothing but a mule.

But the story did get out and as was usual in such circumstances the people were less than charitable, especially the children. We took a delight in following him and chanting-:

> 'The fiddler had an old bowed mare
> To show her foal he does not dare
> Is it an ass, is it a mule?
> Or is he just a bloody fool'

This barracking, to say the least was more than embarrassing to him as he went from street to street selling his vegetables and potatoes. He looked dejected at his old bowed mare pulling his cart, but she looked proud as punch, as she looked around at her off spring trotting behind the cart. This could not be said for the fiddler. He tried to fob off the mule as a stray saying that he was asked to take it in out of charity. He would gladly give him to anyone looking for a good working mule, in exchange for a nominal fee to cover the cost of his keeping and feeding. He went so far as to offer Feathery Burke a share in the sale if he would sell it for him. However Feathery in all his cunning tricks failed to make a sale. Eventually he was forced to abandon the mule some miles into the county of Tipperary.

I wonder how many remember the Fiddler? A harmless poor soul, trying to make an honest living.

THE VISIT OF THE WHITE FATHERS

In the summer of my second year of my advanced education, we were informed that the White Friars from Africa would visit the monastery and address us. We were told that to be addressed by such a distinguished order was a great honour. Some time before the arrival of the friars, our geography teacher acquired a large map of Africa on American cloth. This he used to pin point where exactly the friars came from.

"Now boys I want you to pay particular attention to this map." He pointed to the map with the pointer.

"We should all know something about them and their good work in darkest Africa." He paused as he looked around the class.

"Tell me what are the friars are doing in Africa?" He pointed at me.

"Praying Sir." I replied without thinking.

"Sit down you Amadan (Fool) all priests pray." If he did not want me to answer why did he ask me?

"The friars are in Africa claiming the souls of the savages for Jesus. However there is little need for me to explain their missionary work. They are quite capable of explaining it themselves. In the meantime we should all be praying for them and the success of their mission and their love of Jesus." Here he blessed himself and turned towards the statue of the blessed virgin standing on her pedestal high above the desks surrounded by blue nightlights. This was the signal for us to come to our feet and face the statue. If he and the White fathers knew so much about Africa why did he ask me?

"In the name of the Father, Son and the Holy Ghost." He blessed himself, we followed his example and finished by saying the *Hail Mary* for their success.

Then came the big day, the White Friars were safely in the city. One could not miss them for they looked like *Bean-Ó-Sidhes* in their all white robes.

We were to be the first to be addressed and blessed by them the following day we were informed. We were told to bring our rosary beads and any holy objects we wished to be blessed. Further we were to bring a small monetary donation to help them in their mission. Blessings would be bestowed on us, and a full year's masses would be offered up for the repose of the souls of departed members of the families who gave a donation. Not alone that but we would also receive a signed certificate that we could frame. It was pointed out to us that these certificates were coveted prizes and we should make every effort to qualify for one.

That evening I told mother the purpose of the Friars visit. Leaving the request for money until I was sure in my own mind that I had impressed on her the real purpose of their visit.

"Ma! The brothers want us to bring a small donation to help in their works of mercy in Africa. In return we will get many blessings and a holy certificate to hang on the wall." I awaited her reaction.

"A small donation for Africa did you say? Well now, don't you know that your cousin from Manchester is stationed there with the British army, God forgive me but why not let the British look after them. After all it is part of her empire. I have enough problems making ends meet here." Mother it would appear was not convinced that a donation to the missions would do much good. The real truth was that mother had no money to give to anyone. She felt that charity should begin at home. I knew that I would be despatched off to school next day without any donation. I was also well aware that this would displease the Brothers and that I would suffer for it at a later date. I had to use all my chicanery in overcoming their displeasure to say the least. That night I searched through our medal drawer. This was the drawer where all the medals, crosses, scapulars and relics were kept. These we received on a regular basis from my eldest sister who was a nun in the Franciscan order stationed in Florida U.S.A.

We had more relics of the true cross than there were trees on mount Calvary or Cratlow woods. We had more relics of the saints than there were saints in the encyclopaedia of *Lives of the Saints*. If anyone ever needed a holy medal of any saint, then we were in a position to supply it. As I believe were most families in the city, of that I had no doubt. In the collection I found two large bronze medals. To what saint they belonged I did not know, and as a matter of fact I cared less. They were of the same size as a penny. I hoped that they would fool the brother and my generosity to the friars would not go unrewarded and that it would gain for me the coveted certificate. I filed the eyehole from the medals and put them in my pocket.

Next day there was great excitement in the monastery. The classrooms were closed and we were directed to the chapel where mass was to be celebrated by the friars. Some of the boys had several pairs of rosary beads, some statues and others holy pictures. It was like a sales room with all the holy pictures and relics. Me! I had my two counterfeit coins. When all the pupils were settled in the seats, the sacristy door opened. The brother superior came forward to the altar followed by the other brothers and lay teachers from the secondary college. From the doorway came a man in a long white cloak with a cowl over his head, sporting the longest beard I ever saw. He was followed by six others dressed the same, they looked as if they were wearing burial shrouds. All were singing the Gregorian chant. They glided across the floor like *Bean-Ó-Sidhes*. These must be the friars, we whispered to each other. One backward glance from the superior and we were struck dumb once again. Mass was celebrated by the head friar and his brother priests, with the brothers acting as Sacristans or acolytes as they were better known in Limerick. There were so many on the altar steps that they were tripping over each other much to our amusement. There was a lot of singing of hymns but no communion was given except to the priests and brothers. When the mass was completed, the superior and his brothers went and sat in the two front seats of the chapel. These had been reserved before hand for them. Those with objects to be blessed were told to hold them up. There was a noisy movement in the chapel as the boys held their beads, books, pictures and statues high in the air.

The old bearded priest came forward accompanied by another friar carrying a brass bucket containing holy water and in his hand he held the aspergillum. It was made of bamboo with a bulbous attachment that had small holes in it to soak up the holy water. It looked more like an African drumstick with holes in it and I presumed that what it was, to impress us no doubt. As the old friar blessed the sacred objects his assistant dipped the aspergillum into the bucket of holy water and sprinkled it over us. With this part of the service concluded the head friar invited his fellow priests to sit on the seats provided for them at each side of the altar. Looking down at the captive pupils seated before him, he stroked his beard. He made the sign of the cross over us, before tucking his hands into the wide sleeves of his garment. Then he enlightened us on their work in Africa. He spoke eloquently and sincerely of their work in saving the souls of the Africans for Jesus. We were so enthralled with his stories that we sat there without so much as a murmur from us. We were shown slides of their work in darkest Africa. We were also shown pictures of Elephants, Lions, Crocodiles etc; Then he sprung the greatest surprise of all. He called on those of us who felt that we had the vocation to put up our hands. There was no need to ask further, every hand in the chapel was raised high. Some were so excited that they were standing up in the seats waving their hands to draw his attention.

The brother superior looked around at his pupils with a smile on his face. I waved my hand towards him and wondered if he saw me. We all wanted to go to Africa and save the souls of the black babies for Jesus. I doubt very much if that was the real reason. I suspect that we were caught up in the euphoria of his sermon and the chance to get out of Limerick. The good friar smiled down at us and called on the Holy family to bless us and our vocation. We on our part were sure that he would take us all back to Africa with him.

Me! I saw myself as a knight of the crusaders on my white charger going into battle against the Saracens. My white cloak with the cross of Jesus boldly embroidered in red on the front for all to see , bringing fear into the hearts of the unbelievers. I felt that if he called me, then I would bring more converts into the church than any of the others. In me he would have a real asset. One of the chosen few. I had a genuine vocation

"Many are called but few are chosen." He told us. Having called on the Holy Family to bless us once again, he done no more than return to his seat and sat down. This was a great disappointment to me and no doubt to many of the others as well.

There was a pause before two of the Friars rose from their seats and bowing before the Blessed Sacrament went into the sacristy, only to return shortly afterwards. One was carrying a large cardboard box, the other a statue of a black boy kneeling. His mouth was open with a big smile on his face. He had a big red tongue and he looked like a baby blackbird waiting to be fed. The head kept nodding up and down as he was carried into the church. What kind of a saint was this I thought? We knew most of the saints and as far as I knew none of them were black. The statue, for that is what I took it to be, was placed on a small table that had been placed in front of the Altar as was the cardboard box.

The head friar rose to his feet and going across to the table opened the box. From it he withdrew a scrolled certificate and held it up for all to see and admire.

"One of these will be presented to each and every pupil making a contribution to the missions." He displayed the coveted certificate from side to side. Its golden scroll reflecting in the light from the chapel windows.

"Now those of you making a donation come forward and place your coins in the mouth of the black boy." He pointed to the black statue, only now the head no longer bobbed up and down. He was still smiling. I thanked God that I would be one of those making a contribution. I also prayed that I would not be found out giving two medals.

The line of boys moved slowly forward to where two of the friars sat with fountain pens in their hands and piles of certificates before them. When my turn came I placed one medal in the mouth of the black boy. I watched as the medal slid down into the mouth of the statue. The head with the beguiling smile and thick lips nodded as the medal hit the mechanism controlling the head. Nobody seemed to notice that I had donated a filed down medal. Seeing that I was about to get the coveted certificate I put the other medal back in my pocket. I could use it elsewhere. I moved forward and one of the friars asked my name. This he entered on the certificate and smiling he handed it to me. Finally when all the boys had made their contribution the box and the statue was removed. Now although I had got my coveted certificate I wanted more than anything else to become a White Friar. Plucking up courage I left my seat and nervously approached the head Friar who was still sitting on his chair smiling. I stood before him spell bound and lost for words.

"Is there something that you wish to ask me, son?" He looked up at me like the saint that he was. I knelt in reverence before him, I knew that the brothers were watching and I intended to impress them.

"Yes father! I would like to be a Friar just like you. I know that I have the calling." I rubbed the palms of my sweating hands together behind my back.

"I know that you would and I admire your courage, but we must remember that many are called but few are chosen. Give it careful thought and if you feel the same way when your schooling is finished you can write to me. God bless you." With these words he made the sign of the cross over me and dismissed me from his presence with another blessing. I had never been so blessed in my whole life. I was excited as I ran home from school. I could hardly wait to tell mother that I was to become a White Knight. Going through the front door like the proverbial rocket. Ignoring my dog for once I began to tell mother of my commitment.

"Wait up a minute, will you. What are you blabbering about?" Mother came from the kitchen wiping her hands.

"Ma! I'm going to be a White Friar and I got this for you." I handed her the rolled up scroll.

"This is very nice, but how did you get it seeing as you had no money? What have you been up to this time?" She unrolled the scroll and studied it.

"It's like this ma! I gave them a medal on account and they let me have it."

"You gave the friars a medal on account of what? They gave you this, now that's one for the books. How did you really get it?" She interrogated me.

I broke under the pressure and told her the story of the filed down medal and my promise to let them have a penny at a later date.

"Did you tell them all this before you decided to become one of them?"

"No Ma! But I'm sure he knew that I have the calling." By now I could see myself in darkest Africa dressed in white with a long white beard.

"Well all that I can say is, that I hope when his time on earth finishes, that God will be kind to him and measure his big heart. Not his pea sized brain for listening to you." I did not understand what she meant by this remark at the time. When I did next day, it was all too late for I had lost the calling. I still had the sacred medal left and my mind was already working overtime as to where I would spend it. I knew this shop over in Quinn's lane off John Street not too far from the school. It was managed by an old lady with poor eye sight. Not alone that but the lighting in the shop left a lot to be desired.

After school I would chance my arm and try and trade in the other medal for a Chester cake. Leaving school in the afternoon, I sauntered down John Street and entered Quinn's Lane. Well I thought to myself, as I pushed the door open, in for a penny, in for a pound. The bell above the door clanged to announce the arrival of a customer- Me!

"I'll be with you in two shakes of a lamb's tail." It was the voice of the old lady with the bad eyesight; my luck was holding. I waited at the old wooden counter for her to come out from her sparse kitchen and serve me.

"Now son, what will it be? I doubt if I have very much left." She looked round at the bare shelves. I was glad that she did not remember me from previous callings to her shop.

"Have you any Chester cakes left?" I asked.

Reaching under the counter she produced a tray of cakes. Out of respect for cakes, she called them Chester cakes. Our name for these cakes was, *'Sweepings of the Loft'.* There were three miserable stale cakes left on the tray probably a week old. I wouldn't be surprised by the marks on them if the rats had been at them. Rejected no doubt by more discerning customers.

"How much do you want for them things?" I pointed to the miserable few cakes.

"How much do you think? A penny each, of course. Do you want one or not?"

"Are they fresh?" I dared to ask.

"Fresh! They were fresh when I got them, why what's wrong with them?"

"Oh alright, I'll take that one." I picked the biggest one on the tray and that was not all that big. I handed her the medal and began to leave the shop with my cake. It was then that I heard the roar from the kitchen.

"Come back here you Fecking skuttering Git. Try to rob a decent woman would you?" She came rushing round the counter and confronted me before I could lift the latch. Why did I think that this little old lady could not move? Like a lioness attacking a Zebra she was upon me before I could wink my eye.

"What's wrong Ma'am, I paid you didn't I?" I looked at her in all innocence.

"You give me back my fecking cake at once and take this with you." She reached out her claw like hand and caught my free hand and banged the medal into my palm. Then she grabbed the cake although by this time I had taken a bite out of it.

"What's wrong with it anyway?" I innocently looked at the medal sitting in the palm of my hand.

"Do you take me for a blind fecking fool or something? One of them was fobbed off on me last week, if you must know." Her face was so close to mine that I could feel her spittle on my face. I didn't know women swore.

"Come to think of it now, I'm nearly sure as hell that you are the same little fecking caffler. Yes it was you, I'd know that sour puss anyplace. Get out of here before I call the guards." She pushed me out of the door and slammed it behind me. I looked down at the medal in the palm of my hand. I heard the bell ring and the shop door opened again .

"If I ever see you next or near my shop again I'll have the guards on you. Now feck off." I looked back to see her shaking her fist at me.

Next day there was uproar in the school, a sacrilege had been committed. We were assembled once again in the chapel. From the altar steps the good brother superior, denounced the perpetrator of an evil deed to the fires of Hell.

"Some boy. No! Some Devil, with nothing but evil in his mind, put a medal in the good friar's collection box. Not alone a medal but one filed down to make it look like a penny. A sacrilege and an abomination before Almighty God." Spittle formed on his mouth and I thought he was going to have a heart attack, then what would I do? I would be blamed for murdering him and swing on the gallows. He looked round the chapel hoping to find some clue on the faces of the pupils.

"This is it." He held the evidence above his head for all to see. "Which one of you carries the mark of Cain?" I thought this a bit over the top. After all Cain carried the mark because he murdered his brother, Able.

"I tell you this, no good will come out of it. Not alone did he cheat the friars and stole, yes stole, the certificate, but he desecrated a holy medal dedicated to St Theresa." He looked with shocked horror at us. So it was the medal of Saint Theresa that I filed down. I thought to myself, I should remember to ask Delia to send us some more from the convent.

"Will the boy. No! Will the blackguard who perpetrated this evil sacrilege in the house of God now stand up and confess his sin before Almighty God?" He looked around the chapel hoping to see who would be brave or foolish enough to stand up. There was no way I was going to confess. Why I would in all probability be stoned through the streets of Limerick like Saint Stephen was.

"Very well then: Remember there is a viper amongst you. A viper that carries the Mark of Cain! You will all remain behind for one hour extra for the rest of the week. I hope the Devil who perpetrated this evil deed has sleepless nights as he fights with his conscience. If he's taken in his sleep he will go straight through the gates of |Hell into the eternal flames of Hell." Had I known there would be all this hullabaloo over a simple medal I wouldn't have taken the trouble. Still I was taking no chances and went to a country church and told what I had done in a round about way. This act on my part saved my immortal soul from Hell fire.

THE LADY AND HER KEY

Over the archway from our room in the Strand barracks there lived a strange lady and her cat *Tibbles*. She kept herself very much to herself. Where she came from was a bit of a mystery. She was always immaculately dressed with not a hair out of place and as predictable as the *Angelus* bell. Always leaving her room at a precise time and returning approximately an hour later.

Nobody seemed to notice that she had not been seen for two days. That is with the exception of my mother.

"I'm worried about her next door. I haven't seen her for the last two days. I'd best go and see if she is alright." She told us. Knocking gently on her door she waited, then she knocked again and called. "Are you alright in there?" As there was no response she gripped the handle and turned it. The door swung open as she slowly pushed it inwards. "Anyone home?" She called as she moved deeper into the room. The room was in darkness as a heavy curtain had been drawn across the window.

"I'm over here. Would you please see to Tibbles?" A voice softly called from the recess of the room. Mother went and opened the curtain. The room was flooded with light. The room was so small that the bed took up most of the floor space.

"Are you not well then?" She asked.

"I'm not too bad but I cannot get out to see to Tibbles."

"Never mind your cat for now, when did you eat last? I think I had best send for Doctor Holmes." Mother retreated from the room and called to me.

"Go into town and fetch the doctor. Tell him it's urgent. Now don't take that dog with you," she warned.

"Who will I tell him to come to?" I questioned.

"I don't know her name, and anyhow she could not answer the door. Tell him to call here first."

In spite of mothers warnings Bruno accompanied me. We made our way into the city and to the doctor's surgery, which was also his home. The servant girl informed me that he was out on call. She promised that she would inform him of the urgency of the situation as soon as he returned.

That evening the doctor called and mother took him across the hall.

"I'm afraid that she is incapable of looking after herself. Do you know if she has any relatives?" He asked.

"I don't think she has anyone, doctor."

"Then she will have to go into the City Home. She cannot stay here," he warned.

The outcome was that mother took on the task of looking after her. She was not in the best of health and to add to her misfortunes she suffered from

Rheumatic fever. One could see from her face that she was in constant pain. Mother as usual had volunteered me to see to her shopping.

She took on the task of cleaning and tidying up her sparse room and bed. She also made her meals, not that she ate a lot. Bruno and I were always on hand to clear up. She forever smelt of camphorated oil, which she used liberally on her joints to ease her pains. Peeping over her collar could be seen a blanket of thermal yellow wool. A sure sign that she had chest troubles. At night she would sit huddled over the grate of her range, seeking heat to ease her pains, her faithful cat Tibbles sitting on her knees. Whenever I could I would go to her room and keep her company. Bruno and her cat got on well together and she liked that. She took to telling me stories and after a time I asked her if she would mind if I brought a few mates in to listen. Soon my gang became regular visitors and she seemed grateful for the company. In the evenings we took a sadistic delight in going to her room to be frightened by her ghost stories. The stories always related to her past and the beautiful farm she once owned.

"Did I ever tell you children, that we once owned the finest farm in the Golden Vale of Limerick?"

Although she had told us this story over and over again we could not help but to be enthralled as she built yet another story 'round it. Slowly she would remove her cat from her lap. Raising feebly to her feet she would hobble to her sideboard and retrieve a large iron key from the drawer. We were never allowed to fetch the key for her; that was her prerogative. Like the Priest fetching the sacred host, her key too was sacrosanct to her. Hobbling back to her seat she would painfully sit down. Patting her lap to encourage her cat to rejoin her. The cat needed no encouragement, for no sooner had she resumed her seat than he was back on her lap. Leaping from the floor to her lap he would go round and round in ever decreasing circles, until finally he settled down and began to purr. We presumed that she liked the cat on her lap for the extra heat he provided.

"Is that not the finest key, you ever did see?" She would with great effort hold the key in her hand that was badly deformed from arthritis.

"It is indeed and big enough to open *King John's Castle.*" I would enlighten her. This would bring a smile to her face.

As she slowly turned the key in her hand over the heat of the fire, the flickering lights from the flames passed through the key. Shadows would manifest themselves on the bare walls. Their reflections, mockingly dancing in the glow from the fire. Apparitions, perhaps of the ghosts that she reincarnated nightly with her stories mingled with the shadows.

It would be a hard hearted person indeed who could not but sympathise with her, as she looked far beyond the grate, tears of memories past filling her sad eyes. Composing herself she would find a temporary home for the key in her apron pocket, much to the annoyance of her cat at being disturbed.

"Now children! Who would like to hear a real true story?" Looking from one to the other with that mischievous twinkle in her smiling eyes she would ask.

"Oh yes please!" We would move that much nearer to the fire. Crossing our legs to make ourselves more comfortable. Before settling down a fresh sod of turf was screwed into the fire. Sparks raced up the chimney, never to be seen again. Settling back in her seat her story opened.

"It all happened in County Limerick a long, long time ago............

"In our townland lived a very handsome young man, not that far from our farm, I tell you. He fell in love with a young maiden, the only child from an adjoining farm and she with him......"

The story in the classical example of all love stories told of their love for each other and the joy of both parties of parents at such a fine match. This part of the story was soppy to us and we waited anxiously for her to finish with it and get on with the real story.

Then would follow the climax of the story........

"It was the day before the wedding, all arrangements had been finalised. That same evening the handsome young groom took some of his guests to visit the church He wanted to see for himself how the preparations for the great day were progressing. It was dusk by the time they reached the old graveyard guarding the entrance to the church. A mist slowly rose from between the ivy clad tombstones as an owl tooted from the safety of a pagan yew tree. This, in itself children, was indeed a bad omen. The young man should have taken heed, but he was too captivated in the euphoria of his wedding."

Here she paused and looked around at the door, a silence prevailed for some time. Not one of us would dare follow her gaze. We kept our eyes firmly fixed on the fire. Returning her gaze to the fire, she picked up the poker and held it in her knurled hand. Holding firmly onto her cat. With the other hand she riddled the fire, sending comforting sparks hopping and jumping round the grate. Her cat again showing his displeasure at being disturbed curled up in an ever tighter circle. Replacing the poker in the corner, she continued the story...........

"Seeing a human skull lying at the side of the path, the groom picked it up. "God's peace to all the dead this blessed night." Here she blessed herself and encouraged us to do likewise.......

"He being in the best of good spirits and meaning no harm at all, looked into the vacant holes where the eyes once had been, so he did and addressed the skull.

"You too are invited to my wedding reception to morrow." Her voice took on a sombre tone as she looked round at her assembled listeners.

"God protect all of you round my fireside this blessed night, he did so he did." Then he placed it gently back where he found it.

Next day the reception was held in the grand mansion of the Grooms parents. Carriages came and discharged their distinguished guests and moved on. The orchestra played a *Strauss* waltz, as the handsome couple moved gracefully across the floor." At this point she hummed and swayed to a few bars of the waltz and told us how wonderful the mansion looked that night.

"Later that evening at the stroke of midnight when the guests were enjoying themselves, there came a knocking at the great oak doors of the mansion. This drew the attention of the butler. Opening the doors he was confronted by a young gentleman who stepped from the shadows into the light of the tapers. There was no sign of a carriage, which the young man would have needed to reach the isolated mansion.

"Where has your carriage gone to, Sir?" The butler inquired of him.

"I have no need of a carriage for my journey here was short." The young man who wore a silk top hat and tails replied. He carried an ebony walking cane with a gold top. No doubt a man of great wealth. Stepping into the great hall he took off his white silk gloves and scarf. Removing his top hat he placed all inside and handed them to the butler.

"Would you kindly inform your master that I have come to his wedding reception at his personal invitation."

"May I ask your name Sir?" The butler requested.

"My name matters not. He did not ask it of me, nor was it given." The butler looked puzzled at this reply.

"Just tell him that the gentleman, he so kindly invited to his wedding yesterday evening has arrived."

As she continued her story by the light of the flickering candle; we were so frightened at this stage that we had our coats over our heads.

The old lady made no effort to allay our fears, rather did she continue her story with more and more gory details. The butler departed and delivered the message as instructed.

"I'll go and see to this guest personally. He must know of me. Yet I find it hard to place meeting him yesterday." The puzzled groom replied. Seeing the young man standing in the great hall, the bridegroom racked his brain; He was trying to think of when and where he invited him and who his mysterious guest was.

"Well my young friend, what makes my wedding so special that you want to attend?"

"I Sir! Had no intention or desire to attend your wedding, yet you personally sought me out and invited me. Please forgive me for my late arrival."

The groom looked at him in surprise and anger.

"I invited you? I fear Sir, that I do not know you. Nor have I any recollection of inviting you to my wedding. Your impertinence deserves my contempt."

These fine words she used meant little or nothing to us; but they sounded ever so grand.

"Last evening you and your friends were walking through the local graveyard, which is my home now. The skull that you picked up and invited to your wedding belongs to me. I Sir, am here at your personal invitation." The groom looked at the fine young gentleman standing before him. He was shocked when he saw the flesh slowly melt from his head to reveal a bare skull. The bridegroom collapsed to the marble floor in a deep faint. The guests gathered in haste to help the unfortunate bridegroom. The visitor collected his belongings and opened the great door vanished into the misty night.

The groom grew weaker by the day. Specialists were brought in from the great hospitals of London and elsewhere but to no avail. The groom died some weeks later and was interred in the same churchyard where he had met the skull.

His beautiful bride never got over the shock and lived as a recluse in the mansion. She neglected the house and lands and dismissed the servants. Finally with all her money spent she was forced to sell the estate and seek refuge elsewhere.

The next night there would be a different story but all related to her precious farm and key. We heard later that she did own a large farm in the county. That she and a boy from an adjoining farm fell in love and were married. Within three months of the wedding the husband developed tuberculosis. He died shortly afterwards. Mother maintained that the story she told us, was indeed a true story. It was her own wedding that she was relating to.

One day much to our surprise, she decided that she wanted to go to church. Mother tried to advise her against it and offered to bring the priest to her. She would not hear of it and insisted on going to the church alone. Daily she more or less staggered to the church. It must have been by super human strength and determination that she got there and back. Then one day she failed to return to her sparse room. The news soon filtered through that she was found slumped in the seat of a city church, her life now past. Near by was the key that she treasured so dearly. It had slipped from her hand as she died. We never did find out who she was or where she came from. She was buried in the paupers graveyard in Killeely.

The following poem I wrote to her memory. A tribute to her for the many hours of enjoyable story telling she thrilled us with.

THE OLD RUSTIC KEY

The old rusty key, she took it down,
'Twas worn thin with rust, and brown;
Why had she kept that key, you ask?
She has no home, her life now past.
That key is all that she had left,
Of the life she knew, the joy she felt.

The old church clock ticks the hours away
The widow kneels, her prayers to say;
And Christ upon his cross looks down,
He too, a key he gives her now.
With tear dimmed eyes, she calls to him
"Please God, forgive me all of my sins."

Was that a door she heard open wide?
She looks around, then gives a sigh;
Is it the cry of the Bean-Sidhe wail?
Has someone else come in to pray?
Perhaps her Tom has come home soon;
Or yet the children home from school.

Is that you Tom? She calls to him,
Or are my lamps just getting dim;
The shadows now grow more and more,
They beckon her, they call her home.
She rises slowly from her pew and smiles;
The shadows move to be her guide .

The Priest he hears the door bang closed;
He knows it's late, there'll be no more;
On entering his church, all is empty and still,
There's just the shadows that dance at will.
At the high Altar he kneels for a final prayer;
Yet his minds not easy, there's someone there.

He casts his gaze along the seats
No sound, no sight, his senses meet;
"But wait, what's that"? He hears a sound
"Was that a key, fall on the ground"?
He strains his eyes in the fading light,
He sees a figure within his sight.

He calls out once, who can it be?
"Who's in my church, alone with me?"
There is no answer, there is no sound;
He's frightened now, He looks around.
Yet in his fear he moves to see;
The widow dead beside her Key.

The Sexton now he rings the bell
Her time has come, it's her parting knell;
They laid her down beside her Tom,
Her time on earth had come and gone;
The priest looked down at the rusty key
On her coffin he placed it and shed a tear.

I don't expect there are many, if any, who remember the crippled old woman and her cat Tibbles. They lived in one small room in the Strand barracks in Limerick? I remember her not alone as a fine Sean Scealuide, but as a gentle lady. I also remember her in my prayers. I feel sure she would find this simple little ghost poem, in relation to her own mysterious life a real compliment.

GOD BLESS YOU MR KEANE

In my young days there was no social security as we know it to day. The only extra help that the poor could hope for, apart from the help given by the Society of Saint Vincent de Paul, was the niggardly mite begrudgingly handed out on Thursdays at the dispensary in Gerald Griffin Street. Many waited for days in trepidation, for the few shillings they hoped to get. These were already overdue to the Huxter shop, the Pawnshop and the rent man.

This day was more or less like a market day. Friends and neighbours gathered to exchange gossip and to meet old acquaintances and relatives.

Newcomers would shuffle uneasily unsure of the procedure as to how to apply for desperately needed help. The proud would make vain efforts to conceal their true identity without success. Strangers were marked down for special attention. Tension would mount as the clock on the wall slowly ticked the time away. High noon was fast approaching.

I remember listening to the conversations as I stood with my sister in the well of the hall waiting and hoping.........

"Where is that man to day. God but he is cutting it very fine?" Patrons would stamp their feet on the cold floor trying desperately to keep warm.

"I wouldn't mind too much but today of all days. I was promised a real good pair of boots cheap, if I got there on time. Too late now I fear." The speaker looked up at the clock in despair. The assembled people had a thousand reasons as to why Mr Keane should be on time.

"There he is now! Look that's himself and about time too, I must say."

Tom Keane, a native of Ardnachrusha (Parteen) in the county of Clare was some six feet six inches tall and weighed in at about seventeen stone. He had a voice that could be heard all the way into county Clare or so the poor people vouched for. He needed it for it was the only weapon that he had to control his obstreperous beseeching clientele. Mr Keane, was like a God, it was he who decided who would get and who would go without. As judge and jury he was the man who decided who got a few shillings and who went home disappointed. Some people called him the *Devils Advocate*. Others were not so complimentary and derided him for his lack of charity. He was called, the *Hoor's Ghost* from Clare, the *Mongrel*, the *Cur*, the *tyrant*, the *Country Bumpkin*, *the Git* and the ultimate accolade *The Son of a Black and Tan*. He was accused of picking the pockets of the poor of Limerick to line his own. Such slanderous remarks washed off him like water off a duck. Mr Coffin his sidekick came in for more abuse.

"His name suits him, so it does. How many poor creatures did he send in their coffins to Saint Lawrence's I wonder? The dead of Limerick will remember them two in the next world." The rhetoric would continue from his disgruntled customers.

"Shame! They wouldn't know it if it were staring them in the face."

They were none of these, for by all accounts behind all the bellowing they were kind, generous and fair men. Just because they were given the unenviable task of selecting those in most need did not justify this form of character assassination. The money allocated to them for distribution to the needy did not justify such unwarranted criticism. All were needy but some were more needy than others. Many were desperate and starving. They would be blessed for their generosity by the family, that had cursed them the previous week for being excluded from the allocated money, the most that any family could expect to get was two or three shillings (Twelve new pence). To get this sum one would need to be a widow with no less than seven orphans. When the name of the recipient and the amount was called out, there came gasps from the crowd. It was as if one had won the lottery.

"Good morning, Mr Keane. Isn't it a lovely morning, thank God?" Greetings and accolades came loud and clear as he made his appearance. Hypocrisy knew no bounds when need arose.

"A fine man indeed and a real credit to the community and his family." Came a resonant compliment from one woman hoping that he had heard and seen her.

"Ah no truer word Brige, and a real Christian too."

He was used to this hypocrisy and compliments, they bounced off him like water off a duck as he made his way to his office. He had heard them all year in year out.

"Did you see the bag? It looked heavy this week. God is good we may be in luck."

"We may, we may indeed. I for one feel it in my bones Josie. Why I even made a novena to St Jude and spent my last halfpenny on a candle."

Some could be seen on these occasions with their beads hidden under their shawls as they prayed that divine intervention would intercede on their behalf.

"Will you just look at the queer one over there, Josie? Has she no shame at all?" Brige directed her gaze towards a woman leaning against the wall.

"Where, which one are you talking about. Do you mean her against the wall?"

"The very one, a real brazen madam if ever I saw one. Will you not make it so obvious with your pointing? She'll spot us and think that we are talking about her."

"Well we are talking about her are we not? What about her anyway? She looks no different than you and me, except that she has a coat on "

"That is where you're wrong. What you don't know is that her husband is working on the sly for a farmer in Mungret. Now do you understand my meaning?"

"I've got a good mind to tell Mr Keane." Brige looked across at the woman, unable to hide her jealousy.

"You'll do nothing of the sort. Why that's Phyllis Cleary, as decent a woman you'll not find walking on this side of O' Connell Street." Josie looked at Brige in hurt disgust. By this time Mr Keane had come out from his small office, minus his topcoat.

"Would two of you men kindly bring out the table and put it here?" He indicated where he wanted the table put.

"Do you want the chair too, Sir?" Willing hands fawned and grovelled trying to gain his favour.

"Yes please, if you would be so kind." He took his watch from his pocket and opened the flap on the front.

"Not a bit of bother at all Sir." The men grovelled before him.

With the table and chair now in position, the men returned to the well of the building and joined the assembled crowd. Mr Keane was in no great hurry as he placed the portmanteau on the table. Taking his glasses from his pocket he polished them before placing them on the bridge of his nose.

"Did you see them glasses? I'll bet that they never came off a corpse." Brige whispered to Josie. Glasses taken from the dead would find their way into the stalls outside the milk market for resale.

"Will you hold your whist. He might hear you, you know." Josie poked Brige in the ribs.

"Good morning everybody." Mr Keane looked down at the assembled people from his rostrum.

"Good morning Sir, and many more of them to you. God love and keep you, Sir" The salutary answer was predictable.

"Now let me see." Opening the ledger he ran his fingers down the page.

Then sitting down on the chair he opened the portmanteau. From it he withdrew an assortment of monies. There were a few half crowns, florins and shillings but mostly coppers. It would be a lean week this week for most of the assembled people. Half crowns, florins and shillings together with the smaller denomination coins were all laid out in descending order of value. From the inside pocket of his coat he withdrew his fountain pen. Screwing it open he pointed the nib towards the ground and shook it. Then he tested it on the ledger to make sure that the ink was flowing freely.

"As I call out your names would you please step forward and sign for the money allocated to you. In the meantime would you please refrain from talking to each other. That way we'll all get home earlier, thank you."

"Mrs O'Brien, one shilling and threepence." His voice boomed.

As each name was called, the person entitled to the benefit came forward, to receive whatever few shillings they were allocated. Some weeks a family may get a half crown. The next week one shilling and sixpence and nothing the next week. There was no set pattern of payments. The cruel parting was when a mother or Father who had stood all morning in the hall, found that their name was not called. Mr Keane was not insensitive to their wants, but he had only so much money. As they looked up at him with pleading eyes, he would look up from the ledger and shake his head.

"I'm really sorry, but there is no money for you this week." He'd apologise.

Perhaps it had come to the notice of those in charge that the son or daughter or husband, as the case may be had got a few days work that week. Be it malice by a jealous neighbour, be it true or not there would be no money. It was in this atmosphere, where what little pride one had was stripped bare of, that my sister and I paraded week in week out. Mother would not demean herself to attend. Parents or elder members of the family were obliged to stand in all humility, hoping for a few shillings. This to alleviate the hunger within them and their brothers and sisters at home. Would a mother get enough to buy a half pint of milk for her baby? Would a father get enough to buy a bag of penny loaves? It all depended on how far Mr Keane could stretch his allotted money.

It was here before the bigots and the saints that one waited to receive what we to day call Social Security and take as a right. This was a degrading means test, not by an appointed board, but by the whole population of the city.

There was no hiding place when it came to allocating the few shillings. Everyone knew each other's business.

IS THERE A DOCTOR IN THE HOUSE?

When the poor became ill, they were obliged to go to the dispensary off St John's Square in the city centre for relief. Should you be too ill to attend in person then you sent someone to the dispensary to make an appointment for the doctor to call at your home. On appointed days, the doctors would be in attendance for a set time at the dispensary. Their rooms were more like confessional boxes, lined up each side of the hall. Outside were wooden seats on that one sat and waited their turn to be seen. The floor was of bare wooden boards; these were washed daily in hot water and carbolic soap. This we presumed was to prevent any epidemic from breaking out. It did nothing to alleviate the discomfort of the patients who had to wait in the cold and damp, for there was no heating whatsoever. Bottles and jars of all shapes and sizes were to be seen, openly displayed by the patients. It mattered little what the complaint was, the treatment seemed to be the same from the common cold to a dislocated shoulder. That is my childhood memory of the place. The doctors got little pay from the City Corporation for attending to needs of the poor, and nothing at all from the patients. Having listened to the symptoms from the ailing patient, he asked more often that not.

"Have you brought a bottle?" The patient would produce the obligatory bottle.

"Good, take this to the dispensary." The patient was then handed the prescription and sent on his/her way. At the dispensary further down the hall the prescription and the bottle would be handed in. The cork would be removed from the bottle and a funnel placed in the neck. This was then placed under a large cask and filled with a foul tasting liquid called, *'Cascara'*

Two regular visitors to the dispensary were Josie and Mary from our parish. I suppose one could call them hypochondriacs. They were as well known at the dispensary as was the parish Priest in his church. I relate just one of the occasions when as usual the two old friends met at the dispensary.

"It's yourself Mary did you bring your jar?" The man in the dispensary asked of her.

"Just what in the name of God do I want a jar for? How much of this stuff do you expect me to drink? There will be enough in this bottle to kill a horse."

"Don't be all that smart with me now, the doctors note also states that you must have some zinc ointment so I need a jar to put it in."

"Look! I've got so much ointment from him now." She pointed towards the doctors door, "that my husband uses it in place of Brylcream."

Mary having collected her *Cascara* and ointment returned to the hall. As she was about to leave the premises, who should she meet but her friend, Josie.

"Well now aren't you the sight for sore eyes. How the Hell are you anyway?" Mary asked.

"Oh it's no use complaining; I could be worse or dead for all that lot care. I'm dying and that's the truth. Before you see me again they'll be waking me." Catching her breath she huddled under her shawl and took a fit of coughing.

"You should get something for that cough, Josie. Is it the same one I saw you with last week?"

"It is indeed the very same one that I had last week and the week before that. Only now they have caught up with each other bad cess to them." Josie came from under her shawl her eyes streaming.

"I'm no better than you myself. Before I got up this morning I had to feel myself. I'm going to die I told himself lying beside me"

"What's wrong with you now? You'll not be happy until I put you in the box." He grunted and he half asleep. No sympathy at all for my aches and pains. I think that I'm going mad as well as everything else."

"Sure me old pains are playing me up as well. I looked in the mirror this morning and barely recognised myself. There are people better looking than me being laid in their graves, I thought. We are all getting old Mary." They both made their way down the hall trying to comfort each other.

"You should try rubbing *Camphorated Oil* on that chest of yours. My Tom swears by it."

"He would swear if I asked him to rub my old chest. Why it's like a scrubbing board for sure." Both women took a fit of laughing.

"Look now what you brought on." Josie took a bout of coughing.

"Nothing to what it made me do, I just peed in my drawers." Both women again burst into peals of laughter.

"Why don't you take a drop of the horse medicine there. At least it will give you the runs and make you forget your cough." Mary could hardly get the words out without bursting out laughing.

"Ah stop! Stop will you now, you'll be the death of me," Josie stamped her foot on the ground trying to suppress her laughter.

"I told you that stuff would turn you into a horse eventually. Will you look at yourself stamping the ground like a stallion," Mary was now in great form and raring to go on.

"Oh! I've tried everything to get rid of this cough, why my Sean swears that I'll still be coughing when they put me in the coffin. Still never mind me, what did the quack give you as if I have need to ask?"

"You should know better that to ask such a stupid question, I got the same as always, a bottle of Cascara and a jar of zinc ointment for good measure." Mary produced her bottle and jar from under her shawl.

"Snap! I know how you feel." Josie took her bottle and jar and clinked them against Mary's.

"Do you know, looking at the state of them." Mary nodded towards the waiting patients, "Horses are treated better than us. Don't you agree with me?" Mary adjusted her shawl over her red hair.

"Did I tell you that Mary McCafferty died last week? I went to the wake and started thinking as I sat beside her corpse, God forgive me."

"Whatever would you be thinking about at a wake?"

"I was thinking that God would come and take me in me sleep very soon. Come to think of it poor Mary, rest her soul looked healthier than me and she in her coffin. I felt like telling her to move over and make a bit of room for meself. My Tom was not too concerned when I told him. He laughed and said that it would not too soon for him. I think he has another woman on the go, he never comes near me. Know what I mean?"

"Another woman, another misfortunate creature you mean. I don't know what you're complaining about. My old man is like a randy stallion. If you're all that eager for your oats you can borrow him and welcome. He'd soon satisfy you and put a smile on your sour puss."

"Here was I ever telling you about our Sean?" Josie pulled at Mary's arm.

"No! Why what's the matter with him? He looked alright the last time I saw him," Mary stopped dead in her tracks and looked Josie in the face.

"Well he got this..." Josie looked around her to see if anyone was in listening distance then she continued. "Well he got this ringworm in his head. My Tom shaved his head and took him to the doctor here. He told him that he must have picked it up from another boy. Then he gave Tom some blue stuff to put on our Sean's head, you know what I mean?"

"No as a matter of fact I don't know. We never had anything like that in our family, thank God." Mary blessed herself in indignation.

"Well to cut a long story short," Josie ignoring Mary's cutting remark continued, "Tom put the stuff, that you never saw or heard of before, on our Sean's head and covered it with an old tam of mine and sent him off to the Christian Brother's school at Quay Lane.

"Well, what's so wonderful about that?" Mary was not impressed.

"Ah! You'll find out in two shakes of a lambs tail if you are patient. Our Sean was sent back home again by the brother's. Do you know Mary, I just could not believe my eyes."

"Whatever possessed them to send him home?" Mary was by now getting impatient with the long winded story.

"Will you get on with it. My man will be waiting for his bit of dinner."

"I thought he might be waiting for something else" Josie again took on another fit of laughing that brought on her cough.

"Serves you right for having a dirty mind." Mary was most upset.

"Dirty mind, look who's talking. It was you who told me that her husband was a stallion. Never mind I'm losing track of the story. The other boys it seems grabbed the tam from his head and threw it over Thomond Bridge and into the river.

"But that wouldn't prevent him going to school Josie."

"No Mary, God bless the poor unfortunate child. Everyone was teasing him and calling him a Blue bottle. It's the toe of me shoe they would feel up their arse if I caught them at it."

"Really, go away, I don't believe it; that sounds incredible." Mary was not taking this piece of gossip very seriously.

"You may well stand there and laugh, Mary Quigley, but let me tell you that it was no laughing matter to our Sean."

"Oh don't be so serious, get on with your story," Mary apologised.

" Tom took him back to school and do you know what?"

"I won't know until you tell me, so I won't."

"The brother's told him to take him home and bring him back when his hair grew. What do you make of that now. Is that not one for the books"?

"Come on now Josie let's get out of here. Sure this place gives me the creeps."

Mary hooked Josie's arm and together both women left the hall and turned into John Square.

"Here Mary, what say we both go down to Frawley's pub for a bottle or two of stout and to Hell with it all?" Josie tugged at Mary's arm.

"What about your old man, he'll be waiting for his oats, won't he?"

"He knows what to do, and if not then he can tie a knot in it." The women could hardly restrain themselves.

"You're right for once Josie. It will do us both the World of good. It's the least we deserve and why not".

"Do you know before the day is out we could be the talk of the town," retorted Josie.

"Well when they are talking about us, they are letting some other unfortunate alone."

Together they made their way down through the *Irish town*, laughing and giggling to each other all their misfortunes forgotten for the moment. One has to appreciate that the economy of Ireland was more or less stagnant during the war. Britain a rich nation with an Empire treated her poor no better. They too were dependant on charitable organisations and what was known as *'The Parish'*.

THE DENTIST

I dreamt that I climbed a tall tree and sat in the branches. Fruits of all kinds grew on the tree and I began picking them and putting them into my mouth. As soon as I bit into them I spate them out again for they hurt me. I picked another one ignoring the pain and tried again to eat it but the pain returned. I picked the fruit from my mouth only to find that it was made of stone. I tossed the fruit into the garden but it rebounded and smashed into my mouth causing me intense pain. Shaking the branches I watch the fruit fall to the ground. I tossed from side to side trying to escape as the fruit rebounded and attacked me.

I awoke to find myself sweating and to add to the misery of my persistent chilblains. I was also suffering agony, from a severe toothache. Holding my jaw and feeling miserable I left the bed and went to mother's room.

"What's the matter with you?" She looked at me with her soft eyes. She knew instinctively that something was wrong.

My eyes filled with tears for she could not realise how much pain I was suffering. Only my childish mind was capable of knowing the agony of the disaster that had befallen me in the night. She comforted me as best she could but to no avail as the pain grew in intensity.

"We'll soon put that to right." Mother told me I was lucky as this was the day when Dr Holmes would be in attendance at the 'Dispensary'. He was qualified to extract teeth and would have it out before I knew it. Why she thought it lucky for me to be in pain on that day I'll never know.

Now I have no doubt but that the good doctor was well qualified to extract teeth. His reputation as a dentist was castigated, by the poor of the city. The drawing of the tooth was not the only terrifying prospect to look forward to. It was the fact that to have an anaesthetic one had to pay. Mother had no money to pay for it. In fear and trepidation I left the house and took the sorrowful road to the dispensary.

I arrived at the dispensary and sat with the multitude of sick patients on the hard wooded benches.

"What's wrong with you son?" A sympathetic patient beside me asked.

"I've got a toothache," I told her pointing to my jaw.

"Oh God help you son, you'll need to go over there," she pointed to a door further down the hall.

Several men and women sat in silence on the bench. Some had scarves over their mouths. Others had pieces of flour sacks in their hands. All looked as miserable as sin. I took my place at the end of the seat. What frightened me most of all were the people saying their rosary and putting holy water inside their mouths. After what seemed like hours the doctor arrived and entered the surgery.

"First patient," Came the call from inside the door. The patients looked from one to the other before the man nearest to the door rose. Returning his beads to his pocket he blessed himself and looked pitifully at the other patients.

"Good luck now." Came a sympathetic remark from a fellow sufferer. The door closed behind him and the queue shuffled forward. The groans coming from inside the surgery sent shivers down my spine. Slowly the queue melted away. Some on leaving looked back at the closed door and remarked "Butcher"! The sight of the blood and the vindictive remarks was doing little for my ego.

"Are you having the anaesthetic son?" A woman, her head covered in her shawl asked.

"I don't know mam, what is it?" I was grateful for the concern she was showing me.

"Never mind, he'll understand. You're only a child." This remark did little for my already shattered nerves. Finally there was only me and the woman left waiting. She was shivering like a jelly on a plate as she numbered her beads.

"Next!" Came a roar from inside the surgery. The woman blessed herself and kissed the cross before she vanished inside the door. The roars coming from within its confines put terror into me. I was wetting my pants and holding on to the seat for dear life. If I had Rosary beads on me I too would be deep in prayer. Finally the woman appeared with a cloth over her mouth. She took one look at me, and shaking her head staggered down the hall. Half ways down the hall she staggered and fell.

"Next, next!" I heard an agitated voice calling from within the confines of the surgery. Slowly I rose and placing my hand on the handle entered the room. What a sight greeted my eyes. It was more like a Butchers shop. There was a long kidney shaped enamel dish on a glass topped trolley in which were several teeth. Some were as big as the teeth in the pigs heads and bigger. The surgeon in a blood spattered gown stood by a huge chair. On a tray were the instruments of torture. I saw the sweat on his brow and began to tremble.

"Sit down. I won't ate you. What's the problem." My executioner queried. I took one look at him and another at the teeth and was out the door like a bat out of hell.

"Come back here and stop wasting my time." I heard the bull roar.

I saw the woman who had left the surgery before me sitting on a seat and another giving her water as I fled.

"How do you feel, better now I suppose." Mother came from the scullery and looked down at me.

"I couldn't go through with it, he frightened me." I told her.

"You should have had it out. Being frightened of him is nothing to the pain you will have to suffer now. You should have had it out there and then. There will be no surgery until next week." She was a great comfort to me in my agony. She was right as usual. The pain grew intense and I was feeling miserable. Next day was worse and mother told me to put cloves where the pain was. Nothing seemed to ease the pain.

"You should smoke a cigarette, that will kill the pain." One of my mates advised.

"Where would I get a cigarette?" I pleaded.

"Come with me, we'll soon get one." Up O'Connell Street we wandered. My pal keeping his eyes peeled to the ground.

"Quick, there's one." A man entering the Augustian Church discarded the butt of his cigarette in the gutter.

"Here it's still alight." Putting the butt in his mouth he began drawing in the smoke.

"Let me have a drag when you're finished, look it's a castle butt.(Castle being the name of the cigarette) They're good smokes." I put the cigarette to my lips and began to draw the acrid smoke into my mouth.

"Drag it into your lungs." He instructed me. I took a deep breath and nearly collapsed on the pavement. The pain in my tooth was forgotten as I fought for breath. Holding my chest with one hand I began coughing.

"Have you no better things to do than take up smoking." A good Samaritan came forward and gave me a clip around the ear. I staggered to the steps of the church and sat down. When I regained my composure I returned home still in pain and discomfort. The cigarette cure having done more damage than good.

"Go over to 'Barringtons' hospital, they might be able to help." Mother advised. I left the house alone and crossed the city to the hospital casualty department.

"What's the matter with you?" The nurse asked.

"I've got this awful toothache." I informed her.

"A toothache, I'm sorry but we cannot help you. You'll need to go to a dentist."

"I've no money, can't you do something?" I pleaded.

"Sorry, this is a casualty department. Try the dispensary to morrow."

"I've been there and got frightened." I pleaded with her.

"Oh well, if you won't go to the dentist what do you expect us to do about? " With that she dismissed me.

"I see you had no luck there." Mother looked at me in sympathy on my return.

"If he tied a string to the tooth and then to the knob of the door, I could slam the door shut and it would come out." Brendan offered yet another cure.

"Whatever gave you such an idea." Mother looked shocked.

"I saw it in a Laurel and Hardy movie." He confessed.

"I know who'll do it for you." Taking down the tin box containing her envelopes and note paper she sat at the table.

"Pass me the ink and pen, there's a good boy." Opening the pad she began writing a letter.

"Now you know the Carnagie library in Pery Square. Go up there and at the corner opposite St Michael's Protestant Church you will find dentist Coogan. Give him this letter, remember to say a little prayer on the way. Sealing the letter she put it into my pocket.

"Here put this over your face." Taking her woollen scarf from behind the door she wound it round and round my mouth. Arriving at the imposing Georgian building I climbed the scrubbed steps and rang the bell. The door was answered by a young maid dressed in a black and white uniform.

"Yes, is there something you want?" She looked me up and down.

"I have a letter here from my mother for the dentist." I offered her the letter.

"I'll see that he gets it, thank you." She began closing the door.

"Excuse me, my mother told to see the dentist." I stood my ground.

"Mr Coogan you mean."

"I suppose so, if that's him."

"Come in and sit down there. I'll give him the letter. I'll not eat you." She smiled when I hesitated at the doorstep.

I sat looking at the imposing hallway and wondered what he could do for my pain.

"So you have a problem with your tooth. Come on inside and let me have a look." A man in a white coat came into the hall. I was shepherded into a room that was surgically clean.

"Now sit yourself down here." I was invited to sit in a leather chair. Soon as I sat in the chair he tilted it. I was now a captive and he could clamp my hands and feet to the chair and butcher me. I saw that happen in a movie in the Tivoli cinema once. A nurse entered the room and adjusted the chair leaving me in a prone position. The Dentist came forward with a syringe and having assured himself that the contents were flowing freely he told me to open my mouth. There was no escape now I was about to be drugged and murdered. I obediently opened my mouth and putting on my St Anthony face I looked pleadingly towards him.

"Don't be so nervous, I'm not about to murder you." He laughed. From my point of view he could have chosen a better way of saying it. I felt the needle probe deep inside my mouth.

"There now, just relax, don't be so tense." He smiled as he looked at the now empty needle. I was left sitting in the black leather as my mouth began to go numb. I wondered how long it would take for my body to die. Then it all came back to me, I now knew that I would not feel any more pain. The same happened to me before the nun stitched my hand in Saint John's hospital. Content that he was my saviour I lost all fear. Soon the offending tooth was removed and I left the surgery.

As I related in 'Dare You Ripple My Pond' mother had many rich friends and relatives in the city. This must have been one of them.

CIBBY EYE LASHES AND THE WOMAN FROM CRATLOW

Cibby Eye Lashes was a cat that kept very much to himself. Not that he was an unsociable cat, rather reserved and proud. I could say that he was just plain lazy, but as he was my cat I had to defend his reputation. The fiercest *Kerry Blue* dog gave him a wide berth, not that he would attack any of them, he was far too enthralled in his own importance. Why waste time and energy running from a mangy dog? This was his philosophy. When an inquisitive dog dared to approach him, he would sit on the pavement and give a warning look. This was enough to deter the bravest of them.

A widow woman driving an ass and cart on which sat a milk churn came daily to the barracks selling fresh milk. Her worldly possessions consisted of a thatch cottage, a few acres of scrub land, a couple of hens and a milch cow. Her one cow produced her only source of income, the milk which she sold where and when she could. She took a great liking to my cat, or was it the other way round. It mattered little for as soon as that ass and cart came down the Strand, Cibby was off down the stairs to meet it and the lady from Cratlow.

Now Cratlow was a very small community in county. Its only claim to fame was its haunted wood where the people of Limerick went at weekends in the summer for their picnics. Cibby Eye Lashes would fall in under the cart and trot like a dog in time with it until it reached the gates of the barracks. At the gates the woman would come off her straw seat and lead the ass inside. That ass would never enter the barracks, unless he was led in by the reins. Perhaps he was aware of the ghosts of ages past lurking in the old arch. My cat would come from under the cart and rub himself against her legs.

"Oh you are a lovely cat," she would tell him as she bent down and stroked him. This action didn't do her much for her arthritis, for she found it difficult to straighten up afterwards. The cat would roll over at her feet. He would do anything for a free drink of milk, just like some humans I could mention. Mother blamed me for the way I trained him. Taking his dish, which she carried especially for him, she would mount the cart and opening the churn and fill the measure with milk. This she would put into his dish and present to him as if he were Royalty. With his tail in the air he would make for his dish and lap away at the milk to his heart's content.

"I'd give my right arm for a cat like you." She'd stroke him as he consumed his dish of milk. Why she took such a liking to my cat I could not comprehend. There were thousands of cats looking for new homes. Cibby would raise his tail and purr between lapping the milk with his long tongue. Along with everything else my cat was a born beggar. Mother hearing the cart approaching one morning, went to purchase her pint of milk and as usual the cat had got there before her.

"You've got that cat spoiled you know. He's only playing up to you for the milk." Cibby looked up at mother and then returned to stroking the woman's legs with his body.

"Ah no! He's a lovely fellow; I bet he would soon send my rats and mice running, wouldn't you pet?" She retrieved his dish from under her straw seat and filled it with foaming milk fresh from the churn.

"There, get that down you. You know a good drop of milk when you see it, don't you?"

"Don't tell me that you have rats. They frighten me to death whenever I see them. Do you know my son, the one who owns that cat? He fishes them out of the river with his fishing rod and turns them loose on the road. I try stopping him you know but he's a real terror." Mother looked with horror at the woman and shook herself.

"Is that himself sitting on the wall with the dog?"

"None other: They are like two brothers. Where you find one the other will not be too far behind. His name is Bruno."

"Bruno! Why didn't you call him after a saint?"

"No, Bruno is the dog. His name is Louie."

"Oh I see now, sorry. Silly me." The woman half laughed. Why did mother always bring 'Bruno ' into the equation when talking about me?

"You were talking about the rats."

"Will you not be talking missus. Sure I hardly get a wink of sleep with them scurrying to and fro around the old cottage. Every scrap of food I have to keep in tin boxes," she raised her arms towards the heavens seeking divine intervention.

"And you say that you are not frightened. Why I'd no more stay in a place like that, than I would in a graveyard."

"Did you ever think of going to Saint Bridget's well over at Mungret? They say the water from it will drive the rats away." Mother looked aghast at the woman.

"I've been to the holy wells and God knows elsewhere. You see I've lived with them so long now that they don't frighten me at all. Perhaps if I got rid of the little beggars I'd miss them." She looked down at the empty dish that Cibby was trying to lick the pattern off.

"Tell you what I'll do, that is if you really want to get rid of them." Mother looked pleased with herself.

"What do you suggest? Send for the *Pied Piper* to entice them away." The woman laughed to herself at the very idea of it.

"No! Nothing so dramatic! What I was about to suggest was that you borrow the cat there. He knows you and a few days in the country chasing rats would do the lazy brute a great deal of good." Mother crossed her arms. The cat by now had finished with the milk and was sitting between the asses front feet washing himself.

"That's very kind of you and I must say much appreciated on my part. You are so considerate. Do you think that he would mind coming?" She looked down at the cat.

"Mind indeed! What say has he in it anyway? He's only a cat. Borrow him and welcome."

"Tell you what I'll do then, that is if you don't mind. To morrow please God I'll bring a good big box with clean straw in it and when I've finish selling my milk I'll call in and collect the cat. How about that arrangement?" She nodded to mother as she called her donkey forward.

Next morning the milk woman left the straw filled box at the house and went on her way peddling her milk.

"Don't anyone let the cat out this morning. I have a job for him." I took little notice of this instruction as I left the room for school.

In the afternoon I returned home to find mother and the milk woman calling the cat.

"What do you want my cat for?" I looked with deep suspicion at the large cardboard box filled with straw.

"Oh don't worry about your blessed cat. We're only borrowing him to get rid of a few rats in this woman's house. Where is the brute anyway?"

"He's sitting on the window sill. All you have to do is to call him." I told her.

"Perhaps you could get rid of her rats, they seem to know you personally." Mother half laughed. Was she being sarcastic?

"There, see that. I've been calling the brute for ages and he ignored me. You walk in the door and he greets you as if you were someone important, just shows you." Mother looked at my cat.

"Seeing that he's your cat, you had best call him. He will listen to you." She glanced at the cat.

I called to him. He stretched himself and jumped off the window ledge and slowly sauntered across the floor.

"Don't you hurry yourself, you may do yourself an injury." Mother sarcastically remarked. When the cat came within reach of her she grabbed him and unceremoniously dumped him into the box and closed the lid.

"That's no way to treat my cat. Why didn't you ask him nicely?"

"Now look here you, less of your cheek if you know what's good for you." She warned me. All was quiet within the box as the milk woman picked up the box and left the room.

"Isn't he real quiet, not a murmur out of him," She put her ear to the box.

"No wonder he is so quiet. He's in shock not knowing what has happened to him," I told her. How would she feel being dumped into a dark box? The poor thing could have died from a heart attack for all they cared.

The milk woman was late in turning up next morning. This worried mother.

"Whatever could have happened to her? It's not like her to be late. God, I hope she did not have an accident." Mother looked worried.

"What about my cat? Nobody seems to be worried for him, do they?" I intoned.

"There's your cat, what about him?" My sister Phyllis pointed to the cat as he sauntered into the room.

"What's he doing here on his own? I sent him to Cratlow only yesterday."

Mother scratched her head in disbelief. Going to the window she looked out expecting to see the milk woman on her cart.

"That's strange, she's no where to be seen. How did he get here?"

Sometime later there was a knocking at the door. On opening it mother was confronted by the woman from Cratlow in great distress.

"Oh Missus"! she wailed. "You'll kill me for sure. Didn't I go and lose your lovely cat." She wrung her hands together in anguish. Then she continued to relate what happened. "I let him out of the box in the house, when I got home. I never expected it of him. He flew at the window like a bat out of hell and tore the curtains, not that they were all that good anyway." There was no stopping her as she continued. "Then he took it upon himself to wreck the room. I had no alternative but to let him out. Why he was far worse than the rats, in the way he behaved. I thought that he had lost his senses. I'm worn out believe you me. I must have searched every shed and barn between Cratlow and Bunratty without success. I'm speechless from asking all the neighbours if they saw him. Not a hair of him is to be seen. The poor creature must be half way to Galway by now and it's all my fault." She was really distraught at the thought of losing the cat.

"Will you calm down, come in and rest your feet, there is no need for all the fuss and bother. Before you get anymore upset look over there." Mother pointed to the cat sitting in the window washing himself.

"Is that yourself? You poor thing, you must have been frightened out of your wits, I am sorry." Reaching out to the cat she called to him.

"Would you tell me in the name of all that's good and holy, how did you get home?" The cat did not run to greet her as he usually did, he looked across at her with daggers in his eyes.

"Would you credit that, he must have travelled at least five miles home, but how did he know the way? That's one for the books." One could sense the relief in her voice as she spoke. As she reached nearer to the cat, he rose and made a dash for the open door and was gone,

"I think that I must have upset him," she looked at mother.

"Have your tea and forget the cat, he'll be his old self by this time to morrow."

"Do you think that he will ever forgive me? Where has he gone to?"

"Gone to? I have little doubt but he is sitting on the river wall with the dog and his master, telling them all about his misfortunes."

"His master? You mean Louie. I saw them on my way in doing a spot of fishing?"

"Fishing! Fishing is that what you call it. Tell me what boy in his senses would spend his time with a dog and cat by his side fishing for, of all things, Rats"?

Cibby Eye lashes did eventually make it up with the woman from Cratlow. He had no alternative if he wanted to enjoy his free dish of fresh milk.

She never did ask to borrow the cat again. Perhaps it was for the better.

HEADS AND TAILS

Mother was always at her best when adversity struck, and that was often indeed. It was her unquestionable faith that sustained her, for she was a born optimist. To her there was never anything really wrong that could not be put to right. She was adamant that God really loved the poor more than anyone else. He would take care of them when the whole world had abandoned them. If he loved the poor so much how was it that the rich prospered. Sometimes I wished that if God did not love me so much then I might have a chance.

'"Why is it Ma, if God loves the poor so much does he ignore us? We never seem to have anything." I would ask of her periodically.

"Never ask such questions, God moves in mysterious ways. We will get our reward you wait and see. Mark my words." Patting me on the head she would try to console me.

Little did I know that my childish questions were causing her anguish. How was I to know when I complained of the pangs of hunger, that I was breaking her heart. There was little she could do about it. Sometimes when she had no money she would send me on a free message.

"Will you ever go to the Yarmouth Fish Store and ask for some cod's heads for the cat." She would ask me as she removed the special bag made of waterproof American cloth from its peg. Off I would go up Roche's street in the city, the bag slung over my shoulder. Arriving at my destination I would spend a few moments playing with the polecats and ferrets outside Casey's store. These animals held me spell bound with their yellow eyes looking out through their wire mesh cages.

Next to them were the rabbits in separate cages, old adversaries watching each other. The rabbits, watching cautiously, every movement of the ferrets. The ferrets perplexed at not being able to get at the rabbits. When I went to feed the rabbits with a cabbage leaf through the wire mesh they came forward unafraid. Perhaps they felt secure in the knowledge that they were in separate wire cages and that they had the added protection of me. Well I thought so and told the rabbits that I would protect them. When I tired of playing with the rabbits I would go on to the fishmongers. On the marble slabs were arrayed fish of all shapes and sizes. Some looked really fierce to me, especially the cod with their sharp teeth. Under the cutting bench inside the shop, in the sawdust lay the heads and tails of the fish. It was these that I was seeking.

"Can I have some cods heads for my cat please?" I would ask of the fishmonger preparing the fish.

"Help yourself son." He would point his knife at the pile of discarded heads and tails on the floor. They were only too glad to be rid of them. Searching through the pile I would select the heads with the most flesh on them and put these in my bag. I'll always be grateful to the memory of one fishmonger who was my benefactor and my friend. If he were not in the shop I would saunter around the streets awaiting his return. I had all the time in the world to spare.

I relate one such occasion, but it was usually the same every time I encountered this generous fishmonger I called Pete. Perhaps he knew that the fish heads were not really for the cats, who knows! The rain was lashing down as I approached the stores with my dog in tow.

"So you're here again, come on in." He put his arm round my shoulder and brought me into the shop.

"Here, you cannot come into the shop." He looked down at Bruno walking three steps behind.

"That's my Dog, Sir."

"Tie him to Casey's blind, he'll be alright there." He instructed.

"Now stay here and be quiet, I won't be too long, good dog." Bruno looked up at me and began to bark. I held my hand up and warned him to behave. He returned to the pavement and settled down. I went back to the fishmongers.

"I hear that you're the boy who feeds all the alley cats of Limerick. You look more like Oliver Twist, the more I see of you." Mother would not have appreciated this remark about her son. She always said that I had a face like Saint Anthony, always sorrowful. "Never mind those old heads on the floor, come over here." With my bag swinging by my side I approached the block where he stood. "Now let's see, you usually have cods heads and tails for your cats, is that not so?" He lifted up the peak of his hat with his Knife edge.

Going to the window display he removed two big Codfish by their mouths and placed them on the slab. From them he cut a more than generous portion of heads and tails. "Open your bag son." He swept the heads and tails into the bag, the weight of it forced me to drop the bag on the ground. "Too heavy for a little one like you, no doubt." He looked at me as I composed myself and picked up the bag.

"Oh no Sir; it's just that when you dropping them in I lost my grip."

"There's a few mackerel over there in the bottom of the boxes. They are damaged, you can take them. That is if you can find use for them." Again he pointing to a pile of fish boxes. Nervously I approached the boxes, not wishing to disturb the cash paying customers. There I removed a few damaged mackerel, that were crushed when the wooden lid was fitted.

"Not like that son." The voice of the fishmonger rang out. With no more ado he scooped up what fish were left in the box and put them in my bag.

Staggering out the door with my bag full of free fish, he called after me.

"How far have you to go son?"

"Only as far as Killeely, Sir."

"Killeely, half ways to Clare. Here take this and catch the bus." Reaching into his pocket he took out a penny and handed it to me.

"Hold on a minute." He called after me as I prepared to leave the shop. He returned with a large greaseproof bag and making a hat of it placed it on my head.

"There! That's as good as any sou'wester is that. You look like Captain Courageous." He smiled.

" Thank you Sir, thank you very much."

"Don't forget to say a prayer for me at the shrine of Saint Anthony," he called out. This was the only payment he asked and all that I could offer him in return for his generosity. What else could a hungry child offer him but his prayers that cost nothing. I was sure that he knew the fish heads were not for the cats but for a hungry family. I felt sorry for lying to him and wondered if God would accept my prayers.

"I won't forget, I promise. Oh thank you Sir, thank you very much." I promised as I collected Bruno and raced down the street as fast as I could to Cannock's where the Killeely bus stood waiting.

We entered the bus and went upstairs to the front seat. This was the favourite seat, when we could afford the bus fare. I could see all before me and would wave to my pals from my lofty perch.

"Where are you going to?" The conductor stood beside me.

"A Child's ticket all the way to Killeely." I held up my coin to him.

"What of the dog? He cannot travel on the bus. He shouldn't be on the bus anyway. See the sign *No Dogs allowed.* I looked up at the notice printed in English and Irish.

"But we go everywhere together, can't he stay this once please? It is pouring with rain outside. If he goes then I'll have to go too."

"Put him under the seat and if the inspector comes 'round, I know nothing about him." Issuing the ticket he retreated down the stairs.

"You heard that, Bruno, you can look out the window for now. If anyone comes up the stairs you must hide under the seat." Bruno wagged his tail and I knew that he understood.

I told my mother about my friend Pete and she said his name must be Peter and was probably appointed by Saint Peter himself to look after me. Perhaps she was right after all when she said that God moved in mysterious ways.

Mother would remove the fish heads and tails from the American bag and turn it inside out ready for scalding in hot water. The fish heads and tails would be washed and placed in the big pot together with onions and carrots and boiled. She would then make a thick paste with cornflower using the stock from the fish. This would be added to the pot. Flavoured to taste and when ready served up piping hot it was eaten with relish. Cibby Eye Lashes and Bruno would have their bowls filled from the pot. I often swallowed the fish eyes but they never did me any harm.

When the money stretched to it, we would have Pigs heads, back bones complete with tail. This was a meal fit for a King, when served with boiled cabbage, parsnips and champion potatoes in their jackets. Many a Limerick father put away a few of these meals after a few jars of Guinness. We had breastbones, eye bones, spare ribs, strips and skirts, knuckles, why the list was endless. We had more variations of food that the best restaurants. The best of all were the *Lots*. Say what one will about Limerick bacon and all the rest, but lots were the greatest. All the little bones called Lots would be boiled together with parsnips, carrots, onions and pearl barley, when boiling mixed herbs would be added to the pot. The aroma of this succulent dish would fill the whole street and be the envy of those who could not afford it. When there was sufficient left over we would invite our mates in for a bowl. That's the way it was when I was young. You might not have a lot but what you had you shared.

"We're like Browns Cows, all in the same field," mother would remark. I could never understand her sayings.

When it got cold it would turn into a jellied mass, it was said that not alone did it do one good but that it put a good lining on ones stomach.

There were indeed many ways of keeping hunger at bay in those far off days. I have no doubt but that other readers will be reminded of their own parents dishes made to alleviate the pangs of hunger.

The problem at the time was that there were too many hungry people and not enough food to go round. Then again there was plenty of food but no money to buy it.

SAINT VINCENT de PAUL

The poor of the city were helped where possible by the society of St Vincent de Paul. Someone had to do something to relieve the dire poverty in the city. The challenge was taken up by this charitable organisation. Most members of the society it must be appreciated did their best under such trying circumstances. Others we felt were religious bigots who believed that they could buy the souls of the poor. Before offering any charity they insisted that the family led the lives of the saints. To some it was compared to the demands made on the starving Catholics during the great *Hunger* when whole families were denied a bowl of soup unless they adopted the Protestant faith.

It was these people who seemed to dominate the distribution of the charity. The head of the charity was the local Parish Priest. The money for this charity came mostly from the business community of the city and the foremost of these were the Protestant's. Though there were but few of them, they never hesitated to help where help was needed. There were also the church door collections and the poor boxes in the churches. Apart from the clothing, boots and bedding, there was a further voucher usually controlled by the local Shopkeeper. These vouchers were stamped with a list of groceries one could obtain up to the value of the voucher. The list I'll remember to my dying day, for it always read.....

Bread- Butter- Milk- Meal- flour- Tea- Sugar.

To obtain one of these coveted vouchers one had to be in dire straits and live the life of a saint. The family had to be Roman Catholic and seen regular at the altar rails, of a sober disposition and members of the confraternity. We qualified for one of these vouchers, which was brought to our door on Thursday nights. Two members of the society would call and quiz mother before surrendering the voucher. Had she received any money from England or elsewhere? Did she come into money or receive a gift or clothing and so on? This was a necessary means test as there was only so much money available and so many in need. At this time one of my elder brothers was in college in Manchester studying for the Priesthood. Then came a letter from him, telling us that he was coming home on a holiday. We looked forward to seeing him again after his long absence. Perhaps we were more anxious to see what he would bring back from England. Finally the great day arrived and he landed on our doorstep with a large suit case. He laid the big case on the table and opened it. Much to our disappointment, there was not a toy to be seen.

"These are for you." He said holding out a jacket and trousers to me.

These items of clothing were well worn and of little use to me. They were too light and looked funny.

"I can't wear these. Everyone would laugh at me." I held the trousers up against myself.

"They are called pyjamas, you wear them in bed, silly!" He informed me.

That evening I put on my fine pyjamas, they were far too big for me. I found it necessary to roll up the sleeves and the trousers legs. They were not comfortable at all. Still I was determined to show them off to the first person who came to our door. It so happened that above all evenings, this was the evening that the St Vincent de Paul members were due to call. When the knock came, I was off like a hare to open the door. I was confronted by the two members of the society, standing open mouthed before me. I thought that they were surprised at my pyjamas and I was right but not in the way I expected.

"These are my new pyjamas, and you wear them in bed." I paraded before them like a Peacock.

"Will you take no notice of him and his antics, he's just showing off." Mother pushed me back into the room. "Will you not come in out of the dark. You'll see better that way." She held the door open to the two men.

The man with the book looked at her and then at the man holding the voucher. The elder of the two looked at mother and sarcastically remarked." Is it pyjamas now for your children? What next I wonder?"

"It's only an old pair his brother brought from England and gave to him." Mother looked across at the table where I was sitting sulking.

"Come here and show these nice gentlemen your new pyjamas." She called me forward.

"Did I hear you say you have a son in England, is that right?" He opened the book and moved into the room where the light was better.

"There seems to be no mention of this in the minutes." He studied the book intently. "This matter requires further investigation. Don't you agree John?" He looked to his partner to confirm his findings.

"I couldn't agree more, you'll have to go to the office to morrow evening and explain yourself to them ma'am. Good night to you and God bless you and yours." He returned the coveted voucher into the file.

"Excuse me, you forgot to leave the voucher." Mother called over the banister as they retreated down the stairs.

"Call up to the office to morrow night about seven and they will explain all to you," mother looked after them; disappointment showing all over her face. She said nothing to me, I only wished that she had, for I felt guilty for us losing the voucher. It meant that we would have no supper and no breakfast going to school next day.

The following evening mother wrapped the old pyjamas in brown paper and tied it with a string.

"Come on you, get your coat on, we have a lot of explaining to do. You are not taking that dog either. Do you hear?" She was annoyed with me and she could not help showing it. Off we went to the offices and sat in the hall waiting to be called before the committee. Finally our turn came and we were ushered into the committee rooms. At a long table, covered with a blanket, sat six men and in the centre a Priest. The chairman who was the Priest introduced himself and his committee to us and told us the procedure of the meeting. The two men who came to our house were also sitting at the table.

"Well now Ma'am, it has been reported to us, that on your own admittance you have a son in England. Is this the truth?" Folding his arms he waited for mother to explain her conduct.

"That's right Father, one of the eldest boys is in England, you see...." Before mother could finish explaining, he had the report open before him

"There is no mention of this in here." He tapped the book that was open before him.

"No doubt like all good Irish boys he sends money home to help the family. Is that not so?" He looked right and left at the other members of the committee, all of whom nodded in full agreement.

"When two of the committee members called last evening, you had the children ready for bed and they wearing pyjamas. Can you explain to the committee just what is going on here? This is a very serious matter and must not be treated with flippancy." He continued to chide mother.

"There was only one pair of old pyjamas and he was fooling about wearing them." She went on to explain that my brother was studying for the Priesthood and that he was not earning any money. Further to that, he was supported by the Church in his learning.

"We are proud and honoured to hear that your son is studying to become a Priest and we wish him every success." The Priest no longer scowled. He smiled at mother. Then he composed himself and continued with the interrogation.

"Never the less there is the matter of the pyjamas. Perhaps you would explain just how you can afford such luxuries for your children?" Mother explained, as best she could, as to how she came to have the pyjamas.

"There was only one pair as I told you before and he was wearing them." She pulled me before the table. Then she opened the parcel and produced the offending pyjamas for all to see. "You see they are threadbare and don't even fit him. As a matter of fact he doesn't like them, do you?" She held the rather large offending articles against me to show the committee how large they were. She stretched them and as she did so there was a tearing sound.

"There is no need for that, take them away and wait outside." The Priest looked embarrassed.

"Please take a seat outside and take your son with you. Don't forget the parcel, thank you." An elderly gentleman spoke up. Mother and I left the room and sat on the bench outside.

"Well! We'll soon know just what it is all about. No thanks to you, won't we?" She looked down at me. "Oh do cheer up. It wasn't your fault. Nobody is blaming you, least of all me." She tried to cheer me up. Finally the door opened and we were called back into the room.

"Sit down please." Mother was offered a chair. I was left standing by her side.

"There seems to have been some misunderstanding here. It is all of your own making. All you had to do was explain the circumstances when the committee members called." The Priest tried to excuse himself by putting the blame on mother.

"Here you are Ma'am." The elderly gentleman interrupted the proceedings and held out the coveted voucher to mother. He seemed to be embarrassed by the whole proceedings.

"It's a cold night, take this and get the bus home and put that boy to bed. He should not have been brought here in the first place." Mother took my hand and gently squeezed it.

Through the icy cold of the city we made our way. Down the length of O' Connell Street, cross Sarsfield bridge for the final trot home to the Strand barracks. She had no intention of spending the few coppers she was given on a bus fare. She could make far better use of it.

As she opened the door she was confronted by the other members of the family collected round the stove for warmth. Then waving the voucher in the air she called.

"One of you go at once to the distillery, before the shop closes. Get some tea, bread, margarine, milk and sugar. This night we are going to celebrate."

There was no further chastisement of me for the problems I caused on the night I wore pyjamas. Still I felt that it was all my fault and so I shed a few silent tears on my pillow.

THE WOMAN IN BLACK

We had many peculiar characters in the old city and outside of it. I have referred to some in my previous books. Here we meet another of those eccentrics. I must stress that these people were harmless. We would not remark on a person who broke an arm or a leg. Yet we took a sadistic delight in tormenting people who were suffering from a mental disorder.

One of these was the *Woman in Black*. It was obvious from her dress why she got this name, for she was covered from head to toe in a black dress. Her long black dress reached down to her toes and beyond. Over her shoulders she sported a black shawl with tassels on the ends. To cap it all, on her head she wore a wide brimmed black hat. This was held in place with a wide black ribbon that went over the top of her hat and under her chin where it was tied in a large bow. The woman in black was a *Bean- an- Bótar* or Woman of the Roads. She was a well known figure round the villages of County Limerick, Clare and Tipperary. Whenever she took it upon herself to visit one of the villages, the people would purposely close their doors and pretend not to be at home. As most of the doors of the villages were seldom if ever closed, there had to be some logical explanation for this unsociable behaviour. Country folk were known throughout the land for their generosity. Why then were they loath to give the bread of hospitality to this poor woman of the road?

Why didn't the Parish Priest, in his God fearing sermons condemn the people for their lack of Christian charity? It could well be understood and appreciated why the children were so afraid to approach her. Her appearance and her conduct made them to say the least apprehensive. What then were the explanations and excuses from the so called God fearing, kind and generous country folk? The reasons as to why she was so unpopular are many and varied, I relate but one. Reaching a house where the door remained open, she stuck her face round the jamb of the door and called out.

"Oh I see you are having a bite to eat. Now isn't that civil of you." Before the family could recover from the shock of seeing her toothless grin, she was in.

"Will you get up there and show some manners to your elders," the youngest would be ejected in no uncertain terms from his/her place at the table.

On the thumb of her right hand she had a fingernail, that was about an inch long and as broad as a kitchen knife. Having evicted the child from its rightful place at the family table she sat herself down and joined the family. Taking a flowery potato in its jacket from the dish in the centre of the table, She held it in her left hand. Using the nail on her right hand as a knife she proceeded to peel the potato, much to the disgust of the family present.

"Would you like a plate and knife for that?" The woman of the house placed a clean plate and knife before her.

"There is no need for you to put yourself to any trouble on my behalf." Reaching into the centre of the table and using her nail as a fork she retrieved a large slice of bacon from the centre dish, this she proceeded to ram into her mouth. As the grease from the bacon ran down her chin she used her sleeve to wipe the surplus away. This before she rammed the remainder of the bacon into her mouth with her thumb. She looked for the world to see, like a squirrel with the pouches of his jaws filled.

"I suppose you'll be making a sup of tae to wash this lot down?" She asked as she cast her gaze towards the hob and the steaming kettle. The other members of the family making their apologies left the table in disgust. The family, who by now should be settling down to their tea and home made soda cake, had no alternative but to abandon the family table and leave it to the woman in black. She continued to eat her fill from the bounty filled table, not in the least embarrassed by the sudden departure of the family. Having partaken of her fill she rose from the Table, let out a few belches and scratch her backside.

"You don't mind if I take a few of the spare potatoes with me, do you?" The remainder of the boiled potatoes looked at greedily with beady eyes.

"Take them and welcome, sure I'd only feed them to the chickens," the despairing housekeeper replied. Not only did the woman in black scoop up the remainder of the potatoes from the dish into her bag, but the remainder of the Limerick bacon and a good half of a soda cake.

"Thanks for the food now Ma'am. I hate to leave such lovely people; but sure I can call again, can't I?" The woman of the house had no intention of encouraging her to stay. Her conduct and the fact that she was as allergic to water and soap as is a rabid dog, did not make her the most congenial of company.

As she proceeded through a village on another occasion her target was the parish Priest. Some mischief maker had informed her that the parish Priest was looking for a cook and housekeeper and had put her name forward.

"Good day your reverence. Fine day, thank God." Scratching her head she greeted him with a toothless grin. Escape for the luckless Priest was out of the question. He had no alternative but to acknowledge the greeting.

"Good day to you and God bless you." He tried to pass her. She was having none of it for as he tried to pass around her she blocked his path.

"I wouldn't like to think that a man of the cloth was purposely avoiding a poor woman of the roads." She looked questionably at the Priest.

"God forbid Ma'am! Whatever gave you that idea?" He knew in his heart and soul that he was fibbing, but then surely his God would understand the predicament he found himself in and forgave him. As a Priest he was well able to protect himself against aggressive people and acquired situations. The woman in black was different, he had as the saying goes, met *his match.*

"Is it true what they are saying father? Are you really looking for a good cook and housekeeper?" She asked.

Looking aghast at her, his mouth fell open, as his brain worked overtime to find an excuse of an answer.

"I was up to last week, then the Reverend mother of the Good Shepherd Convent in Limerick came to my assistance." He dared not look her in the eye.

"Is that so, father? so you are fixed up then" She had another little scratch.

"I am indeed. She sent me a respectable girl." He again tried to pass her.

"Thank God for that father. I was going to offer my services on a temporary basis, if you understand my meaning." She laid her hand with the long nail on the priest's arm. The way he shuddered, one would have thought that the Devil had struck him. Perhaps he had, when he felt the long nail biting into his arm and saw the toothless grin of the woman standing before him.

"That was kind of you and real considerate, I'll remember you in my prayers." With these words ringing in her ears he left her and was off down the road, thankful no doubt for escaping from her clutches.

The story was told, be it fact or fiction I cannot verify, that she lived at one time in a small cottage along the banks of the river Fergus near Ballynacally in the County Clare. She was an only child and her parents were basket makers. Her father would cut the sallies and stack them beside the bank where he and his wife would collect them and take them back to the cottage. These they would weave them into cisceans, baskets, cribs etc; when she was ten years of age her mother died and her father brought her up alone. She quickly learnt to follow in her mother's footsteps and grew up to be a fine strong girl. When she reached the age of sixteen. She came to the notice by a local widower, who asked for her hand in marriage. Her father who was now getting on in years agreed although her suitor was twenty six years her senior.

"He was a good man that took me out of the rushes," she would boast.

Tragedy happened a year into their marriage when he was collecting stones to build a haggard from an old ruined building. As he struggled to remove a stone the whole wall gave way and buried him. They brought him back to the cottage where he died that night. Heartbroken she abandoned the cottage and took to the roads always wearing black clothes in mourning for her lost love.

There are many stories told of the men and women of the roads. I would be inclined to accept this story as a true account of what happened to her. It is doubtful if anyone could have invented this story about her life.

MY SISTER MARY

My sister Mary was the proverbial magpie. She hoarded anything and everything. Nothing went to waste. Drawers were crammed with balls of string. These she collected from outlets too numerous to mention. Wrapping paper was neatly folded and stashed away. Oxo boxes were filled with a variety of buttons, Buckles, laces and pins. You name it, Mary had it in stock. She had, as far as I'm concerned, the first recycling centre in the universe. This was her hobby and a God send to mother whenever she searched for a button to replace a lost one. Mother maintained that she would make a grand nun, for she was as quiet as a mouse and seldom took offence. She was also very canny with the shillings, a good sign for the proverbial nun, perhaps a reverend Mother even. She had other ideas and had no intention of donning the habit.

She had a very good friend who was also named Mary, who lived over on King's Island near to King John's castle. She unfortunately was born with one leg shorter than the other and as a result needed a high shoe. However this did not stop her limping. She also had a turned eye. Mother was worried because they were always together, the two Mary's I mean. Not because they were companions but because of Mary's limp. For some reason best know to herself mother believed that Mary's limp was contagious and could be passed on. Don't ask me why or how.

"That poor girl, God be good to her, will she ever find a man? What with her limp and her eyes looking both ways at once. I'm sure that God had his own reasons for inflicting this punishment on her." This was not meant to be an uncharitable castigation of the girls infliction. It was her way of explaining her sympathy for others.

On one occasion mother was sitting by her fire when they both arrived at the house. She sat for some time studying poor Mary.

"I'm off now ma'am, good day to you," Mary hobbled from the kitchen.

Mother rose from her chair and studied her intently as she hobbled down the road. Returning to the kitchen she watched our Mary's movements as she walked around the room.

"Mary, when you go out with your friend what side of her do you walk on?" She finally asked.

"What side do I walk on, I don't know, why?"

"No reason, it's just that you seem to be developing a limp in sympathy with your friend. You should try walking one day on her right and the next on her left. That would balance you up."

"Ma! How could you, you'll be telling me that I'm crosseyed next."

"I'm only telling you for your own good. If you don't want to listen then I cannot make you."

On another occasion after the men from St Vincent de Paul Society came and left the voucher for food, Mary instructed me to fetch the messages. The voucher had to be taken to a huxter shop owned by a member of the society in the Distillery. It could only be used to obtain from the following list according to the value of the voucher........

Bread-butter-milk-meal-flour-tea-sugar.

"Now listen, here is a penny, it's not for you. I want you to bring back a packet of *Beecham's Pills*. Tell no one and bring them directly back to me."

I felt I were on a covert operation as I collected Bruno and raced along the Strand.

Having collected the groceries I then purchased the pills as instructed. Bruno jumped on top of the river wall at the *Treaty Stone* and raced down to the steps looking for his enemies the water rats. I sat on the stone steps and peeled a few skinnings from the loaf of bread that I hoped would not be missed, then I turned my attention to the small twisted paper containing the pills. Cautiously I opened the packet and peeped inside. In the bottom lay five little black round pills. I took one out and placed it on my tongue and mistakenly swallowed it. I tried to regurgitate it but it had gone. Taking out another I gripped it between my teeth to hold it. The pill disintegrated in my mouth and tasted awful.

'How could anyone eat these?' I thought as I tried to dislodge the taste from my mouth.

I went down the steps and washed my mouth out in the river. I returned to the steps and sat down. Looking down at my hand I noticed that the remainder of the pills had fallen from the wrapper. Where had they gone to? I had to find them or else. I searched around the Treaty stone for them without success.

"Oh God help me, St Anthony come to my aid," I prayed as I looked across at the large statue of Christ on the cross in the grounds of Saint Munchin's Church. I would have gone inside and made a novena if the church had been open. I sauntered down the Strand wasting as much time as possible to delay the inevitable. As I passed by one of the gardens I saw small black berries growing from a bush. I collected five that looked like the pills I had lost and put them in the wrapper and twisted the neck. I knew that if Mary found out she would twist my neck.

"What kept you? Don't tell me that you were ratting again?" Mother looked up as I entered the house. Mary called me into the scullery where I handed her the make believe pills.

"You're a good boy, say nothing to nobody." She patted me on the head like a chastised dog. All seemed to be in order for she opened the packet and seemed satisfied with the contents.

That night I got the runs and spent most of the night running to and fro to the lavatory. I never did find out if the berries did her good or not.

When it came to baking she had the delicate touch of a surgeon. Her baking was second to none. That was when we could afford the necessary ingredients. She used to make scones which for some unknown reason we called *groggle cakes.*

The principle ingredient for these was Bran, which was cheap. This she blended with a little flour and sweetened condensed milk. We never bought condensed milk it was out of the reaches of our meagre resources.

In the dock area of the city was *Cleeve's* milk factory and it was behind it that we scavenged for the milk. Tins of sweetened condensed milk, damaged or with signs of rust were taken and buried in a dump behind the factory. As the employees buried the tins we waited in the rushes until they left and then promptly dug them up again. We also collected them from Cleeves dump at the top of the Quarry Road in Killeely.

It was this milk that she used for the cakes. Sometimes we would pour the milk on a slice of dry bread and eat it. It was a bit messy but wholesome. My cat, Cibby Eye Lashes would give his eye teeth for a share of it. I would swap some of the scones with my mates but I never told them where the ingredients came from.

As the war was raging in Europe and the far East there were few if any luxuries to be had.

Cocoa shell's were another commodity that could be bought cheaply and boiled and the residue used to make a kind of watery cocoa. One morning as I entered the kitchen Mary had two tin plates set out on the table.

"I've made a special treat for you this morning." She tossed her sandy hair out of her eyes as she spoke. She was forever experimenting with dishes with me as the taster.

I looked down at the plates of steaming cocoa shells and wondered if she was finally going out of her mind. Mother should have been studying her mind and not her hypothetical limp.

"What are they?" I pointed to the strange looking food set out before me.

"They are cocoa shells, good wholesome food. Now taste what I've discovered." She came back with a rusting tin of Spring time sweetened condensed milk which she had boiled and poured some on top.

"Try it. I bet it tastes good?" she encouraged me. I suppose hunger is the best sauce and cautiously I picked up a half spoonful and put it in my mouth.

What was she trying to do, poison me? I never tasted anything so vile in all my young life.

"You don't think that I could eat this. It tastes awful. Did you eat some of this yourself?" I asked as I spat it out into my hand.

"No! I made it especially for you and Brendan. I take it that you don't like it then?"

She offered the offending food to Cibby Eye Lashes who after sampling a few laps was showing signs of distress. Flicking his tail into the air, which was his signal of annoyance he walked out of the door. Bruno came in to see what the cat had left, took one sniff, looked at it suspiciously, he looked at it again and growled at it before leaving.

I guess the road to Hell is paved with good intentions. I felt that my animals were cursing whoever presented them with the food.

I had the habit of bringing home a selection of vegetables and potatoes. Some I would pick up in the milk market. Others I would acquire from some unsuspecting farmer. On this occasion I went with my dog for a walk into the country and stopped at an old mansion at Ballynanty Beag. This was before the grounds were turned into allotments and finally a housing estate. The purpose of my mission was to collect as many daffodil bulbs as possible for my father's grave. I dug up a generous box full and returned home. I left the box under the table planning to plant them the following Sunday on the grave.

The following day was Friday and mother waited until evening before she went to Parnell Street. It was here that the bacon merchants of the city had their premises. In one shop owned by the Maher family one could buy a variety of offal, bacon etc that would make the teeth water. When she saw the shop about to close she would make her dash inside. Then would follow a bargaining session that would do credit to a bazaar in the Casaba. The result was that mother always came home with a back bone or two or a few pounds of lots, or skirts. Sometimes she would haggle for and get a half pig's head. There was always something to be had on the cheap. On this occasion she came home with a bag filled with lots. These were small little bones; what they came off I never knew nor did I care. Mary took on the task of making a stew with the bones and a variety of vegetables. Carrots, onions, parsnips, thyme and a pound of pearl barley found their way into the pot. I watched as she skimmed the scum off the pot and put it into Bruno's tin. The smell from the stew was so tempting that I could have eaten the pot itself.

"What does it taste like? Can I just try a drop?" I pleaded.

"You'll do no such a thing, what's wrong with you don't you know it's Friday?" Mother chastised me. It was forbidden to eat or drink anything containing the flesh of animals on Fridays. The stew bubbled and simmered as we waited and watched the pendulum of the eight day clock move slowly backwards and forwards. If only mother would leave the fire then I could open the glass face and push the hand forward, I thought. Finally the clock struck twelve, the bewitching hour of midnight came and the assortment of dishes and plates were laid out on the table. It was now permissible to eat meat, it being Saturday. I could never comprehend why we had to starve on a Friday when there was a good pot of stew on the hob. We could, if we had it eat salmon or any type of fish and eggs but not meat or anything produced from meat.

Bruno jumped up and down as the clock struck midnight. As he was a member of our household I suspect that he too was a good Catholic. Mary filled his bowl with the dregs from the pot. It did not take him long to lick the bowl clean and return to my side begging for more.

It was the early hours of the morning when disaster struck. The first one to complain of stomach pains was Phyllis. She always had a delicate stomach and shortly afterwards Brendan. Phyllis was the first into the toilet were she sat moaning and groaning.

"Will you come out before I skutter my pants?" He wailed holding his backside. She ignored his pleading and continued to moan. I ran into the garden and joined Bruno where he was relieving himself. Even the old Long Can was once again brought out for use. Suspicion fell on the stew and more so the meat that mother purchased. She assured us that the meat was fresh and could not be blamed; no more than the vegetables. The cause remained a mystery until Sunday afternoon when I went to collect my daffodil bulbs. Someone had mixed them up with the onions. As I was sorting the onions from the bulbs mother asked me what I was doing.

"Someone took my box and dumped my bulbs in with the onions." I informed her. Without saying another word she went out into the yard and looked in the compost.

"Mary where did you get the onions from?" she asked on her return.

"In the box, why?"

"Do you always have to answer a question with another? The why and wherefore is that you put some of his daffodil bulbs in the stew. What kind of an Amadan are you anyway?"

"What about my daffodils?" I piped up.

"What about them? You nearly poisoned us all with your stupid bulbs." Mary was not too pleased with me.

Collecting what remained of my precious bulbs I placed them in a bag and was about to leave the house when my mother called me.

"Just where are you off to now?" She stood with her hands on her hips at the door.

"I'm going up to the graveyard, Why?"

"You're getting too big for your boots, so you are. What do you mean why?"

"I'm going to plant these bulbs on Dads grave." I held the bag out.

"Oh go on then, I suppose he's going too?" She looked down at Bruno who was waiting his opportunity to escape.

"By the way stop extending that grave. Last week you took in the graves of two soldiers and an unmarked grave to the side. Just because nobody attends them does not mean that you can claim them. Oh go on! Sometimes you are an embarrassment to me."

I had hardly returned home when a man arrived on a bicycle in an agitated state.

"Don't you go away, is your mother home?"

"Ma! There's a man at the door for you." I called out.

"Will you get inside, I'll see to this." She bundled me into the kitchen. This was nothing new to me.

"Yes, what can I do for you?"

"I'm the gate keeper at mount Saint Lawerence cemetery. It's about your son and the grave."

"My son is not dead, you've come to the wrong house."

"No Ma'am; what I mean is the grave of your late husband, God rest his soul. That is your son who answered the door"?

"That's one of them, why what has he been up to now?"

"You know the glass domed wreaths that mourners place on the graves of their loved ones?"

"Of course I know. What about them, what has that got to do with him"?

"Well it's like this, we have been watching the graves because several of the domes went missing, expensive ones at that."

"Are you saying what I'm thinking? He would never steal from a graveyard, would he?"

"He's not exactly stealing them, he's removing them and putting them on his father's grave. Not alone that but that grave is getting bigger by the day."

"Louie, come out here and explain yourself. I warned you, I told you but you never listen. Now put your coat on and return all those domes to the graves you took them off."

"Thank you, Ma'am, sorry for troubling you but you do understand." Touching the peak of his cap he mounted his bicycle and left.

"God Almighty, whatever next? Where will it all end? Will you go and do what you are told? Leave the dead rest in peace or they will come and haunt you. Now get out of here and put everything you removed back to where they belong."

WHOSE GOD IS IT ANYWAY?

Some doors away from us lived Mary and her parents. It was said that no finer family lived in the road, this was not saying a lot for the other residents.

Mary, their only daughter was the apple of her father's eye and the jewel in her mother's crown. A gift from Heaven, or so her mother claimed to make up for the children they could not have. The family was so religious, that it was said that they had direct contact with heaven itself. Her uncle was a Catholic Priest and another relative a nun. It was an open secret that Mary herself was thinking strongly of joining the order of the Poor Clares, this being an order of nuns who gave their lives to the service of God and had a convent over in Galway on Clare island.

Entering her parent's home was no different than entering a Catholic Church. As one crossed the threshold they were halted in their steps by her mother's voice coming from the house.

"Have you taken the holy water and blessed yourself?" Her mother would call from the parlour. Now in the parlour in a place of honour stood a full sized statue of the Blessed Virgin and swinging from her hands the biggest pair of rosary beads seen this side of the Vatican. There was little doubt about it but Mary and her family were indeed a credit to the Church and the community.

Although her family were pillars of the Church, Mary found it impossible to obtain gainful employment. Her father was a grand knight in the Order of the Knights of St Columbia, an organisation within the Catholic Church that looked after their own. Some people said that they were the Catholic Churches answer to the Freemasons and the Mafia. All the influence of her parents and Church were to no avail, there were no good jobs available. Finally against the wishes of her parents she decided to go to England to seek employment.

Mary was lucky for she found a good job in Cricklewood a suburb of London and respectable accommodation near by.

She wrote regularly to her parents telling them in glowing terms that she was employed by a large firm named *Smith's* in the area that made clocks and was saving her money for her holidays. Mary was a clerk in the main office.

Her parents wasted little time in informing the neighbours of their daughter's wonderful progress in London. Her mother was a regular visitor to our home and over a cup of tea would relate and no doubt exaggerate the progress of her daughter in London.

"From the way she talks, you would think that she was the only one with a daughter in England doing well." Mother would say.

All went well for several months, the neighbours got the daily reports on the progress of Mary. Then came the big day, Mary was coming home for a holiday. Her mother informed my mother of the good news plus.

"Kate! You're the first to know, Mary is bringing a nice Irish boy with her. She has become engaged to him." She could hardly restrain her enthusiasm.

"Good for her. I wish them both the best. Tell them to make sure and call."

"Oh I will Kate. Can you imagine it, my little Mary engaged? Where did all the years go to?" She wrung her hands together in joy.

"She's got a cheek talking about her little Mary. She's as big as a seven barred gate and as old as Rip Van Winkle." Mother told us later. Was this jealousy on mother's part?

Who could blame her parents for getting so excited about the whole affair. They awaited in joyful anticipation the arrival of their daughter and her fiancé.

Finally all the anxious waiting was over. They had arrived at Limerick railway station and were met by Mary's father.

"Father this is William," Mary introduced her fiancé to her father.

"Welcome to Limerick Bill. You don't mind me calling you Bill, do you?" Both men shook hands.

"No not at all, and what should I call you?" Bill smiled as he returned the greeting.

"Why you call me Mr McGuire or Sir what else?" Familiarity was not encouraged with your elders in my young days in Limerick.

Arriving in the house Mary and her fiancé were welcomed in the usual manner. Her mother had a bottle of holy water from Lourdes in her hand as she greeted them at the door. She sprinkled the water over her husband, her daughter and fiancé Bill. Mary blessed herself, her father removed his hat and he too blessed himself. Bill it would seem had blotted his copybook, for he looked at his future mother-in-law puzzled. Taking a handkerchief from his pocket he wiped the holy water from his face. Mrs McGuire looked at him, she was suspicious of his conduct. Meditating she replaced the cork in the bottle and blessed herself. What kind of a Catholic had her daughter brought from London? She thought.

Mother and the neighbours kept looking through the curtains to try and see what kind of a man Mary had brought home. There were more neighbours walking up and down the road glancing into the McGuire house than visitors to *Lenin's* tomb. All went well within the house throughout that afternoon and evening. Bill told them that his people were farmers and that they lived in Tyrone. As the conversation revealed more and more information about Bill and his family, the more the McGuires were impressed. Indeed they were of the opinion that Bill would be a good catch for their daughter. As the hour got late Bill began to feel tired, no doubt from the interrogation he got from the McGuire's and the long journey.

"I think I'll retire now, that is if you don't mind. I really am bushed from the long journey."

"Oh I am sorry Bill. How time flies when one is having a good chat. We'll see you sometime in the morning, please God," Mary's father got up from his chair.

"Where would my room be?" Bill picked up his case and went towards the door.

"Your room! What room Bill? Don't tell us that you haven't booked in any place yet?" Mary's mother studied him.

"I'm sorry, but you see I understood that I would be staying here," Bill replaced the case on the floor.

"Stay here is it? What do you mean stay here?" Mary's mother looked at him shocked.

"There's no way that we could allow you to stay here in the same house as our daughter. We would not tolerate it. What would the neighbours think?" She could hardly restrain her indignation at the very suggestion. She was also suspicious as to their conduct in sinful London. Bill was despatched to the nearest Guesthouse on the Ennis Road. Mary's mother decided to find out more about her daughter's fiancé. Mary began to make her way out the door to her bedroom before she was stopped by her Mother.

"Come and sit down here a minute. I want to have a few words with you." Her mother patted the seat of the settee. Mary sat down and placed her hands on her lap. She knew what her mother was about to ask her.

"Now I want you to tell me the truth Mary. What is going on between the two of you?"

"There is nothing going on, nothing for you to worry about. What do you think of him?" Mary put her hands 'round her mother and tried to change the conversation.

"Would you tell me Mary, is Bill one of us?" Her mother was not one to be put off.

"Not exactly Mom. You see he comes from the north." She was avoiding the question.

"I can deduce from his accent that he comes from the north, but is he a Catholic?

"Well to tell you the truth Mom, he is a Protestant but he does not practice." She hastily added. This she thought would appease her parents. Instead it landed like a bombshell.

"God Almighty, whatever possessed you to find one of them?" Her mother looked at her daughter in horror.

"You will have to tell your father yourself when he comes back. I don't know what he'll say." Her mother wrung her hands.

"Mother, we love each other and intend to get married, and that's that." Mary defended her right to marry the man of her choice. In the days that followed her father, her mother, her uncle, even the parish priest tried to break them apart but to no avail. Of course when Mrs McGuire came to our house she made no mention of this and why should she? It was none of our business anyway. She must have suffered agony trying to keep the secret from the neighbours. There would be no keeping of the secret, for when Bill and Mary went to Mass on Sunday it became manifest that he had no idea as to the service. Mary was seen to nudge him when it came to stand up or kneel down. The poor man would be the only one left standing when all the rest of the congregation were kneeling. It would have been better had the neighbours been told in the beginning. Now everyone knew that Mrs McGuire's daughter was going marry a black Protestant.

Some time into the holiday they decided to go and meet Bill's parents in Co Tyrone. Once again they were faced with the same hostile reception from his parents. Bill's father warned him that if he brought a Catholic girl into his house then he would disown him. No threats and no promises would stop them marrying each other. Their respective families would not be allowed to come between them and their undying love.

The day came when finally they decided to make the arrangements for the marriage. Mary wanted to be married in her own Catholic Church and to this Bill had no objections. They went to the Parish priest to make final preparations for the forthcoming marriage. The Priest listened to all that they had to say, especially to Mary. Having failed to part them, he now made it clear to them what the ruling of the Catholic Church were on mixed marriages.

"Now Mary, seeing that you are determined to marry Bill, I am duty bound to point out the conditions under which I am allowed to join you in Holy matrimony."

Mary and Bill listened intently as the Priest related the conditions laid down for mixed marriages in the Catholic Church.

"You must understand that you, Mary, must do all in your power by persuasion and prayer to bring Bill into the true church." He allowed this undertaking to be fully understood before he continued.

"Any children of this union must be brought up as Roman Catholics. You understand this Mary and you too Bill?"

"Mary, you must not enter any Protestant churches or graveyards and especially you must refrain from attending their services.

Finally the Priest finished laying down the rules much to the relief of Mary and Bill.

"Now Bill, you have been ever so quiet throughout all this. Have you any questions you wish to ask me?" The priest turned his attention to Bill.

"No! If its acceptable to Mary, then it's alright by me." He rose to his feet.

"Good night father." Mary held out her hand to the Priest. Together they left the church hand in hand.

The day of the marriage came and went. Bill and Mary returned to London and to wedded bliss. The McGuires spoke little of their daughter's progress in London now. Naturally they were disappointed. Mother would ask how they were from time to time.

"Oh they are getting on as well as can be expected," her mother would tell her avoiding any elaboration of the subject.

Then one day who should appear on the street but Bill and Mary unannounced. Mary was carrying a baby boy in her arms. Bill was pushing the empty pram beside her. The children laughed and derided Bill, no man in Limerick would be seen pushing a pram. It was not the done thing. Their arrival caused great excitement in the street as Mary proudly presented their offspring. One morning Mary's mother was seen hurrying with the pram with the baby inside, towards the city.

"Did you see who took the pram?" Mary came to the door upset and asked my mother who was on her way to fetch a can of milk.

"I saw your mother with it. She seemed to be going to the town," mother told her.

"No doubt like all grannies going to spoil him," Mary remarked as she returned to the house.

Some time later her mother returned smiling all over her face. Swinging from the hood of the pram was a picture of the Blessed Virgin.

"Wherever have you been, Mother? He should have been fed and changed ages ago." Mary looked in at her baby.

"Don't you think I know what to do with my own grandson? We went to St Munchin's Church."

"What did you go all that way with the baby for?" Mary asked.

"If you must know, I had him properly baptised and blessed." Her mother nodded her head in contentment.

"Mom! He was properly baptised in the Catholic Church in Cricklewood."

"Sure them English Catholics don't know how to do it right, so they don't. Anyhow there's no harm in having it done proper in Limerick." Her mother with a look of happiness entered the house. Mary told Bill what her mother had done that day, much to their amusement.

"If it makes her happy then what harm can it do? Did you tell them that we are off to Tyrone to morrow?"

"I'll tell them now. Will you hire the car?"

Next morning they left early to visit Bill's parents. At the farm Bill's mother paid great attention to the baby. She seldom let him out of her sight.

One day when Mary was out shopping she called Bill into the parlour. She had something important to tell him.

"Bill there is no need to worry about my grandson. He will be alright now."

"Whatever are you talking about mother? There is nothing wrong with him."

"There isn't now. You see when you and Mary were out visiting yesterday didn't I take him to the minister and have him properly baptised." His mother was more than pleased with herself. Bill let out a laugh and called Mary in, then related what his mother had divulged.

"What's so funny, Bill? I told you this in strict confidence." His mother was upset. It was then that Bill told his mother and father that Mary's mother had done exactly the same in the Catholic Church in Limerick. Bill's parents saw the funny side of it and joined in the laughter. Some days later they returned to Limerick and Bill and Mary's dad went to the local public house that evening.

After a few drinks too many Bill related the story of the baptism to her father.

Next morning after breakfast Mary's mother asked if she could take the baby out in his pram.

"You won't be taking him too far this time, will you? We have a lot of packing to do." Mary told her mother.

Sometime later her father came into the room and asked where her mother was.

"Oh! She took the baby for a last drive before we go back to London."

"For a last drive is it? Don't you know where she is gone to?" He laughed

"What do you mean? Where is she is gone to? What's so funny?"

"I told your mother the story about Bill's mother having the baby baptised in a Protestant church and I'll bet you that she's off to have him baptised again in the Catholic Church."

"Do you know something Mary? We must have the most baptised child in Ireland."

"Whatever you do don't ever mention baptism again. You'll drive the grannies stone mad." Her father laughed.

Some time later Mary's mother returned with the baby and there on the hood was a new blessed picture. As far as was known Bill and Mary settled in his home in Tyrone where they had two more boys and a girl. In later years her father took a delight in telling the story over a few pints. Much to the annoyance of his wife.

P.S. Although the family were long gone I have altered the name of the family to avoid any embarrassment.

FEED MY LAMBS, FEED MY SHEEP

When mother sent us to the Christian Brother's at Sexton Street, she warned us to be on our best behaviour. Being accepted into the secondary school was a privilege not to be abused. We were indebted to the good brother's for allowing us to have free access to advanced education. I was not over enthusiastic at the prospects of again coming in contact with the Christian brothers. I had learnt to cycle and already had secured the job as a messenger boy at Lipton's.

"You a messenger boy? You can forget that. Education is no load to carry," mother reminded me. She was trying to give us every chance to better ourselves, but we did not appreciate it. For a poor scholar to be accepted by the brother's into the secondary college free they had to have very good leaving certificates from the primary school. Mother would not have been in a position to pay the fee and buy all the books required for advanced education.

To us advanced education by the brother's meant more punishment and more hunger. It also meant that the journey to college was now several miles longer on foot. Mother did not have the money to pay our bus fares. I took it for granted that we would get the usual bottle of milk and the bun at break time. This at least would alleviate the pangs of hunger. On enrolling we were sent across to the shop where we were provided with an array of books that would do credit to the national library. As our books were supplied free they were stamped by the shop. We would have to keep them spotless and account for their upkeep. Pens, pencils, copybooks and jotters were also supplied free.

Our first day was spent being initiated into the system. No longer would it be reading and writing, this they presumed we had mastered. From now on it would be Latin, bookkeeping, English grammar, Euclid and Shakespeare, just to mention a few of the subjects.

As the hands of the clock on the wall moved slowly towards break time my stomach began to rumble. Reminding me that it was time for the bun and bottle of milk. Then the bell went and we were dismissed out into the grounds of the monastery. There were no tickets issued and no mention of a free meal. We looked around us trying to locate the area where the free bun and milk would be available. Where, oh where was the room in which the food was being served? Search as we might there was no sign of it. There was only one way to find out where to locate the room, ask one of the brothers.

"Excuse me Sir, where do we go for the bun and milk?" I asked a brother who was walking round the grounds reading a book.

"What bun and milk? Don't tell me that you forgot your lunch. You'd best ask your teachers for permission to go home for it at dinner time." He returned to his reading.

Run home to what? There would be no lunch at home. No more than there was a breakfast. Anyhow it would be impossible to get to our house and back again to the school in the space of one hour. We should have realised that if parents could afford to send their children to the college then they should well afford to feed them. There was nothing else for it but to wait until the end of lessons and hope that there would be a dinner when we got home. All that day we sat in school, and as the saying goes, we were all falling with hunger.

"We will have to explain to mother that we cannot go to this school on an empty stomach," my brother grumbled.

"You're right for once. It's senseless coming here if we cannot get a bite to eat."

That evening tired and hungry we returned home and were more than thankful to find that mother had made a pot of Irish stew. That stew was to us *Manna* from Heaven. We could not eat enough of it.

"Well you seem to have met the hungry grass to day." Mother looked across at me as I filled my plate again from the pot.

"It's not that Ma! The problem is that in Sexton Street we don't get any milk or bun." I returned to the table with my well laden plate.

"Did I hear you say that there is no milk and bun? I never realised this. Never mind, I'll do something about it." Somehow or other mother did provide a lunch of sorts for us. This consisted of a couple of slices of bread and margarine each. It may not have been a lot but it helped to sustain us until we returned home. It could not last however. There was little money coming into the house. Mother tried to keep the luncheons going but they soon frizzled out. Then it was back to learning, religion and hunger once again. It was enough having to face the pangs of hunger; It was far worse to see the farmers' sons with their home made scones the size of a barn wall with half a yard of best Limerick ham sticking out the sides.

One lunch break we went into the city hoping to find some food of one kind or another. We had no luck and decided to sit on the seats at the Limerick Peoples' Kilkee. This is situated opposite the Limerick Boat Club. There we intended to stay before returning to the school. Passing down the side of the Franciscan Church, the aroma of roast beef coming from the basement kitchen tickled our nostrils. Curiosity killed the cat, or was it the pangs of hunger? I crept down the steps and opened the door into the kitchen. Was it true? I looked at the table in disbelief, saliva dripped from my watering mouth like a fox watching a coop of hens.

On the table was a large joint of beef on the bone that had recently been carved. It looked so big that I thought it came from a dinosaur. It was the first roasted joint that I ever set eyes on. Next to it sitting in a large dish were piles of roast potatoes. Beside them were little blown up cakes. I was to learn later that they were called *Yorkshire puddings*. I took these to be their afters or desert. The temptation was there. I was not thinking of the sin, I was about to commit by stealing from the poor friars. I grabbed a few handful of the puffed caked and as many potatoes as I could stuff into my pockets and inside my shirt. I looked with gluttonous eyes at the joint. If I could only get a piece off the bone, It was all too much, how could I leave it behind? Without any thought as to the need of the friars I picked up the joint and was up the steps quicker than you could say *Jack Robinson.*

"What's wrong with you? Come back" Brendan shouted after me as I raced for the docks. When I reached the Limerick Peoples Kilkee, I sat on a seat and placed the joint beside me.

"Where did you get that from? Don't tell me that you stole the Franciscan's dinner? You get worse by the day and you'll go to Hell, if you must know." He panted as his eyes opened wide.

"Don't worry, they were finished with it and were about to throw it out." I justified my theft.

"Throw it out, you must think I'm simple minded. What else did you steal?"

"Look I got roast potatoes, little cakes and this." I held up the joint close to his nostrils. I managed to break the bone and give my brother his share, well nearly. We picked that bone as clean as any bone in St. Lawrence's cemetery. It was a grand meal and we ate the little buns afterwards. Brendan wiped the grease from his chin and let out a belch. He rubbed his stomach and let a smile appear on his greasy face that would do credit to a Cheshire cat. Where now was his concern for the poor Friars? God, I felt great and did not feel like a thief at all. I knew in the back of my mind that if I were caught then I would wind up in a Christian Brothers reformatory.

"Thanks St Anthony. That was the best roast joint I had this week." Brendan again wiped the grease from his chin and let out another belch. Then rising from the seat he looked behind him.

"I see some of your friends have heard the good news. You had better see to them." He pointed to two dogs sitting patiently under the seat awaiting the bones.

"I'll let them have it in a jiffy," I told him as I tried with my tongue and little finger to scrape the last vestige of marrow from the bone.

"For God's sake will you give the poor dog's the bone and let's get back to school or we'll be late." He looked at me as I picked the last morsel from the bone. He gave the bone he had to one of the dogs. It was only a small bone and was soon devoured.

"Ok then lads, fair is fair. I'll break it in half." I picked up a large sharp stone and proceed to break the bone.

"Will you stop talking to every stray animal you meet. Do you know you embarrass me." Brendan chided me.

The two dogs sat on their bottoms half rising and half sitting, their tails wagging in anticipation. Finally I succeeded in breaking the bone and gave each dog a piece. The dogs did not leave from under the seat but lay down full length and began chewing on the bones. One or the other would let out the occasional growl to warn off any potential intruder into the feast.

"Tell me! Why is it that wherever you go there are animals of one sort or another?" My brother pointed to the dogs. I was used to his sarcastic remarks and ignored him. We crossed the dock road and went to the public tap with its lion's head and its iron cup on a stout chain to prevent anyone stealing it. There we washed our faces and drank copious amounts of water to relieve our thirst

"Well, I for one am ready to take on the Christian Brothers and the lay teachers too." I slapped by stomach in satisfaction.

"I'll tell you something else, I'll be back there tomorrow for more of their scraps." Brendan looked at me and smiled.

"Don't forget that it's Friday to morrow; a fast day. The pickings might not be all that good." I reminded him.

"Well I'm as partial to a bit of salmon as the next." For once he was in fine fettle after his feed.

"We cannot go back to morrow. You see they didn't exactly give me the roast beef." I half explained.

"What do you mean? I was right, wasn't I. You stole it? Still I should have known better. Oh my God and from the poor Franciscans too. Of all people you stole from the poor Franciscans." He looked shocked as he walked away from me. I caught up with him at the corner of Bedford Row.

"Did you know that you were born in there?" Pointing to the children's hospital I endeavoured to change the subject.

"So what, we all were born someplace. He continued on up the road moaning like the Bean-Ó-Sidhe. Finally I lost my patience.

"For God's sake will you shut up. You enjoyed it as much as I did." He walked on up the road in silence. I caught up with him and warned him of the consequences of my theft.

"There is one thing for certain. You will not be able to go to the Franciscans to confession, will you?" I warned. We got back to the school in time for the usual prayers on the hour by the hour, where I said a silent prayer for our benefactors.

The next day at lunch we again made our way to the Franciscans. I crept down the steps into the basement. I tried the door handle but the door was locked.

"I told you so. They are taking no chances on you pinching their lunch," He whispered to me.

"What do we do now?" I asked.

"I thought that you were the one with all the brains? Think of something." I could see that he was disappointed.

We heard movement inside the kitchen and crept up the steps to the relative safety of the road. We saw one of the lay brothers come out from the kitchen with a container in his hand. Lifting the lid of the bin containing Pig swill he dumped the lot into the bin.

"Did you see what he just done? We could have eaten that." That was the end of that days meal. We did have many successes. I often wonder if the friars were aware that I was sharing in their bounty?

We were told that the Redemptorists better known as The Fathers, gave out little loaves of bread every day to the poor and hungry. We decided to go and find out all about this. Perhaps between us we could be on to a good thing. We arrived at the church and went to the college entrance. A lot of people were assembled in front of the door. We stood there for some time before we were approached by a man.

"Do you pair want something?" He looked at us menacingly.

"No, we're just looking. Why is something wrong?" I asked him.

"If you've no business here then Feck off." Not a very nice remark to make in the grounds of a Catholic Church, I thought.

We went down to the water fountains at the lower end of the church and relieved our thirst. We returned to the church doors and mooched around the grounds killing time. We kept well clear of the bad tempered man. At the same time we kept our eyes open for developments. The suspense was broken when an upstairs window was opened and some Priests and lay brothers put a basket of bread on the sill. The priests and brothers threw the loaves into the crowd. They laughed as men and women swore and pushed each other trying to grab the small loaves. There was calm for a few moments before another basket of bread appeared on the window sill. These they did not throw into the crowd. They picked up the little loaves and pelted them at the gathering. Men and women jumped into the air trying to catch the loaves. This action by the clergy I found most nauseating and had the compulsion to go and tell them so. My brother and I watched the humiliating spectacle for some time before leaving in disgust.

"Do you know I'd love to go up there and throw the bloody lot out of the window." My temper got the better of me.

"Will you not be so stupid. What could you do? We had best be going or else we will be late back."

"Well it is annoying. It is bad enough being poor and hungry. To be humiliated like that." I kicked at the ground in my frustration.

"It is of no concern of ours. Anyhow we will not be coming back here again. Now will we?" He was right of course. There was nothing that we could do. Who would listen to us anyway? It would be pointed out that the Clergy were doing their Christian duty by feeding the hungry. The hungry would not thank us if the Clergy stopped giving out the daily bread. It was a catch twenty two situation that defied a solution. I told mother that evening what we had seen and also of my upset.

"Whatever brought you pair up there? These poor people go there daily for the loaf of bread. The clergy are doing their Christian duty." Mother would never tolerate any criticism of the clergy.

"Well Ma! I thought it cruel to treat the people like that." I defended my assessment of the situation.

"We will hear no more about it now. It is over and done with. You don't understand." She closed the conversation. It is incidents like this that remain in ones memory forever. Whenever I pass the church now, I instinctively look up at that window although the free bread has long since passed into history.

The Franciscans too have all but departed from Limerick. The once busy kitchen is now closed. I'll always cherish the fond memories of their choir and devotion to their calling. I cherish too the days I spent inside their church with my mother seeking warmth from their central heating. I wonder if God will understand and forgive me knowing that it was not to pray that I visited him? I'm sure that he has long since forgiven mother.

COLEOPTEROUS

Sometimes I wonder if I had a death wish or if it was the devil in me. If the devil was in me then he was in the others too.

Two boys were delegated each morning to go to the shop in the grounds and collect a large glass flask of ink and top up the white ceramic inkwells that were conveniently embedded along the tops of the desks. The good brother kept wondering why our desk used up more ink that the others. What he did not know was that I was using the ink to tell fortunes with. It was simple all one had to do was drop a blob of ink on a sheet of paper and fold it over. Then open it up and read what it disclosed, a little exaggeration helped to reveal the secret.

I also had a box in which I kept black beetles that were good runners. I was not the only one. There was one boy in class who swallowed whole big fat juicy worms. These he would find in the drains on Sarsfield Bridge or down O'Callaghan's Strand. I told him that the aborigines in Australia ate grubs from under the bark of trees and that eating them gave them magical powers. I never expected him to follow suit. I was taking no chances, I kept my beetles out of his reach and although I never saw him eating one I could not be sure. From our collection of beetles we would select one or two. These we would dip in the ink and let them run round a sheet of paper, just to see what patterns they made. Perhaps it was a cruel sport but the beetles didn't seem to mind. When we released them they always seemed fit and none to my knowledge ever drowned.

At other times we would select a good running beetle and challenge another pupil to race his beetle against them. This usually went very well until seen by the brother. Then all mayhem would be let loose

There was one occasion when I had a tin box with a selection of good running beetles in it. I selected a real champion in answer to a challenge from another pupil. We lined up the two beetles side by side on the desktop and released them. The rules allowed us to prod them on in a straight line or to pick them up if they should fall to the floor. Off the two beetles raced along the desktop. Mine in the lead by at least two lengths and gaining speed as he scurried to the end of the long desk. In our excitement we did not notice that the brother had crept up behind us. There was a mighty bang on the desktop and my beetle was flattened by the dreaded black strap.

"Who started this little game?" The brother towered above us. The black strap with the remains of my beetle stuck to it was poised and ready to strike.

"What game Sir? He fell off the ceiling and ran across the desk. Thank you for killing him I was scared to death of him." I looked to my mates for confirmation of my lies and at the same time annoyed that the good brother had murdered my beetle. The brother glanced up at the ceiling and then at me. I bit my fingernails in fear.

"There are no beetles on the ceiling. Now, tell me for the last time who is responsible for this?" He moved to the front of the desks where he could get a better view of us. We glanced at each other and then at the learned brother, nobody answered him.

"Of course he's not on the ceiling Sir, you just murdered him." On my God! I could have bitten my tongue, why did I say that?

"Murdered a beetle! What kind of an *Amadan* are you anyway? Very well then, all of you will remain in this evening for an extra hour and study your Latin grammar." As he took a last look along the line of boys before he returned to his desk, he took a step back and looked in shock. There climbing out from the side of the inkwell was the other beetle.

"Where did that come from? One of you brought them into the school." The beetle scurried across the desk leaving a trail of ink behind it. We cringed back in mock fright as the poor creature made a dash for freedom.

"Don't just look at it, kill it before it gets away." He again raised the strap and belted the desk. This time he missed the beetle and hit the inkwell. Ink flew in every direction covering several of the boys in the process.

"Where is he gone to now?" He seemed to be obsessed with the poor creature. Lifting his cassock high he seemed to be dancing to *the walls of Limerick* as he hopped from one foot to the other looking for the missing beetle.

We looked all 'round the floor but could see no sign of the creature.

"He must be hiding Sir. We can't see him." One boy remarked.

"Get up, get up all of you and look for it. There may be more." He again step danced and looked at his feet.

We rose from our seats and opened our desktops seeking the elusive beetle.

It was then that I noticed that my tin lay on its side inside my desk. There was not a beetle left in it, nor could I see any. As I lifted my books out I saw them seeking refuge in the darkness, hiding under the last book. Poor harmless creatures I thought. Why cannot he let them alone.

As I looked up to ensure that the brother did not see them, they in turn made a wild scramble to safety.

"Good God look! Where did they all come from?" The brother pointed to the beetles scurrying along the desktop.

"Look Sir, there is another one." A beetle appeared between the cracks in the desktop only to vanish immediately. The goody goods were pointing out where the poor beetles were seeking refuge. As they came to the surface, they were met by the Brother. Splash! Another poor creature would bite the dust.

"Take all the books out of the desks and clean the desks out. Make sure you shake your books." The brother told us as he retreated to the safety of his desk.

"Just who brought these into the school?" He pointed to a beetle running at high speed across the desk. They never ran that fast for me.

"Do you know anything about this charade?" He pointed to me.

"Not me Sir, they make me shiver." Why did he always pick on me?

From the way he reacted one would think that there were thousands of beetles. There were no more than three or four at the most. That is unless someone else had some that escaped. Finally, what beetles remained were collected and taken outside and put in the garden.

"You want to be very careful in future. These creatures must have got into your books in the park." He warned us.

We were not kept in that evening, as the brother accepted that the beetles got into the classroom by mistake.

FOOD FROM THE GODS

They tell us that hunger of the mind is more quickly satisfied that hunger of the body. I consider myself as good an authority as anybody on this subject. I met many the well fed person whose mind in my opinion was lamentable non existent. I do not mean to be offensive. I noticed that many of the well fed and pampered pupils in my school found difficulty in grasping what the teachers were trying to instil into their minds. 'God loves the poor,' we were told time and time again. Therefore one could draw a very ingenious conclusion in favour of the hungry the poor.

It happened one morning break as we returned to our classroom to collect two copies of the Dandy comic. These we intended to exchange in the second hand book shop in John Street for one that we had not read. If we could not afford to buy the comic second hand, then they would let us have one for two. As I was leaving, my brother opened the desktop next to ours. There, wrapped in tissue paper was the finest soda cake we ever saw. Not alone was there a soda cake but a hunk of cheese as well.

"Will you look at this?" Brendan removed the cake from the desk and lay it on the top. This was *manna* from Heaven to us.

"I wonder what it tastes like?" I reached to break a little bit off the side.

"Leave it alone, I know you." He replaced the cake and closed the desk.

"I wonder if it has *Caraway* seeds in it?" Opening the desk I removed the cake. As I tried to break the piece off, a whole quarter came away in my hand.

"Now you have done it." He looked at the lump of cake in my hand.

"Come on let's eat it. He won't know who took it. Anyhow he won't miss a little bit." I broke the cake and temptingly reached out a piece to him.

"You've got quarter of the cake. He might be taking it home, then what?"

"Look, do you want this or not?" I took a good bite from the cake.

"I don't know. We may be asking for trouble." He hesitated.

"What do you mean taking it home? Farmer's don't buy home made cakes. Their women make their own."

"It must be his lunch then." Brendan hungrily eyed the rest of the cake.

"You may as well try some yourself. There is nothing we can do about it now." I encouraged him to participate in the feast.

"Well! In for a shilling, in for a pound." He took the offered piece and then to my surprise he broke a second quarter from the cake and began to eat it.

"Let's try the cheese." I laughed as I removed the cheese from its wrapper.

Taking a ruler from my desk I cut into the wedge of cheese with it and removed a generous slice.

"This tastes great when mixed with the soda cake. Try it." I masticated the mixture in my mouth.

"Give me the ruler. I may as well try it too." He took the ruler and cut into the remainder of the cheese. We began to laugh at our audacious conduct.

"I think I'll try a bit more." I again took a piece off the cheese. This did not leave a lot, for the piece that was left was now so thin that it broke.

"Look we may as well finish it now. There's no use in leaving that bit." My brother said and I needed no persuasion. Having finished the whole cake

and the cheese, we collected the comics and went to the second hand book shop where we conducted the exchange .

After dinner hour we returned to our classroom and resumed our places. We kept glancing across at the farmer's son trying to read his reaction to his missing lunch. That afternoon the lesson was given by Bagsy and the subject was 'The Geography of Europe'.

"This afternoon the country we will be studying will be Hungary. This country is a member of the Axis powers." Unrolling several maps of various countries, he selected the map of Hungary. Taking the pointer from his desk he tapped the map and turned to the class.

"Can you tell me the capital city of Hungary?" He pointed to the farmer's son.

"No Sir, I can't. But I am hungry." He looked at the teacher with a gaze that would do justice to a Sister of Mercy.

"What do you mean you are hungry? What kind of an impertinent answer is that?" He held the long pointer in both hands awaiting an explanation. I nudged Brendan and tried to stop myself from laughing.

"Those two stole my lunch Sir." He pointed the finger of accusation squarely at us both.

Now how did he know that it was us who had stolen his blessed lunch? He had no proof as far as we knew.

"Who stole your lunch?" He questioned the farmer's son.

"It was them two sir. They were seen in the classroom eating it."

"Come out here both of you." The teacher ordered us out from our desk.

"Did you steal this boys lunch?" He asked Brendan, now Brendan, as I said before, was not one to stand up to any form of interrogation.

"We were hungry Sir! We thought that he was finished with it." He looked the picture of innocence towards the teacher.

"Thought he was finished with it? What did you think he was going to do? Take it home."

"I told him." He pointed the finger of accusation at me. "That he was probably taking the cake home, but my brother said that farmer's make their own cakes, so we could eat it."

"Just what are you blabbering about? You are making no sense at all. Look at me when I speak to you." Brendan looked sheepishly at the teacher.

"What about my lunch Sir?" The farmer's son was on his feet again. The teacher was unable to handle the situation. Perhaps because he had never encountered the problem before.

"You!" He called to a boy in one of the front desks sitting there with his mouth open, taking the whole episode in.

"You mean me Sir?" He looked at the teacher and pointed to himself.

"What is going on here to day. Am I dealing with a classroom of imbeciles? Yes of course I mean you. Go upstairs and ask the Brother Superior to come down here."

The boy returned accompanied by the superior. That meant trouble for us. The teacher explained what had happened as he understood it. Then the farmer's son explained his side of the story. From this point on the superior took complete charge of the situation. His first priority was to see to it that the farmer's son was given a decent lunch. Then he would deal with us.

"You go to the rectory, tell the brother that I said you are to have some lunch." The farmer's son wasted no time in leaving the room. Turning his attention to my brother and me and called us forward.

"You two come with me." With a wag from his finger he was off with the pair of us marching behind. We were taken to the chapel across the yard. The superior stopped at the door.

"You will go to the altar rails and pray and stay there praying for forgiveness until I return. Do you understand?" He opened the door for us and watched as we entered. We began to walk down the church to the altar rails as he had instructed.

"Come back here at once." He called us back to the door.

"What kind of Catholics are you?" He caught my brother by the ear and lifted him off his feet. Brendan let out a scream, which was his usual defence.

"Don't you shout in the house of God." He gave his ear an extra wiggle for good measure. This time Brendan did not scream.

"Don't you know to take the holy water and bless yourselves on entering the house of God?" He let go of Brendan's ear.

"Sorry Sir, we forgot." I made the excuse before he caught me by the ear and at the same time dipping my hand in the holy water font.

"Get in there the pair of you and stay there," he more or less flung Brendan through the door. Like a dancer at a Ceidhle I stepped neatly to one side avoiding the outstretched pincer hand of the superior and entered the church, ensuring that he saw me once again taking the holy water and reverently blessing myself. We heard the door close as we walked down the well of the hallowed church. For some time we did not dare look back. What if the brother had crept up behind us? Had we uttered one word then we would feel the wrought of the dreaded black strap, church or no church. We knelt before the

Blessed Sacrament light. Our hands joined in fear and prayer in that order. As there was no sound coming from the rear of the church, I took courage and slowly looked behind me. The church was empty.

"What do you think is going to happen to us?" I looked across at my brother and questioned him. He made no reply. He must be asleep or in deep prayer I thought, so I gave him a nudge in the ribs.

"What is it? Is he gone?" He still had his hands joined and his eyes closed.

"There's nobody here except us two. What do you think he will do with us?" I asked.

"Look, we would not be in this situation if you had left the cake alone." Once again it was all my fault.

"Didn't you eat your share and enjoy it? There's no use in you putting all the blame on me."

"I'm not interested in that now. If I make a novena quickly to St Anthony I may get off." He again blessed himself and returned to his meditation.

"Return to praying to St Anthony, that's a laugh. We stole the cake and prayers or no prayers, the superior will have our guts for garters." I got no reply, Brendan had returned to his novena to St Anthony. I had no doubt in my mind but that the brother was planning some terrible punishment for us. I sat on the seat ready to accept whatever punishment was about to be inflicted on me. There was no alternative. Brendan! He was so deep in prayer that I thought he had already gone to heaven to speak personally to St Anthony.

Finally the door opened. I slid off the seat and resumed the kneeling position with my hands joined and my eyes closed. We must have looked like little angels kneeling before the altar guarding it. I half opened one eye and saw the black robe of the brother superior towering above me. He had his back to us and was about to kneel in prayer. After a very brief pause he rose to his feet and blessing himself he looked down at us.

"On your feet you two and follow me." I rose to my feet and had to nudge my brother to get him off his knees. We followed the brother out of the church and into the grounds outside. On leaving the church, the superior did not cross the grounds to the classrooms as we expected. Instead he turned right into the gardens and orchard of the monastery proper. He could have taken us out through the door behind the church but for some reason best known to himself did not do so. Then we headed into the monastery. We entered the dining room where the plates from the dinner were still on the tables.

"There you see, I knew that St Anthony would listen to my prayers. He is going to give us a lunch." My brother whispered.

"There is more to this than meets the eye." I whispered back from the corner of my mouth. Me, being a doubting Thomas I had no illusions of a charity lunch.

"Stop whispering you two and come forward." Like two frightened dogs we slowly slid across the floor to face him.

"So you see the funny side of stealing other boys' luncheons. Do you?" Resting his hands on the back of a chair he addressed us.

"If you are all that hungry then you can start here." He waved his hand across the table.

"Start where Sir? What do you want us to do?" I could not understand what he was talking about.

"Start eating. There's plenty of food on the tables. Now eat!" He picked up a plate and put it in front of my brother. The plate contained the bone of a chop, the fat from the chop, a potato and mashed turnip. As ordered my brother began to eat from the plate.

Then he ordered me to pick up a plate and eat the contents. It contained much the same as my brother had. Brendan gingerly ate from the plate avoiding the fat and lay the plate down on the table.

"Waste not, want not. Finish it all up. There is plenty more to be eaten." He slapped his left palm with the dreaded *Black Strap*. So this was to be our punishment. We were to eat the leftovers from the brother's tables. Brendan picked up the piece of fat and put it in his mouth and immediately got sick.

"Now that you have eaten your fill, you can wash this lot." He ordered us.

We spent the afternoon washing the dishes and cleaning the floor. Then we had to return to the chapel to pray for forgiveness for our sins. Finally we got four slaps each from the dreaded black strap and were told to go home. We walked out into the cold windy night and made our way down William Street towards the city centre. As we crossed Sarsfield Bridge I became aware that everything around me was dead. Cold miserable squally rain attacked every bone in my body. The skies looked mournful heavy and dark. Sorrowful tears flowed from an unending dark horizon and filled the river far below. The tears formed into White Horses on the surface of the water and casting their white crests high above the waves raced each other towards the broad Atlantic Ocean. Some leaped onto the backs of others and impetuously challenged the hesitant to follow their lead. It was as if the river knew that the cold north winds were approaching fast and not wishing to be strangled in its fetters of ice was racing towards the security of the ocean. I wrapped my thread bare pullover around me as my shoulders stooped lower and lower to avoid the squall coming through the stone spindles of the bridge. It was all in vain. I looked out through the squall only to note that Brendan had long since left the bridge. My chattering teeth told me that I was the only living thing and that if I did not stop dreaming and move off the bridge then a cold death awaited me. When we entered the house, Mother was sitting in her chair knitting.

"Where in the name of God have you two been? I've been worried sick. What kept you?"

"We were kept in all afternoon by the superior." Brendan had to let the cat out of the bag. He had a mouth as big as Galway Bay that could not be kept closed.

"There must have been a good reason for you two to be kept in so long. What happened?" Instead of letting me tell the tale my way, he wasted no time in telling mother the whole sordid story. If he was expecting sympathy he was asking the wrong person. In so far as mother was concerned the Brothers could do no wrong. Mother was not alone in this belief. It could be said that most of the parents whole heartily agreed with all of what the Brothers said and did. It is doubtful, if they really appreciated the punishment we suffered. It was not until chastisement became sadistic punishment that they done anything about it.

Mother rose from her chair and went to the *Singer Sewing machine* and removed the belt.

The belt from the sewing machine had been used to chastise the family for as long as I could remember.

"I warned you. I pleaded with you to behave, But no! You had to shame me."

"It wasn't my fault Ma. It was him." Again Brendan tried to fix the blame on me.

"One of you is bad and the other is worse. If the devil made you he matched you." Then she gave us both a good whacking with it and sent us straight off to bed.

"Saint Anthony must have been out when you were praying. Whatever possessed you to tell her?" Brendan was weeping tears that would do justice to the mother of Dolores and had no inclination to take any notice of my chastisement.

"I told you to keep that big mouth shut. Now look what you caused?" I continued to castigate him. He was too busy crying himself to sleep to take any notice of my remarks.

Alone with my pain and discomfort I turned my face into my pillow and cried tears of resignation. How could the God I loved so much be so cruel to me?

THE SNUFF BOX

A long retaining bank that prevents the river Shannon from flooding the low lying land runs from O' Callaghan Strand out to the first light house on the river and beyond.

This lighthouse is affectionately known as *The Snuff Box*. That was donated to the city by the Spillane family. Who had the biggest tobacco and snuff factory in Munster. I remember the factory well and the head office in Sarsfield Street. The front of the building had two huge Irish wolf hounds made out of mosaic tiles each side of the front entrance. Whenever we decided to take a day off from our schooling we would mouth off out the bank. We dare not be seen in the city. Firstly Guard White, the local school policeman would be on the look out for any schoolboy or girl seen wandering the streets without good reason. These he would detain and return to their schools for the usual punishment. Then there were the neighbours. They wasted little time in telling our parents if they found us in the city during school hours. When this happened, not alone were we punished by our teachers for being absent, but also by our mother.

On one occasion we had not carried out our homework. We were left with two alternatives, we could go to school and get beaten or go out the bank and think of a good excuse for the next day. We decided that the best thing to do was to take the day off and worry about to morrow later. Hiding our books in the cemetery, I sneaked back to our house and called for my dog Bruno. When he heard me gently calling him, he cocked his head to one side. He rose from his slumber and was off like the clappers of hell after me.

"What made you bring him? Must he go every where with you?" My brother was not amused. Bruno and I were used to his remarks, so we ignored him.

Our first concern was to get some food, so we went to the nearest allotments. This took us out the South Circular road where we knew there were several kitchen gardens. I found one that was isolated from the house and reconnoitred the area for a safe entry. Seeing a gap in the hedge I looked inside. In the kitchen garden were rows of onions, carrots, turnips, cabbages and various other vegetables and potatoes.

"You keep you eyes peeled. I'll go through the hedge and get some veg; You sit there and watch him." I told my dog.

"I don't need your dog to watch me. Why do you always have to talk to him? He's only a dumb animal if you must know."

Ignoring his cutting remarks I went through the hedge and crept up behind a shed. Opening the door I found a hessian sack and returned to the garden. I collected a selection of vegetables and pulled up several stalks of potatoes. The potatoes I shook off the stocks and put in a sack. The stalks I replanted in the garden.

"What we need now is a fat rabbit and I know where we will get just that." I told him on my return.

Going to the River Bank I cut some thin sally ash branches and made a snare. I was hoping to catch a hare or a rabbit. Brendan watched as I carefully set the snare along the rabbit run.

"Now you go up the bank and wait, I'll tell Bruno to chase the rabbits."

Taking my dog to the other end of the bank I ordered him to fetch the rabbits.

Away he went but not along the rabbit track as he was supposed to. He made instead for the waterside. That dog seemed to have a fascination with water rats. I watched as he ran along the edge of the river throwing water to his left and right. I shouted after him but he ignored my commands. Then he vanished from view. I waited patiently for his return. I would chastise him later for being disobedient.

"Jesus help me; Oh someone help me." I heard Brendan cry out. I thought that he had rolled down the bank and into the Shannon. I was about to run to his assistance when I saw him come running along the bank as if the hammers of Hell were chasing him. Behind him ran a big water rat with the snare around his neck and behind him Bruno.

"Save me. Please kill it. I don't want to die." He yelled with his arms open. He sounded like *James Cagney in Boys Town*. Now I had been bitten by a rat before (*See 'Dare You Ripple My Pond' Book one*) and was taking no chances. Stepping as neat as a ballerina to one side I let Brendan and the rat have free passage. They passed me like a pair of express trains. As they passed I called my dog to come to my side. Without stopping he took one look at me from the side of his eye and continued the chase. I'd swear that I saw him wink at me. Perhaps he was apologising for not obeying me. I'd have words with him later about it. Somehow or other the snare came adrift from the rat who took a detour into the Shannon. Bruno raced after him but that wily rat knew the water better than Bruno.

"What sort of a snare was that? I could have been bitten or worse. Don't you know that rats go for the throat? Doesn't that mutt of yours know a rat from a rabbit? " Brendan panted as he lay stretched out on the bank holding his hand to his chest. His theatricals had to be seen to be believed.

"Sometimes it doesn't work out as planned. There's no need to insult Bruno. He done his best." I tried to explain.

"Work out! Done his best! Only you and that useless mutt could catch rats instead of rabbits." Why he was so angry I could not understand. Still Bruno seemed to be enjoying the outing. When the situation died down we put the remainder of our plan in operation. We found a bucket on the River Bank. This we rinsed and half filled with water from the river. We washed the potatoes and vegetables and added them to our stew.

"If only we had some salt and a piece of meat, then we would have a feast fit for a king." I told my brother. Bruno ran up and down the River Bank chasing the occasional rat that came in sight.

"Do you know, I could still get Bruno to catch a rabbit for us if I asked him," I informed my brother.

"Don't make me laugh. I've had enough of you and your dog for one day. The day he catches a rabbit, pigs will fly." There was no need for him to continually insult my dog. We collected some big stones and placed several iron rods over them. On this we placed our pot of stew and lit a fire under it. It did not take long for the pot to boil and in a short time we had a bubbling pot of stew. Considering that we did not have any salt or meat to flavour the dish, it didn't taste too bad. A bit gritty but good wholesome food all the same. Having finished our meal we hid the pot and the remainder of the stew. We went back to the banks of the river to scavenge for whatever salvage might be washed up. We must have walked miles and all we found were several sacks tied at the necks. We knew just what they contained. Dead cats and dogs, perhaps a litter of Kittens or Pups.

On one occasion I discovered a drowned body. I told some fishermen and hoped for a reward. I wanted to see what was in the pockets of his jacket but they chased me away calling me a *Ghoul*. The only one who seemed to be having a good time was my dog as he continually chased up and down the River Bank.

"Where does that dog get all the energy from, considering that he has had nothing to eat?" My brother asked.

"He catches all he needs when he goes hunting." I told him and awaited his sarcastic remark. We returned to the seats on the banks of the river and watched the ships come and go. A man and boy came along the bank. The man was in long waterproof waders that were attached to his braces and carried a fishing rod, keep net and basket. He joined us on the seat and remarked on the weather and the fishing.

"I'm waiting for the tide to turn, so that I can do a bit of serious fishing," he informed us.

"That won't be too long, it is at its highest now," I looked at the water level.

The boy went across the grassy sward to a stone wall. Then he took a slab of Cleeve's toffee from his pocket and began to hammer it against a stone. Cleeve's toffee was a huge slab of toffee made in a Limerick factory of that name famous for its rich sweet condensed milk. The slab was serrated into twelve sections. These could be broken off to make it more manageable to chew. It was not uncommon to see boys and girls walking through the town, trying to manipulate chunks stuck in their jaws. The brown liquid toffee trickling from the sides of their mouths. This toffee must have been a God send to the dentists of the country. Having managed to break the toffee into several pieces the boy returned to his father.

"Seamus! Why don't you give these two lads a piece of your toffee?" His father smiled at his offspring.

The boy held the paper containing the toffee out to us. Brendan selected a piece. I looked towards his father who was studying the tide. I grabbed the biggest piece I could find and rammed it into my mouth.

"Thank you very much, Sir, and you too Seamus." I muttered as I began chewing the toffee.

"It looks as if the tide is on the turn. I think that I'll try my luck." The man adjusted his waders and went down the slipway and into the river.

"Stay where I can see you Seamus. Don't come down to the water." The man warned his son who was now sitting on the seat. We sat beside the boy chewing the toffee. Bruno sat under the seat sleeping. When the boy was studying his father I stole a piece of toffee and slipped it under the seat to Bruno. We sat on the bench dreaming away the afternoon. Suddenly there was a shout from the man in the water.

"I've got one, and it's a big one. You two boys brought me luck after all." He shouted to us as his rod bent under the weight of the fish.

"That is a dandy of a fish Sir, make no mistake. It looks like a sea trout or a salmon." I informed him.

"If it is a salmon don't tell the river bailiff." He laughed as he played the fish.

"See your dad caught that big fish for your supper." My brother pointed to the boys father in the water. I thought this a stupid remark to make. He would have to be blind not to see his father fighting the fish in the water. As he watched his father intently I stole another piece of his toffee and a piece for Bruno. The fish rose from the water and dived head long again into the river, trying to free itself from the hook.

"Hold on to him Sir. Play him that's the best way to tire him." I gave of my expert opinion.

"Dad's caught a fish. Dad's caught a fish." The boy jumped up and down on the seat and as he did I again helped myself to his toffee. Bruno was aroused from his slumber by all the commotion and began to bark and run up and down the grassy bank. We decided to go down to the water edge and watch the battle of man versus fish. Bruno followed not wishing to be left out.

"Go on Sir. You're winning. He's getting tired." Our rhetoric continued as we encouraged the fisherman.

"One of you throw me out my keep net will you?" The man called over his shoulder. Brendan ran up the bank and collecting the keep net returned to the water edge.

"Pass it out to me will you please?" The fisherman reached back one hand and held on tightly to the rod with the other.

"Here you are Sir." Without looking at the man he threw the net into the water towards the man. The net hit the man on the back of the head and slowly sailed away on the tide before it sank into a watery grave.

"What the hell did you do that for? Now I've lost my keep net." He looked over his shoulder rubbing his head and at the same time trying to keep control of the fish.

"Sorry Sir! I must have missed you." Brendan apologised.

'Must have missed him?' I thought. He nearly knocked him unconscious.

The man had no time for further discussion for at this crucial moment, the fish was getting the better of him. That fish fought like a lion up and down the river, his silver body reflecting in the sun as he leaped from the water. If ever a fish was bent on survival then this one was. I was half hoping that the fish would win the day.

"You pull him up this way Sir, and we will throw stones at him." I tried to make amends for Brendan's mistake. Before he could object, Brendan and I began to throw stones at the fish whenever it came to the surface.

"Will you stop! You're drowning me with water." The man shook himself as the stones landed beside him in the water.

"If I had my catapult I could kill him no trouble, so I could." I cupped my hands and yelled. Then I saw Bruno in the water swimming towards the man. Actually he was swimming after the stones. He swam out to the man and began to swim in circles around him looking as to where the stone had gone to.

"Will you call your dog back. He is getting in my....." At this point Bruno swam between the man's legs. The man lost his balance and landed with a splash in the river dropping his rod. We watched open mouthed as the rod was towed at high speed down the river and up again by the fish. Standing befuddled in the water he made a lunge at his rod as it flashed past him only to once again lose his balance and fall into the river.

"God damn it, I'll kill you both and that fecken dog, when I get out of here. So help me God I'll hang for the pair of you." Such rhetoric was not becoming of a Limerick man who I presumed was a member of the confraternity.

"Not very grateful for our help, is he?" Brendan looked out at the man wiping water off his face. Of course he kept falling over. His waders were full of water. Every time he tried to lift his leg he tripped himself up. I looked at Brendan, then I called Bruno out of the water and we ran from the water edge and on to the bank.

"Are you going to wait and see if he gets out alright?" Brendan stood on the bank looking anxiously at the man floundering in the water.

"Take your boots off, Sir. You will get out easier that way." I shouted my advice from the safety of the bank. Taking my advice he reached down to remove one of his waders only to again fall into the river.

"Any more bright ideas will you keep them to yourselves. The curse of Christ on the pair of you. Will you Feck off before I come out or I'll not be responsible for my actions so I won't." The fisherman thrashed and slapped the water in vexation as he tried to retain his balance. Then he threw the wader towards the bank.

"He is not a bit grateful for your advice. It looks as if he will kill us when he gets out." My brother looked at the unfortunate fisherman struggling to get out of the river.

"Do you know what I think? I think we had best get to hell out of here. I didn't think fishermen swore like that. There's poor mother praying for their souls and they're making no effort themselves."

"Mother doesn't pray for these fishermen you fool. She prays for the fishermen at sea. You may as well say that she prays for you when you fish for the rats."

"Pray for me, that's nice, I appreciate that." I looked pleased at Brendan but he said nothing. We watched for a few moments longer as the man tried to get out of the water. Then when we saw that he was about to succeed we made our getaway along the bank.

There was no sense in waiting around to be insulted or even worse.

I returned the next day with my dog and searched the River Bank for the net and rod without success.

THE SLAUGHTER HOUSE

I was forever on the look out for handy jobs that would bring in a few shillings. On one occasion I got the job of helping a man drive a herd of cattle from the cattle market in the city to Cardavon out on the Ennis Road. A well renowned family of butchers had a large farm near by where they bred and slaughtered their cattle and sheep. The farm has long since been converted into a housing estate but the gatehouse remains. We drove the cattle into one of the fields and closed the gate.

"Are they alright mister?" I watched as they settled down and began chewing their cud.

"You done very well young fellow." The drover complimented me.

"Thank you very much Sir," He handed me sixpence for my work.

"Here! Before you go, do you know anything about slaughtering?"

"Slaughtering! You mean killing animals?" I asked him.

"Of course. You see I have a heifer or two to kill and hang and a few sheep also. I could do with a little help. I'll pay you of course."

The mention of payment was enough for me to claim my right as a slaughter man.

"Sure there was many the cow I dropped," I boasted to the man. Never look a gift horse in the mouth, as the old saying goes. In those days one had to bluff one's way. I never had seen a beast killed not alone killed one myself.

"I don't want you to kill any, I doubt if you would be able to. I want you to set and hold the rope."

'What is he talking about?' I thought to myself.

"Oh is that all. No trouble, no trouble at all, I can do that." I followed him into the slaughterhouse adjoining the farm.

Inside were two round machines filled with minced meat, which smelt of herbs and hanging up on a rail were the cleaned intestines.

"This is where we make the black and white puddings and sausages, I'll let you have one or two before you go home," he promised me.

We then crossed the room and out into a large stone area surrounded by animal pens.

In a pen situated in a dark corner were two mean looking beasts. They eyed me suspiciously as I entered.

"Get the rope through the ring in her nose and bring her out here." He pointed to one of the animals.

I had no intention of entering the pen. The look of the two beasts was enough to deter anyone.

"Come on good cow," I held my hand forward to the beast from the safety of the pen wall.

The animal obediently came forward and smelt my outstretched hand. Then it snorted and I pulled my hand away.

Taking the end of the rope I threaded it through the ring in the animal's nose and opened the pen gate. This was becoming a simple task I thought as the animal obediently followed me.

"Put the rope through the floor ring and secure it tightly, will you?" he called to me from a small room in the back. I was going to ask him what he meant but then thought better of it.

I threaded the rope through the ring in the floor as asked. Then I threaded it through a ring on the side of the pen. I was doing very well or so I thought.

Finally I hooked it through a ring hanging from the ceiling. As there were no more rings that I could see I presumed that this was the correct procedure.

I pulled on the rope as hard as I could. As I pulled the animal went down on its knees until its head was touching the ground.

So far so good, I was pleased that I had done so well. The animal snorted and eyed me from her position on the floor. If she could get up I was sure that she would have my hide for garters.

"Are we all ready then?" The slaughter man came out from the back room.

In his hand he held an axe. Not the usual axe, but one with a flat head on one side and a spike on the other.

From the dim recess of the building I looked across at the animal and felt sorry for her.

"Is the rope secured?" He asked as he vaulted the wall.

"Ready as it ever will be." I replied in a professional tone, or so I thought. I coiled the rope around my hand. The slaughter man stood one side of the animal and spitting on his hands he blessed himself. Raising the axe above his head he measured the distance from the animals skull. With a mighty swing that would do justice to the *Blacksmith of Limerick* he hit the animal squarely between the eyes.

I closed my eyes and said a quick prayer for the animal. I was brought back to reality by the rope tightening 'round my hands. The animal let out a roar and backed away quickly as blood poured from a gaping hole in its head. I was catapulted into the air, still holding on to the rope. I found myself in the rafters of the building. I struggled on to one of the crossbeams and sat there watching as the wounded beast ran round the house in a mad frenzy. The slaughter man dropped his axe and vaulted into the nearest sheep pen landing on the back of one of the sheep. He slipped off the sheep's back and all I could see were a pair of Wellington boots kicking the air and the curses coming from somewhere under the sheep.

"What the fecking Hell happened. Where are you son?" Are you alright? Speak to me." The slaughter man appeared from between several sheep.

"I'm alright, I'm up here." I called to him from my perch on the crossbeams.

"Thank God for that, where are you? I can hear you but I cannot see you." I saw him shade his eyes as he looked around for me.

"I'll stick my leg down, that way you will see me," I held on to the wooden truss with my hand and swung my leg over the crossbeam.

"Do you see me now?" I swung my leg backwards and forwards hoping that he would see me.

"I see you, how did you manage to get up there?" He called to me from the safety of the sheep pen.

"Did the rope break on you? You had best stay there for now. That brute is really fecking mad now and will kill you, if you come down." By now the heifer had its back to the wall. She snorted and bellowed in agony as bloody snots formed at the end of its nose.

"I cannot stay here forever. You'll have to do something about her," I called down to the man.

"You stay put where you are son. She cannot last much longer. She's losing a lot of blood." I could see the poor animal in the corner with blood running down its face.

"Will it be long in dying, do you know?" I again called down. I was really sorry for the poor beast and knew that it was all my fault.

"How should I know. We will have to stay put until it dies."

"Surely we can do something for the poor beast. Perhaps I could get to Lord Ross Rose to cure him." Lord Ross Rose was a veterinary surgeon who owned an estate next to the farm.

"Don't talk so fecking bloody stupid, I'm trying to kill it not cure it." I could tell by the tone of his voice and his swearing that he was annoyed with me for some unknown reason. After all I only wanted to help.

We both, from our respective positions kept a watch on the animal as it began to become unsteady on its feet.

"Its going, it won't be too long now before you can come down." The slaughter-man kept up a running commentary on the state of the animal.

"Stay where you are until I tell you it's safe to come down." I didn't need telling for I had no intention of leaving my perch until she was well and truly dead.

I watched in sympathy and said a silent prayer as the animal slowly went down on its front legs. I thought that she might be praying with me.

"Do you think that she is praying." I called to the slaughter man.

"For feck sake will you belt up, you bloody idiot." He shouted.

Then its back legs went and it keeled over with a final roar. Her body jerked in spasms for a few moments then she lay still. We both waited for some time watching for any sudden movement from the beast, but none came. I saw the slaughter-man vault over the wooden pen and cautiously approach the animal. First he looked into its eyes, then he lifted one leg.

"You can come down now young fellow. She's dead."

"How am I supposed to get down from here?" I asked.

"The same way you got up there, I suppose." What did he think I was? a trapeze artist.

I managed to scramble on to the wooden pillar supporting the pen and jumped from there on to the floor. I watched as he picked up the rope and examined it several times.

"This rope is not broken, you fecking little fool. Why didn't you secure it properly?" He was not at all pleased and who could blame him.

"The best thing you can do now is to get to feck off out of here as fast as you can. Don't bother your fecking arse coming back." By this time he was recoiling the rope.

"Does this mean that you don't need me anymore?" I asked.

"Want you anymore? I need the likes of you, like a fecking hole in the head. You little fart. Now get the hell out of here. Feck off will you."

I was going to ask for some payment for the work that I had already done. I could see that he was in no mood to tolerate me further.

"What about the black puddings you promised me." I reminded him

"What about them? Feck off will you, you're very lucky if I don't bury the poleaxe in your skull. Now get the Fecking hell out of my sight." I didn't think that he'd appreciate my help.

WE LOST OUR SOULS IN FLANDERS FIELDS

Uncle Gerald, like so many of his comrades, who had served with the Munster Fusiliers and other Irish regiments in the great war, relived the horrors of it in times of deep depression.

To us children, these were war stories to be listened to over and over again. The more bloody and gory the more we enjoyed them. What we did not appreciate was the torment within the minds of these men who had suffered so much physical and mental torture in the trenches. Whenever uncle Gerald had a drink or two he would relive the battles of the *Somme, Mons, Ypres* and many other battles, in the public houses of the city with his old comrades. I suppose one could say that talking about them had some therapeutic value. We were as familiar with the names of the battlefields as we were with the street names of the city, perhaps even more so.

In deep depression he would speak nostalgically of the *Retreat from Mons'* When the French and British forces were fearful of being surrounded by the Germans and had to drag the field guns for six miles manually because all their horses had died on the battle field. I use the words *Old Comrades* out of respect. The majority of them were between sixteen and nineteen years of age during the First World War. These young men were battle hardened veterans, with bitter memories. During the fiercest battles most of them would have been in their early teens. Some had steel plates in their heads, where a bullet or shrapnel had ripped the head open. They would occasionally tap the steel plate to frighten us children. Others maimed physically through loss of arms or legs or both, would hobble round the streets of the city and be mocked by the children much to their discomfort.

Then there were those who suffered from mental illness. These poor *Yahoos* [fools] as we children called them, felt abandoned by their God and the great British Empire. Yet, after all that lapse of time they still waited for the promised land. *A land fit for heroes to live in* as promised by the Welsh wizard Lloyd George. Others were embittered as Britain reneged on her promise of '*Freedom for smaller nations*'; Their country would not be given her freedom, she would remain shackled to the Empire.

Having indulged in reminiscences of his experiences with his comrades in the local public houses, Uncle Gerald would usually make his way to our house looking for something salty to eat. Why he insisted on having something salty when drunk I never understood. On one such occasion he arrived at the house in a real state of depression. It is to that night I now relate.

Sitting himself down at the big kitchen table, he buried his face deep into his hands. We could see the white of his knuckles showing. Then he addressed mother.

"Kate!" I must have fired a million bullets in the war to end all wars. A war of which I am now thoroughly ashamed." Mother listened attentively as usual, as he tried to relieve his conscience of the terrible burden of guilt.

"Will you not be so morbid? Sure that war is long over and forgotten. The children don't understand what you are talking about. They are not the least bit interested. Let's change the subject. What about it! Tell you what! You give us a little ditty (song) and I'll join in. How's about that?" She tried to wean him away from the subject and his depression.

"It is too easy to say forget, from where you are sitting Kate. No disrespect! It is far harder to put into practice. You could never imagine the nightmares that I endure alone at times. I often wondered, God forgive me, as I waited to go over the top, if there was a God in heaven?"

"That's blasphemous talk and is no way to speak in front of the children. You should be thoroughly ashamed of yourself," Mother chided him.

"I apologise. I'm sorry but talk, that is all that is left now, and like it or not talk eases my mind. You cannot understand just how it felt to see the comrades that you shared your last butt (cigarette end) with shot dead from the top of the trench by a Bosch sniper.

"Was it really like that? Tell us more about it." We were now all ears and could not wait to hear more gory details of the battles. Much to the annoyance of Mother.

"If you must know we were nothing more than a herd of goats led by donkeys. They told us that we were fighting the Bosch for the freedom of little Belgium and the freedom of smaller nations. We fell for their propaganda, hook line and sinker, so we did, and what was the outcome? A million Irishmen died for what? I'll tell you what, to expand the British Empire. I tell you this, the men who died in the trenches are far better off to this day than we are and that's for sure."

"Why do you say such awful bitter things? You should be down on your knees thanking God and his blessed mother for saving you." Mother reminded him.

"Did you say that God spared us Kate? That's a laugh. Spared us for what? To lie in bed at night denied sleep. Tossing and turning as we listen to the cries of our comrades as they lay dying in agony in the bottom of stagnant shell holes. My dead comrades are sleeping peacefully in the former battle fields of Europe, whereas I am suffering a living Hell here on earth." He was silent for a moment.

"Some of them, their arms and legs blown off, pleaded with us to have mercy on them and shoot them, to put them out of their agony. Is this the merciful God that you so readily speak of?"

"You never told us this before. Did you really shoot them? You didn't, did you?" Mother looked shocked at this new piece of information.

"No Kate! I never shot any of them. Others may have. Perhaps I was a coward. Sometimes I wish that I had."

"Ah! God be good to them all, they deserved better than what they got and that's for sure," mother looked across at her brother, as he gazed towards the window with that far away look in his eyes.

"I well remember one man Kate, as well as I know you and you being my sister. His name was Teddy and he came from some place out near Dunass or was it Castleconnell? Well no matter, he will never fish the falls again. We served together, the three of us, myself, Joe and Teddy." Joe was Gerald's other brother. Mother listened to him but did not interrupt the flow of the story. She thought it best to let him get it out of his system.

"Once out on patrol, we found a bottle of best Napoleon brandy in an abandoned farm house. We drank that bottle dry between the three of us. Teddy, God rest his soul, was a marvellous tenor, he could sing songs, the likes of which I never heard before and never will again. He could sing the birds out of the trees. He sung a few bars of one of his favourite songs as he swayed from side to side with his eyes closed."

Sure, if I had the wings of a swallow
I would travel far over the sea;
Then a rocky old road I would follow
To a spot that is heaven to me.
When the sun goes to rest,
'way down in the west

Then I'll build such a nest,
In the place I love best.
In that dear little town
in the old county Down,
It will linger way down in my heart-
Though it never was grand,
Sure it's my fairyland,
Just a wonderful world set apart.

Oh, my Ireland of dreams,
You are with me it seems,
And I care not for fame or renown
Like the black sheep of old,
I'll return to the fold,
Little town in the old county Down

"Do you know Kate, for that brief lull in the fighting we were transported back in memory to Limerick. Although our feet were planted in a foreign soil our hearts were back in old Ireland, as the saying goes. We must have sung every song about Ould Ireland that night and many more places besides. What we didn't realise was that we were fighting Britain's bloody war, as the British were murdering our people in the towns the cities and the countryside of Ireland. Perhaps it was best that we were not told at the time. I often wondered what way we would have reacted. Poor Teddy will never return to the fold."

"Would you like a drink Gerald? There is a drop of *Porter* left in the cupboard." Mother had the cupboard already open and was taking out the flagon bottle.

"Thanks Kate. I thought you'd never ask. You are a good sister to me, and that's no lie. Thank you. Now where was I?"

"You were telling us about your friend Teddy, and the bottle of brandy you found in France." I reminded him.

"Oh yes. So I was. Poor Teddy! Well we returned to the regiment, promising to meet again when the war was over for a reunion in the old city."

By now he had moved to the window sill where he sat on the wide ledge with his hands cupped under his chin. Removing his hand he banged his forehead with his fist, as if trying to dislodge some tormenting evil from his brain.

"Here's your drink. Don't you think that you have punished yourself enough for one night?" Mother placed the glass of porter on the window ledge in front of him and retreated into the room.

"I've started now so I may as well finish and tell you the whole story........

I remember the day well, how could I forget it. Myself and Joe were filling sand bags and repairing the defences damaged in the shelling. We watched the rats scurrying for safety as we moved the bags. Some swam through the stagnant water only to vanish under the slatted pallets. There was the odd ping of rifle fire from the snipers when someone tried to look over the top of the trench. An officer came up and told us to leave what we were doing and to go up the trench and remove a dead soldier who had been shot by a sniper.

We collected the canvas stretcher from inside the supply dug out. It still had blood stains on it from previous use. On the bottom of the trench were slatted boards, these were supposed to protect our feet from *Trench Rot* and to make the distribution of supplies and ammunition easier. They seldom if ever worked, for the water was too deep. We went up the trench for about 100 yards and finally came to the spot where a soldier lay face down in the stagnant water. Nobody had bothered to turn him over. He could have been alive and subsequently drowned from lack of attention for all they seemed to care.

"Did any of you check to see if he was still alive?" I asked a group of soldiers playing cards near to where he lay. They did not reply nor did they look up at us.

As we turned him over we got the shock of our lives. The dead soldier was none other than poor Teddy. Kate, we stood looking down at his young face, then we blessed ourselves and called on Jesus to take his soul to Heaven. I reached down and closed his eyes with my hands. We carried two tags around our necks, one red and one green. On them was inscribed our name, number and religion. Whenever anyone died we removed the red tag and gave it to the administration officer. The green tag we left on the body, this would identify the body when it was found in it's temporary grave on the battlefield. We took him from the trench to the collecting point where other bodies lay awaiting burial. 'What a waste of young lives,' I thought as I looked down at him, and at the faces of the other young soldiers.

You may or may not believe this but the medical orderlies used to snip the vein in the wrist of the soldiers that were brought in. If they bled they were taken to the field hospital. If not, they were buried in mass graves. Nineteen years of age, that was all he was at the time. He should have had his whole life before him, now it was all over for him. I suppose it could be said that Teddy had sent for us that day to take him home to Limerick. That was the last time we were ever called upon to collect a dead soldier from the trenches. He sipped the porter from the glass as he gazed out from the window, his eyes dimmed with tears. He tried unsuccessfully to hide his feelings from us, reminiscing perhaps on the days and nights he had spent on the battle fields of Europe.

"Come on children time for bed. You've been up too long as it is." Mother shooed us from the room.

Uncle Gerald and Joe told us many stories, as did other soldiers of the Great War. I relate just this one to let the reader know of the mental anguish that these soldiers suffered without one word of counselling.

PAYMENT IN KIND

Sundays we usually reserved for our frequent forages into the countryside. On one such occasion, my brother Brendan and I took it upon ourselves to go out past Parteen village and on into the countryside. My dog Bruno looked forward to any outing but seemed to be particularly partial to the Sunday outings. As he heard me going to the drawer and getting his lead out, he cocked his ear to one side and looked up. He was on his feet barking and jumping up and down and, as usual, making a general nuisance of himself.

"Will you, for pity sake, keep that dog of yours quiet. His bark is giving me a headache." Mother could never tolerate his sharp bark. Bruno stopped barking and looked across at mother. Then he sat on his bottom and had a good scratch, again much to her annoyance.

"I'm sure that dog of yours does that just to annoy me." She belted him with the towel she had in her hand. Bruno retreated to my side for safety.

"Are you not ready yet? We'll lose most of the day if you don't put a move on." I called to my brother.

"I'm ready! I'm ready, I don't know what all the fuss is about anyway. Let's go." Brendan grumbled as he passed me and went out the door.

I followed him, with Bruno straining on the lead. I was forced to jerk the lead to stop him getting over excited. We went out past the Long Pavement. On out through Parteen village and on into open country. We passed through the townland of *Castlebank* and entered *Drummin*. Passing along a boreen, (country lane) we saw a neat vegetable garden to our left.

"Come on, this is just what we have been looking for. Let's get something to eat." I suggested feeling the pangs of hunger.

We both crawled along the hedgerow, avoiding the open ground where we would be seen from the house. Then we went through the hedge. With my dog I crept along the neat rows of vegetables.

"There are some carrots over there, I'll go and get some." Brendan left me and crawled along the side of the garden. Bruno crouched down beside me as I went to a spot where there were onions growing. That dog had it all off, he knew when to keep quiet and out of sight. I picked two big potato onions and a head of white cabbage, then I rejoined my brother.

He had a bunch of carrots in his hand. We made an orderly retreat to the gap in the hedge.

Moving down the lane we made our way to a meadow where we sat under a hay stack and made sandwiches of the onions and cabbage leaves.

Bruno ran round and round the meadow, chasing every rabbit and hare that dared show their faces above ground, not that he ever caught any. They were far too fast for him.

"Here, take the carrots down to the stream and give them a good wash. We'll eat them on the way." Brendan threw the bunch of carrots towards me and stretched out under the stack of hay.

"Don't you strain yourself, you may do yourself an injury," I told him.

I rose from my comfortable position under the stack of hay. I picked up the bunch of carrots from where he had thrown them and went down to the stream. As I knelt on the bank washing the carrots, Bruno came bounding down the meadow in pursuit of a young rabbit. The rabbit saw me and swerved to one side and ran up the field. There was no such luck with Bruno, he could not stop and landed in the middle of the stream.

"You stupid dog. Look what you've done? You soaked me." I called after him as he vanished into the next field as the rabbit emerge from the other bank. Returning to the haystack, I saw Brendan stretched out fast asleep. I shook the water from the carrots in his face.

"What the hell are you doing? Are you stupid or something?" He jumped to his feet.

"Come on let's get a move on. There is no time for sleeping." I looked around the field for Bruno. There was no sign of him, so I called his name. He must have heard me first time. He came running across the field, barking to let me know he was coming.

"Alright, shut up. We know it's you," Brendan shouted at him.

We left the field and went down the lane chewing the carrots as we went. As the day wore on we again began to feel the pangs of hunger. It was time to retrace our steps for home. On our way we passed an isolated cottage. There was nothing special about the cottage itself. There was however something special on the window sill. It was this that attracted our immediate attention. On the sill was a soda cake cooling in the gentle summer breeze. We both looked at the cake, then at each other. There was no need for words. We knew just what each other was thinking. If it were at all possible we would have that cake for ourselves and Bruno.

"You wait here and I'll go up to the house. If anyone comes out I'll ask for a glass of water. You hold on to Bruno and don't let him follow me." With that I went up the long lane to the farmhouse. Arriving at the cottage door I knocked and waited. There was no answer so I again knocked only this time much louder. Again there was no response.

"Hallo! Is there anyone at home?" I shouted. Still no response. I reached up and looked in through the window. I was no more than six inches from my goal, the soda cake. The aroma from the freshly baked cake filled my hungry taste buds. I tentatively laid my hand on the cake. It felt warm and crisp. I had visions of it sliced in two with lashings of butter on it. I went to the corner of the cottage and peeped round the gable end. There was little sign of life with the exception of a few hens scratching the ground all was silent. I ventured further afield and went to the rear of the cottage. The clothesline stretched from a hook embedded in the kitchen wall to an old apple tree. A line of fresh laundry fluttered gently in the breeze. I looked at the apples on the tree. There's nothing worth taking, just a few miserable russets. The thought of collecting these I dismissed. I had my mind set on a more lucrative find. I returned to the window sill at the front of the house. In one swoop I grabbed the cake and was off like a bat out of hell. As I ran helter skelter down the lane way, Bruno saw me and began to bark in excitement. There was no time to tell him to be quiet.

"Did you get it?" Brendan shouted to me as I came near to him.

"What do you mean, did I get it? What do you think this is?" I panted as I patted the warm cake under my pullover.

"Come on then let's get out of here before someone spots us." We ran down the lane-way and on to the road. There was nobody to be seen as we trotted along the roadway.

"Stop for a minute, I've got a stitch in my side," Brendan called as he held his hand to his side. We sat down on a large rock beside a stream at the side of the road. Even Bruno was glad of the rest. We cured our thirst in the fresh running water of the stream. It was at this point that Bruno, ever alert, cocked his ears up in the air and began to bark.

"So I caught up with you two *Scallywags* at last." A man dismounted from a bicycle and approached us. There was no hope of making a break for freedom. We were caught and would have to face our punishment.

"Come with me you two, and bring that dog with you." He pointed to Bruno who was still barking. The man ordered us back up the road and fell in behind us pushing his bicycle. We went up the lane-way that we so recently came down. Round to the back of the house and on into a field of Swedes.

"Right you two get in there and weed that field. You do know a weed from a Swede don't you?" He looked at us both.

"And by the way before you start I'll have the cake back." He held his hand out for the scone. He left us alone in the field for the best part of an hour, weeding the Swedes. It was not that hard a task. The Swedes were rather large and there were not too many weeds to pick. Then we saw the man once again coming down the field towards us.

"What do you think he will do to us?" Brendan asked .

"He might have sent for the guards (police). I heard that the country Guards are tough." I warned him.

"That has cheered me up a lot, thanks," he remarked sarcastically.

"Come on you two, and him." He pointed to Bruno asleep at the side of the field. We rose stiffly to our feet and came out of the field to meet him.

"Take your boots off before you come into the house." He looked down at our mud encrusted boots. In my minds eye view I envisaged a guard waiting in the kitchen to arrest us. In trepidation I entered the cottage with my brother and my dog. There was no sign of a guard. That brought some relief to us both. On a large serving plate were thick slices of cake covered in butter and home made raspberry jam. A young woman looked at us both as we stood on the threshold of the cottage door.

"Aren't you two the fine pair of spalpeens (mischief makers). Stealing my Soda cake, just like that. I have a mind to box the ears of both of you. She wagged her finger at us and half laughed. She returned to the fire and pushed the crook with the big iron kettle resting on it over the open turf fire. Returning to the table she picked up a large enamel teapot.

"Will you two sit down. You look like a pair of statues standing there. Tell me where do you hail from anyway? You're not from these parts."

"We're from Limerick. He's my brother and this is my dog." I told her.

"Limerick! You'll be townies then. You came a long journey to steal my cake. What will your parents say when they find out what you were up to? What does your father work at?"

"We don't have a Father. He's buried in Saint Lawrence's."

"Sorry to hear that. God rest his soul. When did he pass away and from what?"

"We don't know. We were too small at the time. Are you going to send for the guards?" I asked unable to stand the tension any longer.

"No, not at all, at all. Just sit yourselves down now."

We both retreated to the nearest kitchen chairs and sat down. Bruno lay flat out on the floor and kept looking up at the woman. The woman returned to the hob and removed the lid from the teapot. She pulled the crook forward and tilting the kettle poured boiling water into the pot. She swirled the water round and round in the pot as she went to the half door and rinsed it out." What's your dog's name then?" she asked as she went to the dresser and took down a tea can. She opened it and put several spoonfuls of tea into the pot.

"His name is Bruno and he is a first class ratter." I told her as she again went to the open fire and filled the pot with boiling water. This time she put the lid on the pot and returned it to the table and covered it with a knitted cosy of various colours to keep it warm.

"Whatever came into you to steal my cake?" She asked.

"We have been out all day and were really hungry. We are sorry." Brendan apologised.

"So am I Ma'am." I hastened to add.

"There is little use in being sorry. Stealing is a serious offence you know." Brendan hung his head in shame. At this point the man entered the cottage and removed his Wellington boots and put on a pair of slippers.

"How is the supper going then? Chasing after these two has given my appetite the edge." I saw him wink at his wife.

"It's all ready. The tea is in the pot." She lifted the lid off the kettle and with a ladle reached inside and retrieved two boiled eggs. The man pulled his chair in front of the table and sat down. The eggs she placed on a saucer in front of him. We had established by now that he was her husband. Removing his cap he placed it on his knee. Blessing himself he said his grace. Then he blessed himself again.

"You done a good job on the Swedes. Thank you." Brendan and I joined them at the table. We were not given any eggs. There was plenty of soda cake and jam and we were soon making short work of it. Before we left for home the woman went to a large round iron pot sitting at the side of the hob and took out a bone and gave it to Bruno.

"Now the next time you are hungry, remember to ask. You might not be so lucky if you try that again." The husband warned us as we left the house.

THE BUDDING SAINT

Lent and Easter were special to us. It was then that we, in all sincerity and with contrite hearts atoned for all our past sins. Just to remind us how special it really was, the clergy covered completely from view every statue cross and picture in the churches in purple robes. All were covered with the purple mourning cloth with the exception of the *Stations of the Cross*. As the stations were solemnly read there would be a pause for thought. Then the choir would break into a verse of the *Stabat Mater*.

We were obliged to spend at least one hour each day on our knees in the church throughout that week in penitent prayers. On Good Friday of that week no meals would be cooked. We were obliged to survive on bread and water alone. Not that we saw too many meals anyway.

It was little wonder as I knelt in the church my stomach rumbling like a soul in torment. I used to hallucinate and see the statues rise up from under their purple coverings. These phenomenon's I kept to myself. After all there were more than enough people seeing miracles that week without me adding to the rumours.

On Good Friday we were awakened early and sent to the church to kiss the cross. Now while most churches had the ordinary crucifix, there was always the exceptional one where they had a relic of the true cross. There were times when I wondered just how there could be so many relics of the true cross. We had a drawer full of our own at home. These were sent to us, from America by my sister, who was a Nun. Then I would shake my head to clear it of these bad devilish thoughts, bless myself and return to my prayers.

Come the afternoon, we were once again obliged to return to the church for the Stations of the Cross. The Stations continued all day without respite. Mother took us to the stations once again at two o'clock. The reason being, that she wanted us to witness the sky darken at three o'clock. The time alleged that Christ was crucified. Standing on the banks of the river Shannon, she would keep a wary eye on Cannock's clock and for good measure the dockyard clock too. She was waiting for the chimes to ring out three o'clock. At this hour she would tell us, the sun would darken and the earth tremble. She was not alone in this belief. We could see others standing there waiting also for this phenomenon to happen. Should a cloud happen by chance to stray across the watery sun on that cold spring day, then this was enough to convince her. She would take us home contented. Satisfied that Jesus had shown us the day and the hour that he had died. How she knew that Christ had died at 3 o'clock GMT was beyond my comprehension. That same evening we were once again taken to church for more praying. When it came to bedtime we were sent off to bed still fasting and praying.

The following morning being Easter Saturday we were allowed to eat and catch up with any chores we were forbidden to carry out on Good Friday. In the evening our first communion suits and white shoes were taken down, as were the girls dresses and shoes. All the shoes were of white canvas. We would make good the scuffs and marks by whitening the shoes from a tin of whitening using a small paint brush. Then we placed them 'round the fire to dry. They were never placed too near to the fire for the heat would turn them yellow. Should the weather permit it they were placed on the window sill to dry. Finally we would wash down in preparation for the big day on Easter Sunday. Next morning, having fasted from midnight we would be dispatched off to Mass still fasting. Not even a spoonful of cold water would be allowed to pass our lips.

As we entered the church the statues and pictures, which were so solemnly covered all week in the purple mourning covers were now once again displayed in all their gaudy splendour. Rows and rows of candles in their shining brass holders surrounding them. Their halos of electric light bulbs lit up. We children were always ushered up to the front seats of the church. When the time came to receive Holy Communion, the acolytes came forward from the high altar to the marble balustrade and set out the linen and lace cloth the full length of the rail and closed the brass ornate gates. Seat by seat, we were sent to the rails to receive the Blessed Sacrament. Our hands joined and our holy medals hanging from our breasts like battle honours. The girls in their white frocks, white shoes and halos of wax flowers followed us to the rails. After mass, we returned home to a breakfast of *Packet and tripe.(See Dare You Ripple My Pond Book One)*.

Afterwards weather permitting, we went to visit the graves of our departed to pray for the repose of their souls. In the afternoon mother would insist on going for a walk out the Snuff Box bank, to see the sun dance in the heavens. The sun, many claimed, danced every Easter Sunday in the heavens to celebrate the rising of Christ. Mother seemed to have an obsession with the planets, the sun and their relation with God. Was it the innocent belief of the people or was it brain washing by the clergy? I'll never know.

Out on the *Snuff Box* bank there is a little grass park where one can sit on the seats and watch the ships go by or do a bit of fishing. This little park overlooked *Corcanree*, the city dump. This is directly across the majestic river Shannon on the Circular Road. Here mother would rest before instructing us to look into the sun. That mother of mine must have been very naïve indeed to tell us to look directly at the sun.

"Can you see the sun dancing? Isn't it wonderful, blessed be to Jesus and his holy name." Looking at the sun she would bless herself and call on us to do likewise. Sure enough after looking at the sun for some time it would appear to be dancing. So too would the big black dots before our eyes.

I remember on one such occasion, as I stood looking at the sun. The big black dots got bigger and bigger and I got dizzier and dizzier. The river and the bank began to spin round and round. I found myself moving backwards until finally with a splash I landed in the river up to my waist in water.

I will never forget the face on my dog Bruno. He looked down at me and began barking his head off. He must have thought it a great game, before he leapt off the seat and joined me in the water.

"Get off me you stupid dog." I splashed him with water as he swam around me. That water was cold enough to freeze a brass monkey and I wasted no time in making for the shore.

"What are you doing in there? Have you no sense and you in your best clothes? Come out of there at once, you fool." Mother looked at me as I struggled out of the water. Did she really think that I had purposely jumped into the freezing water of the Shannon for a swim in my best clothes?

"Ma! I couldn't help it, I fell in." As I looked up at her I saw her spinning round.

"Get out of there at once. You and that stupid dog! He must have tripped you up." She looked at Bruno as he came out of the water and shook himself dry. Bruno jumped round and round the bank as he continued drying himself in the grass.

"Stop that stupid yelping and sit down." She chided my dog.

Bruno lay down in the grass, gave mother a dirty look and stopped barking. When I came out of the water and in reach of mother's hand she gave me a clip round the ear.

"Just what do you think you and that animal were playing at. Look at you? Acting the fool again serves you right." She again gave me another clip round the ear for good measure. Much to the amusement of my brother.

"It's not that funny." She then gave Brendan a clip around the ear. Served him right.

"But Ma! I saw the sun dancing in the heavens. Then the whole world began to spin and dance. You were spinning too." I told her as I held my ears to protect them from further punishment.

"You saw what? I told you so, didn't I. Thanks be to God." She blessed herself and much to my surprise she hugged me to her breast, wet clothes and all. Gone was the anger that she had shown me previously. Was she seriously telling me that falling into the cold water of the Shannon was some kind of miracle performed by God?

I was not happy at all about the will of God. When I prayed to him to relieve my chilblains he was never around. Yet he turns up and dumps me in the Shannon on a cold spring day.

"Never mind now. I'll soon have you as good as new." She took my hand and led me across the grass sward. My shoes were by now an oily brown and squeaked as I walked. Water oozed from the lace holes. My velvet suit and white shirt clung to my body. Water dripped from me as I shivered.

"Some of you go into that field and collect some kindling. We'll light a little fire." Mother sent the other members of the family off to collect dry wood.

She collected dry grass and leaves and when the others returned she lit the fire.

"Now take off all those wet clothes and I'll dry them." She removed her coat and handed it to me.

"Put that on you for now. It will keep you warm until your clothes are dry."

"Ma! I'm freezing to death." I called out to her from beneath the protection of her coat. My nude body felt every ripple and gust of cold air that blasted its way up the river.

"Come nearer to the fire. You'll soon warm up." She called as she wrung water from my soaking clothes. As she wrung the water out of each item of clothing she hung it on the stone wall dividing the bank from the adjacent field.

"Are they dry yet Ma?" I kept calling to her as I huddled nearer and nearer to the fire for heat.

"Be patient will you, Rome wasn't built in a day." She returned to the stone wall and felt my clothes.

"It's no use. You'll have to come home in the coat. There is no sign of them drying in this weather." She ran her hands over the wet clothes.

"Ma, don't be silly I cannot go through the city like this." I forgot myself and opened the coat up wide only to expose my naked body. The other members of the family sniggered and held their hands up to their mouths.

"There's no need for you lot laughing. Can't you see the state that he's in?" She chided them. Then she called Brendan my youngest brother forward.

"Take off your pullover, and let me have it." She insisted.

"Whatever for Ma? I'll catch my death of cold if I do." He tightened his hands round himself in self-preservation.

"Come on take it off I tell you. Do it at once or do you want me to come over there and do it for you?" She made a move towards him.

"'Right I'll do it, but don't you blame me if I die." He took off his pullover and stood pretending to shiver from the cold. Such theatricals deserved an Oscar. Mother took the pullover and secured the neck with a pin that some how she procured from her own clothing.

"Here try this on you. It will do as a trousers for now." She held the make shift trousers out to me. I did not hesitate but gratefully accepted the dry clothes.

"God but I feel like a million dollars already." I looked down at the warm trousers and stroked them.

"Now put on the coat. If we go home by the bank and across the Strand sure nobody will notice." I was not too worried now as I was much more comfortable and warm and looked a little respectable if that were possible in such a get up. All went really well until we entered Clancy strand on the other side of Sarsfield bridge. Who should we see but Angelene and the mother hen approaching. I thought mother would on this tragic occasion put my shame and honour before her friendship towards Angelene's mother. There was to be none of it. Soon as she saw her; She put her hand in the air and began to call, "Cooee". She sounded like a pigeon. Angelene's mother looked up to see who was calling her. I was convinced that she spotted me first. She seemed to attempt to cross the street. Now her mother had no love for me. Not since the time she found out that it was me who broke the flowers in her garden and repaired them with black cotton and string. She also knew that I fancied her precious daughter Angelene like mad. She had better plans for her daughter. There was no way that I was going to get my dirty paws on her little angel. She could not escape across the road, for mother had come within sight and was making straight for her.

"Oh hallo there Kate, I wondered who was calling me." She cooed like a mating pigeon.

"Isn't it a lovely Easter Sunday Mary, thanks be to God." Mother smiled at her friend Mary. Then she looked down at Angelene." You look just like a little angel. God bless you." She never called me her little angel. Angelene was dressed to kill in a white frock with white patent shoes and dainty socks. On her head she wore a   waxed coronet of flowers. In her hand she carried a basket with a huge Easter egg in it. I hoped that she had bought it for me. (Wishful thinking) All this time the mother hen was looking at me in a peculiar way and ignoring mother's compliments.

"Whatever happened to him?" She looked me up and down.

"Oh him! He fell into the Shannon if you must know." They both looked down at me as I shivered and blushed before the treasure of my life, Angelene.

"He did, did he? I thought for a moment that he had taken a notion to go for a swim with that dog of his. They do peculiar things, him and that dog together." She laughed and looked at me disdainfully like a Cheshire cat. Such sarcastic remarks deserved my contempt. "Sorry Kate. I couldn't help myself. Just a little joke." A little joke indeed my foot. She wanted to embarrass me in front of Angelene. I felt like putting a curse on her.

"Mary! I must tell you how it happened. There he was watching the sun dancing when suddenly the earth moved and he found himself in the water up to his waist." I wished that mother would keep her mouth shut.

"I see. He was the only one I presume? Silly of me to ask." She again looked me over.

I looked across at Angelene hoping for a sign of sympathy. There she stood like the angel she was. I pictured her dressed in her white wedding dress with her halo of coloured waxed fruit and flowers sitting prettily on her red head and me in my morning suit beside her. She looked at me not in love but in sorrow and pity. I was then brought back to reality by somebody tapping on my head. It was the mother hen. My dream turned to a nightmare.

"Ah well, Kate there it is. He does smell a bit! Don't you think? Perhaps you had best take him home and give him a good scrub." She again tapped me on the head like a dog. Bruno wagged his tail. Realising what she had done she took a handkerchief from her pocket and cocking her nose into the air wiped her hands.

"Open your hand, there's a good boy. Here take this and buy yourself some extra strong lozenges. They will prevent you catching a cold. God only knows what else you might have caught in the water." I felt like putting a curse on her there and then. She opened her purse and dropped a penny into my hand. She did not wish to make any further contact with me.

"I'll say a prayer for you." She looked with disdain at me worried perhaps that she might catch some nasty plague from me.

"Must be going now Kate. Take good care of him won't you?" She again looked me up and down.

"Come on now Angelene, don't dally. We don't want to miss our Benediction, do we?" Angelene again looked me up and down. I wish she wouldn't do this. I followed her green eyes with mine. Whatever was she thinking? She smiled at me and gracefully tip toed after her doting mother. Her Easter basket on her arm. The chocolate egg was not for me after all.

I looked lovingly after her as she left and waved to her. She looked back at me and waved back. In the excitement of seeing her wave back to me. I let go of the coat only to expose my near naked body and makeshift trousers to her and her mother. Angelene kept looking at me as she walked backwards, only to trip over her mother and fall. Her mother reached down and picked her up before dusting her down. I ran up to ensure that she was alright. Her mother saw me in my Tarzan outfit and gasped.

"Oh my God! Will you cover yourself up this instant and go away." She grabbed her daughters arm and picking up the basket hurried up the strand. It was then I looked down at myself and realised just why she had tripped.

The story of how I saw the sun dancing and the earth moving soon got round thanks to mother. It did not raise too many eyebrows. There were plenty of parents in Munster who took their children out on Easter Sunday to see the sun dancing It was a wonder that half the children were not blinded by this tradition of looking directly at the sun.

What amazed some of the religious fanatics, when they heard the story was how I had walked on the water. No matter how I tried to deny it and explain that I had got dizzy and fell into the water from watching the sun too long, they would have none of it. The hand of the Lord moved in mysterious ways. It was becoming to say the least, embarrassing to be stopped in the street and have my head tapped for luck.

I was of the opinion that mother thought that Bruno and I were trying to brainwash her into a state of madness.

EASTER HOLY WATER

Winter had shed her gloomy mantle and the flowers were bursting forth from the slowly warming earth. The snowdrops were the first to awaken and toss their heads in the gentle breeze. It was early spring and the migratory birds could be seen and heard returning to their nesting grounds on the banks of the great river. There was noisy activity in and around the river as birds and game sought the most advantageous nesting places.

It was a mild afternoon and with nothing better to do I sat by the window with my cat on my lap and my faithful dog sitting astride my feet. With one leg crossed over the other I was at peace with the world. In my hand I held a book written by a favourite writer of mine. It was *The key above the Door* by *Maurice Walsh*. The book was of great interest to me as it was to my teachers, the Christian Brothers. It was part of our English lessons and we were expected to transcribe to his ability as a writer. I was determined to finish it by evening but as the lazy afternoon wore on my eyes became dim and confused. Then the words disappeared off the pages as I involuntarily slipped off to *Tir-na-nÓg*.

"Isn't it fine for some." I was awakened from my slumber by Mother calling. The book fell from my lap and landed on my dog Bruno who gave a little yelp.

"Get up from there and take yourself off to the Jesuits, right now." Mother instructed me to go to this church and no other, for a bottle of the precious holy Easter water. Why she needed more holy water I failed to understand. We had bottles upon bottles of it from Ireland and Europe. During Easter week water would be blessed and the parishioners invited to take it home. In some churches the water would be specially blessed by holding some embalmed part of the anatomy of a saint over the water. Now it so happened that in this particular church the water had been blessed with the body, the arm or some other part of a Saints anatomy. "Now you make doubly sure that you get the holy water blessed by the saint and no other or else," she warned me as she handed me a clean half whiskey bottle. This was a flat bottle with a spring on cap.

"Alright Ma! I won't be too long. Come here Bruno. We have a message to run." He barked and jumped as I tried to put his lead on and knocked me over.

"You stupid mutt. Stand still will you?" I cautioned him.

"You're not taking him to the Church, surely?" She looked incredulously from me to the dog.

"I'll tie him outside. He'll be no trouble, will you?" I tapped him on the rump.

"Go on then, and don't dilly and dally, do you hear?"

All went well and we were soon back in our old hunting grounds along *Clancy Strand*. When we got there the Shannon was in full flood. I saw several of my old muccas (*mates*) looking over the River Wall. I knew what was happening and so did Bruno. He stood for a moment ramrod straight with his hair standing on end and one foot in the air. The water rats were being driven from their nests, by the rising water. They were making desperate efforts to find alternative secure accommodation. Bruno made a leap and landed like a ballerina on the wall where other dogs were running up and down barking.

"Will you look at the size of that pair? Big as beavers they are?"

"See that fellow trying to make the castle? He's as big as bloody Tomcat. Pity he won't make it." We watched as the rat was carried down river on the fast flowing tide. The river by now was lapping the roadway as trees, carcasses of animals, oil drums etc: crashed into the bridges on their way to the sea.

"Half of that rubbish is dumped into the Shannon up in Cavan and we have to suffer it." One smart Alec remarked. This remark we ignored for we had more tempting offers on hand, RATS! Bruno ran along the wall and collided with another dog going in the opposite direction. The dog slipped off the wall and plunged into the fast flowing river.

"Quick come on, get him out of there before he's swept away." The dog was trying to swim for the steps but was being carried down the river with the tide.

"Come on, run. Follow me." I made a dash along the road towards the Strand barracks slipway.

"Here he comes! Call to him," I challenged his owner as his dog was swept past Curragower.

"Come on Prince, swim for it. There's a good dog," his master encouraged him from the slipway. Prince made the slipway and shaking himself jumped back on the wall none the worst for his ordeal. We watched the rats. We chased them along the road with sticks. Girls and women screamed as fathers threatened to call the guards. The dogs tossed the rats into the air. Boy, were we having a great time.

'Ding, Dong. Ding, Dong,
What do you want?
We want calico
How many ya- ards'

"Bloody Hell. Is that the time?" I looked in disbelief across the water at Cannock's clock as it rang out my death knell.

"It can't be. The church will be closed and I'll be killed or worse if I don't get the Holy Water." The Doomsday bell continued to strike the hour of nine. The churches would be closing their doors.

"Now make sure that you get the miraculous water blessed by the saint or else.....". Mother's words haunted my nightmare. It was now a battle against time. Collecting my bottle and calling to my dog we raced along the Strand. The clock slowly chimed out the hour and was joined by the dock clock. Like a death knell the chimes continued as I raced over Sarsfield Bridge and up Henry Street. I prayed that the church might stay open a little longer, it being Easter. High noon was fast approaching as I entered the crescent. All my efforts were in vain for by the time I reached the church the doors were closed tight against me. There was nothing that I could do. I would have to make up some excuse. Taking my time I again crossed Sarsfield Bridge. I felt dejected and alone with my dog. Even he ran away when we came to the end of the bridge. All he wanted to do was chase rats; the cause of my troubles. As I turned into the Strand, Eureka! There before my very eyes was the solution to my prayers or was it temptation by *Satan* himself? I would fill the bottle from the horse's trough. Mother would be none the wiser. I could sneak the bottle out in the morning and fill it in the church with real blessed water. 'God be good to me but I have the makings of a genius,' I laughed to myself as I removed the stopper and plunged the bottle into the trough. I watched as the bubbles left to denote that it had filled.

"So you made it at last. What kept you?" Mother took the outstretched bottle from me. Removing the stopper she wasted no time in blessing the four corners of the room. Then she blessed the family calling on us to bless ourselves.

"Now bless yourselves and say a little prayer. This is no ordinary Holy Water it was blessed by Saint Urban himself." She proudly held the bottle and kissed it.

(Saint Urban was a child martyr. His embalmed body is enshrined in a casket in the Redemptorists Church in Henry Street Limerick.)

I felt like confessing that poor Urban, the boy saint was sleeping peacefully in his glass casket in the church. He would never condone my cunning scheme. Then I thought that it did not really matter for to morrow morning I would put the matter to right. After all, discretion is the better part of valour.

Next morning I emptied the bottle and returning to the church filled it with real Holy Easter water from the barrel. No harm had been done and what she did not know would not harm her. The matter had been forgotten by me, until one afternoon later in the week when a neighbour called in to see mother. It was one of those chance meetings so popular in Ireland. I entered the kitchen and saw them having a cup of tea and gossiping beside the range.

"Oh, it's you, is it? I wouldn't know you without that dog of yours." The neighbour looked me up and down.

"Did you get into the church the other night? You left it very late?" She asked.

"What night was that, Marta?" Mother cocked her ear.

"The night of the blessing of the Easter water. He done his best but sure the Church was long shut. If you need a little drop you can have some of mine Kate. I got a fair sized bottle, so I did."

"Thanks all the same, Marta. I have a bottle of my own, haven't I, Louie?" I didn't like the way she said it. Marta left the house shortly afterwards. I wished that she would stay. I was about to leave the house when she called me back.

"Come here you, you little caffler. What is in this bottle?" She held the bottle of holy water up before me.

"It's Holy Easter water Ma. Honest I swear it is."

"Swear It's holy water. More like Shannon water if I know you. Now I know why you were so late getting back. You and that coss of yours were down the Strand chasing rats. That's where you were. Can you deny it?"

"It's real Holy water you wanted, honest." I again tried to convince her.

"Holy water indeed. Get out and take that mongrel with you." We both made a dash for the door. I opened the garden gate and began running down the road.

"Take that with you. There was me like a fool kissing Shannon water. Don't you come back here until you pray for forgiveness." The rhetoric continued. *CRASH!* Both myself and Bruno were showered with the holy water. I looked 'round and saw the bottle broken on the ground. The precious Holy water was slowly draining away down the channel.

Twilight was descending over the Clare hills and slowly obliteration the setting sun before my faithful dog and I returned to the house that evening.

Mother was very happy, very happy indeed, when I entered the house. I was on the verge of leaving again as I feared the worst, she had finally blown her top. I had finally succeeded in driving her mad.

"I must admit I was wrong over the Holy water. You were seen at the church the other morning collecting the holy water. Fancy me throwing it down the street." She placed her hands on her lap and again laughed.

"What's so funny about that, ma?" I asked rather hurt and surprised.

"Oh don't be so serious. Our road must be the only one that got blessed by Saint Urban unintentionally.

That was my mother.

THE OLD BRIDGE AT QUINPOOL.

QUINPOOL Bridge is a little known crossing point on the Long pavement outside the haunted glens of *Killeely*. Beneath it the waters of the little river *Avondoon* meander gently to join the mighty Shannon. What unspeakable secrets this insignificant river holds we will never be revealed. Today people would be hard pressed to find it unless they were familiar with the area. The place where all the ghostly sightings are seen is known as *The Point,* a swimming area well known to the swimming community of the city.

Yet in times long past it was a very important crossing between the counties of Limerick and Clare, *(Read 'Dare you Ripple my Pond').*

There are several stories told of strange happenings in the vicinity, of the fogs that appear and disappear. Of the birds that for no apparent reason stop singing and of the bitter cold on a summers evening, The drying up of the little *Avondoon* River. I relate three of these stories. One which I was witness to. The first story I tell happened on Christmas eve in the year 1631........

The gates of the city of Limerick had been locked and secured for the night. Far beyond the citadel and the city gates at Thomond, the ferryman waited at Quinpool on the river Avondoon for any stragglers from the city wishing to cross into Clare. He listened as his faithful dog chased the wild life in the woods of Cratlow. Finally the dog tired of his hunting and returned to the boat and sat in his usual spot on the prow of the boat, where he soon succumbed to sleep.

As the ferryman sat drowsing in the boat, he felt a distinct chill in the air. The like of which he had never experienced before. He pulled his heavy cloak tighter round him and cursed the weather. Looking across to the Limerick side of the river he saw a cloud of dense fog slowly coming towards him. He watched as the cloud moved nearer to the water's edge and stopped. Ever so slowly the cloud dispersed and from it stepped a tall man wearing a black cloak with red lining and on his head a cocked hat. The ferryman took the oars in his hands and was about to row to the opposite shore and collect the fare when a foreboding came over him. He sensed that there was something sinister about the man.

The man saw him hesitate and challenged. "Take me across the river at once." The ferryman who under normal circumstances would be more than willing to accept the fare was frozen to the seat of his boat in fear and trepidation.

"I demand to be taken across the river." Again the gentleman's voice boomed out across the fog shrouded waters.

Blessing himself, the ferryman called on his God to protect him. He would not take his boat from the Clare side of the river. His dog was awakened by the sound of the stranger's voice and stood up in the prow of the boat. With his hair standing on end and his ear cocked he looked across at the strange man. He began to shake uncontrollably and finally fell dead into the bottom of the boat.

Once again the stranger demanded that the ferry be brought across. With strength beyond comprehension, the ferryman took the oars in his hands. He rowed not to the Limerick side but to the banks on the Clare side. Leaving the boat he ran, with legs feeling like lead, to the nearest cottage. Banging on the locked door, he called for it to be opened in the name of God. Finally after what seemed like hours. The door was opened by the master of the house. Who half carried the exhausted ferryman into the house.

When the ferryman recovered he related what had taken place to the master. The story he related was beyond comprehension and the master asked him over and over again, if it were not all a figment of his imagination.

"Perhaps you were asleep and awoke when you heard the call?" he was asked.

"If what you say were true then what about my dog? I'll not return to the ferry this blessed night." The master saw that the ferryman was frightened of returning to the ferry and so let him spend the night on the cabin. Next morning they both returned to the ferry. There they saw the body of the dog still in the bottom of the boat. Removing the dog they placed him on the bank of the river.

Entering the boat they rowed across to the Limerick side. They walked along the bank to where the stranger had stood the night before. Then horror of horrors. Looking down at the spot where the stranger had stood they noticed that the grass had been burnt black. To them it was a sure sign that the Devil was out and about in the countryside. Like all such stories the message soon spread throughout Limerick and Clare, that the Devil was out looking for souls. It was claimed that he had visited the burial grounds near to the haunted glens of Killeely to steal a body and had been thwarted in his efforts. Whatever did or did not happen that Christmas Eve, it put the fear of Christ into the local inhabitants. As ferrymen refused to undertake the task after dark, it caused major inconvenience to the citizens from both counties.

Finally, the ferry service was acquired by a Scotch man from Dublin. Who had no fear of the *Devil*. He dismissed the fears of the people as superstition.

He demanded and got large payments for his service. This he could do, as there was no competition. Nobody else was willing to accept the challenge. He became more and more audacious in his demands for higher and higher payments much to the detriment of the local citizens. One morning as the local people approached the ferry, there was no sign of the ferryman. His heavy coat that he wore to protect him from the night air was in the bottom of the boat. Of him there was no sign. For several days the people waited for him to return but he was never seen or heard of again.

In the year 1634 the matter came to the attention of the mayor and the corporation of Limerick. They decided that the only alternative was to drain part of the bog at *Monabraher* and build a new road and a bridge at Quinpool at an expense to the city. Known in later years as *'Rice's Bridge'*.

To this day the old bridge still exists. On it's foundation stone can be read, the inscription in Latin .....

'Hung ponten ac-vialmstratam- fierifectit Petrus Creagh- Filivus-Amdre maipcivitatis-Limericensis sumptibus eldemcivitatis Anno Dei 1635.'

Translated it reads.......

'Peter Creagh, son of Andrew Creagh- mayor of Limerick City had this bridge and street constructed at the expense to the city in the year of our Lord 1635.'

The incident is now more or less forgotten. Yet there still remained a mysterious awe over the area.

> 'A man from Dublin came, 'twas said a Scot,
> A patent for the ferry he had got,
> Twixt Limerick and Parteen; he did demand
> So much money to be paid in hand
> That the city, with him refused to deal,
> Resolved a causeway to make for public weal
> Through Monabrahar bog-twas that year done,
> And so the man away with his patent run,
> The disappointment operated so.
> He died by the way, no more of him I know.'

My second story relates to 'The Headless Coach and Horses...........'

In the year 1690 after William of Orange defeated King James of Scotland at Derry, he marched south to capture Limerick. On his way he took Galway without firing a shot as the city capitulated. His spies told him that Limerick would not surrender. It would not be easy to capture as it sat on an island. He sent part of his army to Parteen (An Poirtin. The little Port) where they encamped in the bogs of Monabraher at the Long Pavement. From this point he hoped to attack the city at Thomondgate. What his scouts failed to discover was that General Patrick Sarsfield had deployed Raparees [soldiers] to the woods at Cratlow to defend the road.

Gunpowder had been placed under the bridge at Quinpool. A raparee was stationed there with instructions to light the fuse and blow the bridge should the army of William break through. It is said that the raparee died at his post before he could light the fuse. This allowed the detachment of William's soldiers to attack the city from the Thomondgate side. Be this factual or not, it is rumoured that it is his ghost that is seen on the bridge trying to make amends..............

Then there is the story of Peter MacAdam, a poor Scottish fisherman of the Shannon. It is also said that he betrayed the city by disclosing to the army of William the ford at *Carraig a Chlougragh (Now known as The Red rock or Bloody Rock)* from where they could easily cross and attack the city. *(Lax Weir-Salmon Weir)* A bloody battle was fought on Thomond bridge where thousands were massacred. In return William gave him a handsome amount of gold and granted him a large parcel of land in the area.

It is true that the MacAdam family lived in Springhill House on the river Blackwater. The family tomb is in the old Churchyard at Killguane near Parteen village and dates back to 1700. MacAdam's received some 1,800 Irish acres of the best land in the region. The family crest reads ...

'Under This Crest We Shall Conquer.'

The people of Limerick and Clare still hold this family responsible for their betrayal. In by gone days it became a pilgrimage to go on the day of the anniversary of his death to the graveyard and desecrate his grave and curse him and all belonging to him. Whatever the truth of this story, there is no doubt but that they were a powerful family in the locality. It is rumoured that the ghost of Peter MacAdam accompanied by the Devil walks along the Long pavement and stops at the old bridge at Quinpool on the anniversary of the betrayal.

Could all these stories of haunting in the area be explained? Could the years wipe it from the memories of the people? The problem is that these sightings keep occurring over and over again..........

One fine summer evening Paddy Gallagher, a well known jobbing builder from Saint Nicholas Street took my brother Brendan and me to swim at a sandy spot known as *The Point* situated below the metal bridge of the *Old Clare Railway.* Paddy had his usual menagerie of dogs with him.

Having finished our swim, Paddy suggested that we should take a stroll along the old railway track to Ardnachrusha. It was our intention to cross above the *Tail Race,* by the *Travellers Rest (where no doubt he would stop for a pint)* and return to the city via the fairy Fields at Corbally, a comfortable and scenic walk along the river Blackwater.

As we reached the power station, the weather began to deteriorate and we decided to return to the city by the shorter route. This took us along the Long pavement towards the bridge at Quinpool. Briskly we walked along the road. The dogs running ahead chasing the odd rabbit that appeared. Nearing Quinpool Bridge over the river Avondoon, we saw the lights of Limerick. We were near to home. Our minds were far from the ghosts of Quinpool as we went towards the city. It was then that a strange incident occurred. The dogs stopped as one in the road and refused to go on. The hair of each and everyone of them standing on end then as one they escaped to the stile at the banks of the Shannon at the *Point* and ran howling along the bank. Someone or something on the bridge had frightened them. Paddy called in vain for them to return. Putting his hands across our path he stopped us in our tracks.

"Will you look at the old bridge?" He whispered.

"What is it? I can see nothing", my brother remarked. Looking down at the bridge all we could see was a mist rising from the river Avondoon.

"Whatever is the matter Paddy? I can see nothing." I strained my eyes to see just what he wanted us to look at.

"Never mind boys. Follow the dogs over the stile. You are not meant to see." By now the air was getting distinctly cold. Yet Paddy made no effort to move.

"We are not welcome here this evening. Bless yourselves and pray for the dead." He instructed us. Standing in the centre of the road we prayed as a group for the repose of the holy souls. Finally Paddy guided us across the stile and on to the bank. There was no sign of the dogs. Half way down the bank, he stopped and looked across at the old bridge.

"The experience we had this evening is not to be forgotten. Is it a wandering soul on the bridge this night or is it the devil incarnate, we may never know?" Paddy seemed to be speaking to himself.

I have since sat on the old bridge and watched the river Avondoon meandering slowly to join the majestic Shannon without hearing or seeing the ghost of Quinpool. Whatever the secret is that little river holds it to itself.

Was I there at the wrong time? I will never know.

A VISIT TO ANGELENE

Mother wondered where the time had gone to, it passed so quickly. It seemed a long time since her friend Mary had moved from the Strand barracks to their new home.

"To day, seeing as we have nothing better to do. We'll both go and see how Mary and her family are settling in. I know you will like that." Mother had her coat on and was adjusting her flowery hat on her head. This was one time that I had no objections to accompanying mother. Putting my coat on I collected my dog, Bruno. Then we set out to see Mary. Well to tell the truth mother did. I had no interest at all in meeting the mother hen. I was hoping to meet Angelene. Mother looked down at my dog scratching himself noisily.

"Do you think it is advisable to take him? You know how fussy she is." Bruno cocked his ear to one side and looked up at her.

"Do you know something? That dog is half human. He knows everything I say. Is that the way you trained him?" She studied me and then the dog before nodding her head in that knowing way. "Oh come on, let's go then. I'm a bigger fool taking notice of you two." Arriving outside Mary's new house mother stood back a pace and looked up at it.

"It's a real nice house. I'll give credit to the corporation for that. Soon now, God willing, we too will have a new house." Opening the front gate we went up the concrete path to the front door. In answer to mother's knocking, Mary came to the door.

"Kate! Kate is that yourself, or are my eyes deceiving me? You should have rung the bell, you know." Her eyes opened wide in surprise on seeing mother.

"Come in, Kate, you are a sight for sore eyes. How nice to see you so soon."

"You don't mind the dog, do you? He would insist on bringing him." Mother apologised for my dog and I.

"He would, wouldn't he. Of course not! I'll open the back door and put him and the dog out. They can't do any harm there. Perhaps he should wait with him when we have a chat." Mother followed her friend into the house.

"You go into the parlour on the left Kate. He can take the dog out the back." The parlour to the left if you please. To the right was a blank wall.

"Would it be asking too much for you to pick up that animal and wipe your feet"? So much for an Irish, *Cead Mile Failte*. Opening the back door she invited my dog and I to play in the garden. For a moment or two he stood still studying and sniffing his new surroundings. Then he was off through the single wire fence dividing the house from the next. Running in front of him were two cats, their tails in the air. One made the sanctuary of a tree, the other he cornered in a back yard.

"Leave my cat alone, you mangy coss. Who owns you anyway?" A woman's head appeared at an open bedroom window. Bruno looked up at the woman but refused to leave the cat alone.

"Right! I'll fix you, you flea ridden coss." She vanished inside the room. The back door opened and *Splash!* Bruno found himself on the receiving end of a bucket of cold water.

"That will teach you to leave my cat alone." She shouted after my dog, as he retreated to the comparative safety of my legs. I heard the back door open again, and looked to see if it was mother.

"Come in son. What was all the commotion about? Not you and your dog again, I hope." It was the mother hen waving to me to come inside. Bruno made to enter the house only to find his way barred.

"Not you. You stay where you belong, outside. How did he get wet?" I made no reply but obediently followed her into the house.

"Your mother is in here." She opened the door to the parlour.

The parlour had linoleum on the floor and a big rug in front of the fire.

The sideboard was littered with ornaments. Two china dogs stood guard one at each end. Family pictures going back generations, were hanging from the walls.

Over the Fireplace hung a picture of The Sacred Heart, that was signed by the Abbot of Kylmore Abbey. Proof that he had blessed the house and family.

Not that the Abbot had ever been to Limerick. They would have sent a donation to the abbey and in return would have received the signed picture. Which no doubt they framed themselves. They didn't have a picture as big as our painting.

"Well what do you think of it so far?" Mary looked lovingly round her parlour.

"From what I've seen of it, It's a credit to you, and that's for sure." I was sure that mother was jealous.

"You must be itching to see the rest of the house." Mother rose to her feet in obedience and followed Mary to the door. I followed behind. There was no bathroom in the house, but there was a flush toilet. The poor old long can has become obsolete in this house. That was no loss, I can tell you. Through the house, mother and her friend went inspecting every room. Not that there were that many. There were three bedrooms upstairs. Returning to the parlour, Mary filled mother in with the other details of the house before she decided to make a pot of tea.

"I'll pour us a couple of stouts, or would you rather a cup of tea?" Mary got up again from her seat.

"We'll have the tea first, if you don't mind, I feel a bit parched." Mother ran her hand down her throat.

"That's fine. Come on into the kitchen, you too son. I suppose you'd like a biscuit?" There was knock on the front door and Bruno began barking.

"Would you get that son. It's probably Angelene coming from town." I made for the door like butter off a knife. As I opened the door a ray of sunshine entered the dull house in the form of Angelene .

"Did you get all you wanted, love. Look who's here?"

"Nice to meet you Ma'am and you." She looked shyly at me from under her long eyelashes.

Mother looked out the kitchen window and was surprised to see a donkey in the next door garden grazing on the sparse grass.

"Mary! Do you know there is a donkey in the garden next door? How did they get him in there?"

"Kate, for pity sake not so loud. They'll hear you. They're very rough people if you must know."

"Come back into the parlour and I'll tell you about them."

Mary had a pot of tea covered with a home made tea cosy, and a plate of assorted biscuits on a tray.

She laid the tray on the table and went to the sideboard and fetched three china cups and saucers and three teaspoons and a mug. I knew that the mug was for. Me! She did not want to take the risk of having a part of her best china broken. Soon tea was served. Mother and her friend settled down in the two armchairs for a chin-wag and an exchange of news.

"I was just telling you, Kate about the people next door. Don't eat all the 'Kimberley' biscuits, there's a good boy." She warned me. I returned the half eaten biscuit to the plate.

"No! Eat that one up yourself. Who wants your leftovers?" Then she lowered the tone of her voice and continued.

"The corporation gave the house to one of the travelling people. The tinkers, you know."

"Now why would they do that? Don't they ever look after their own." Mother interrupted.

"Don't you ever read the papers? It's a new idea to get them off the roads."

"Well I never, of all the liberties! I'll go and find out about this." She was indignant at being snubbed by her local corporation.

"I only wish someone would. I'm fed up listening to donkeys braying at all clocks." Mary crossed her arms.

"You see Kate there is no way into the back garden, but through the front door. So they bring their donkeys, horses and goats through it."

"Didn't the corporation say anything?" Mother moved forward in her seat.

"Say anything! I understand that they also pulled up the wooden floors and used them as firewood and then concreted the floors. Kate, I tell you something will have to be done soon."

"That's a real shame, and they such nice houses too." Mother was sympathetic to her friend.

"A shame is it you say? Look at this." Mary stood up and pulled the settee back. On the wall was a rising damp patch.

"What is that, Mary?" Mother put her hand on the wall.

"It's from next door. It was caused when they put down the concrete floor. It's all too technical you know. No good trying to explain it to you, it's too complicated."

"You're best keeping yourself, to yourself. You don't really know what they are like." Mother advised her friend.

"Come on now Kate. You will have a bottle won't you? Angelene and Louie can have an Olo lemonade in the garden when we chat."

As we sat on the garden seat drinking our Olo and crunching our biscuits the donkey came from next door and looked over the fence. Leaving the seat I crossed and caressed the donkeys nose and pulling a tuft of grass presented it to him.

"If Mom sees you talking to that donkey she will be annoyed. We don't mix with them." Angelene warned me.

I abandoned the donkey and returned to her side. I did not wish to antagonise the mother hen. It was then that the donkey began to bray to attract my attention. In answer to the braying the back door opened. There stood the mother hen followed by mother.

"Are you alright? Did something happen to you?" She asked her daughter.

"I'm alright, it's nothing really. Louie was talking to the donkey and he was answering back." I looked with incredulity at her. Was she too going as mad as her mother?

"Talking to the donkey was he? You had best come into the house." She looked from me to her daughter and back again.

"I'd best be going now Mary. Time is getting on." Mother made her excuses some time later.

I crossed the floor and went towards the back door where the toilet was situated.

"Where are you going to now? The front door is this way." The mother hen barred my way and pointed to the front door.

"I'm going to use the toilet, please."

"Oh! I thought you were going to say *Good Bye* to your friend the donkey. Remember to lift the seat and bolt the door." God in heaven, how could anyone stand that snob of a woman. Sarcasm is the lowest form of wit.

I was more than glad when mother decided to leave and come home, so was my dog by the way he jumped up and down.

Angelene came to the door and invited me to call again, I was delighted.

"Fancy! After all she told us. You go and start a conversation with the donkey." Mother said that she could take me no place without a lead on me.

THE TIVOLI CINEMA.

The Tivoli cinema, was the fleapit of the city. This was the wild west rough house. The only thing respectable about it was It's name. If you never went to the Tivoli then you never really lived in Limerick. Yet I expect every city had a Tivoli cinema similar to ours. It was run by a Skinny Lady, we called *Olive Oil*. A degenerative name taken from the cartoon Popeye. How she ever managed to show any semblance of control was a miracle. Why she ever stayed there must have been her penance on earth. The projection box was forever breaking down. We looked forward to this and took a sadistic delight in throwing whatever came to hand at the screen.

"Sit down you whelps, or I'll throw the lot of you out. Sit down and keep quiet." Olive would run from seat to seat shining her torch. Then the lights would come on and be greeted with a loud cheer from the rabble. The lights consisted of two hands holding a glass torch attached to the wall. There were two on either side of the pits. Barely enough to see where you were going.

"Does your mother know you're out?" We would shout across the seats at the girls. Some would be caught in a corner snogging with one of the local lads.

The upstairs of the cinema was called the *Gods*. Here at least you could have the comfort of a seat to yourself, but that cost a few pence more.

A voice from the God's would call down for the mischief makers to be ejected. This intrusion would be met by another barrage of missiles from the pits below. Then a bag of water would be fired into the pits. This would be answered by more missiles from the pits. The bag did not contain water all the time. Sometimes an uncouth lout would *Pee* in the bag. When this happened there would be a battle royal. Peace would be restored, when once again a Popeye cartoon came on to the screen.

"Olive, your boyfriend is waiting for you. You'll need more that a feed of spinach to satisfy him." Would come the uncharitable remark from the rabble.

"Why don't you try some Cascara from the dispensary, they seem to have gallons of it." A cheer from the rabble would finalise the session of friendly bantering as the lights dimmed. This would be followed by, *Flash Gordon and the Clay-Men from Mars.* A series that ran for years on end and never seemed to come to a conclusion. I wouldn't be at all surprised if it was still running long after I left the old city. He was a proper Hoodini, at the conclusion of one showing he would be trussed up like a chicken dangling on a chain over a flaming volcano. Then the climax... 'See next week, will Flash Gordon escape from the clay men?' The message would be flashed across the screen. The following week he would somehow have one arm free holding a knife that miraculously appeared from no where. He would cut his bonds, which were now transformed from chains to ropes and swing on the rope to freedom. We never questioned as to why the rope did not burn over the volcano.

Not only did Olive act as usherette, ticket collector, game warden, and dog's body. She also sold the sweets. We would watch Olive as she came backwards down the rows, her torch shining on her tray of sweets. On one occasion as she reached our seat, I crept along to the edge and crouching down gently stroked her leg.

"Rats! rats"! I shouted and jumped up on the seat. Pandemonium broke loose with girls screaming and jumping on the seats. One landed on my back and nearly crippled me. Olive dropped her torch. I was showered with sweets. This was our chance to grab what we could before the lights came on.

"Put the lights on, the place is overrunning with water rats." I encouraged a near riot to continue.

"Will you sit down or go elsewhere, your making a show of me." The moth insisted. Brige was my moth that night and was not amused at all the commotion and blackguarding going on around her. She was not my girl friend as such, more a companion of the night. Like most girls from the city she too had airs of grandeur. She suffered from what I would describe as an inferior complex. The poverty of her house was no worse and no better than the rest of our houses and tenements. The wretched walls with their cheap flowery wallpaper or rose wash. The worn out furniture or the teachests. The ugly curtains made from flour sacks and the cold concrete floors. We never noticed this but Brige did and resented it. Her dreams were of the big houses on the Ennis Road and a husband with a good job and a steady income. Her dreams were not about me I'll assure you.

"There's one running up your knickers Brige." I shouted as I placed my hand on her leg.

"God! You're disgusting. Do you know that?" She moved away from me. I moved across the seat in pursuit of the damsel and again caught her leg. She let out such a scream that the rabble fell silent. Her screams attracted the attention of her brother, who was sitting unknown to me some seats away and was twice my size.

"What's happened to you?" He demanded to know of his sister.

"There's a rat in my knickers." She screamed as she searched under her skirt. I made a hasty retreat under the seats. Finally the lights came on. Everyone looked to see where the rats were. Olive looked at her depleted stock and then with suspicion at me.

"Alright where are they? Hand them over." She demanded.

"Hand what over? Are you accusing me of something?" I defended my reputation.

"My sweets and chocolates, that's what."

"Well don't you blame me. It must have been the bloody rats that infest this place that took them."

"The only rats in here are you and your gang."

"Put the lights out. We cannot see the picture." Came the demand as Olive tried to find her missing stock. I fear the rabble had confiscated the sweets and chocolates. Finally with a wave of her torch to the projectionist the lights were dimmed. Satisfied that it was safe the picture continued. We divided the sweets between us in the darkness. Occasionally, and that was not too often, a good picture would be shown at the Tivoli. Getting everyone into the little cinema was impossible. There had to be disappointments. This did not apply to us of course. We had several decoys to hoodwink the unwary. The first showing was at seven o'clock when children would be admitted. The second showing was at nine o'clock when only adults were allowed in. The queue waiting for the cinema to open would stretch all the way along the mall and round the corner into Carey's Road, by the time we usually arrived. There wouldn't be a hope in Hell of getting in. In order to gain admittance we would have to resort to subterfuge. Across the road from the cinema behind a stone wall ran the Abbey River.

On one occasion I looked over the wall into the river below.

"Come and look, do you see what I see?" I pointed into the water and shouted.

"What is it, I cannot see anything?" Another member of our gang enlightened as to the plan ran across and shading his eyes looked into the dark river.

"Over there. Are you blind? Look it seems to be stuck under *Baals Bridge*!" I pointed into the forbidding water.

By this time the patrons in the queue opposite were getting restless and looking across at us. Wondering what all the commotion was about, yet reluctant to forgo their places in the queue. "That cannot be what you think? It looks no way like a body. Is it one?"

A body! There was a stampede to the wall. Some even believed that they saw the body. We left them to it and got to the front of the queue. When the gates were opened there would be a stampede back to the cinema. This worked well for us on many occasions.

On another occasion we thought of working a miracle. We would say that we saw the Blessed Virgin in the sky over Barringtons hospital. This idea we quickly abandoned. We knew what the outcome from the Priest would be if we were found out. The cause of the problem at the cinema was that there was no discipline. When the gate opened everyone left the queue and dashed for the entrance. It was a case of the survival of the fittest. Many timed one found themselves flung from the melee and practically thrown over the stone wall into the river.

Another ruse of ours was to get in the middle of the crowd as they pushed and shoved and pretend to faint. This was not too hard at times, especially when some one let off a series of farts after a feed of Limerick bacon and cabbage. If some one struck a match at this stage, I've no doubt but that the methane gas would have blown half of them across the river.

I, or a pal would fall to the ground in a dead faint and remain still. Brendan or one of my mates would plead for space to remove me. This was a gamble for sometimes the rabble would ignore ones suffering and stamp all over them.

"Make way. Give him air. Can't you see he's fainted?" My brother would plead with the crowd to move away from where I lay on the ground. The crowd would part like the waters of the Red Sea. I would be helped to my feet and propped against the wall of the cinema. I often thought that I should have been given a place in the Abbey theatre in Dublin for my performance. In the meantime one of our pals would have gone to the box office and purchased the tickets. Then I would make a miraculous recovery and join them in the cinema.

Where others would buy sweets or ice cream to eat in the cinema we would buy a few cheap knuckles. Knuckles were the top section of the Pigs toe which were boiled and were available from most shops in the area. Our favourite watering hole was run by a lady called Mary Anne Walshe I believe, at the far end of the *Long Can* behind the *Good Shepherd Convent.* The knuckles would be displayed piping hot in her window. There was many the swear word uttered as a patron tried to extract the long sinew. It had a habit of springing back and hitting one in the eye. The knuckles in themselves were lethal weapons when one was pitched from the back of the stalls.

One had to be fitter than the fittest and full of guile to survive in the old city.

I expect that there are many who remember with nostalgia the old Tivoli or similar cinemas throughout the country.

THE WEMBLEY DANCE HALL

Of all the dance halls in the city I would expect most of the citizens of my age to remember some of the following ... .
'Todsies or St. Mary's Hall.
Other venues were
'The Transport Union Hall (O'Connell Street)
'The 'Wembley' at Watergate.
'The 'Abbey' next to Creagh Lane, my old school.
'The 'Number 9'. Sarsfield band room in John Street.
'The Stella.' Too posh and dear for the likes of me.
'The La Sceala' on the Dublin Road which I never entered.
'The Hop' also on the Dublin Road which we never found.
'Faughs' on the Ballysimon Road reserved for the country folk.
'Meany's' way out near to the falls of Donass. Not worth the bother if you had no transport.

There was another dance hall called *'China Town' or 'The Tub of Blood'* due to all the fights and pitched battles that took place on the floor.

County Clare was a great spot for the Rinnce Fada's. I've always had a great admiration for the Clare folk. They could dance the buckles off their shoes all night long.

Wembley was our dance hall. It was known locally as the *'Hop'.* It was a firetrap and death trap rolled into one. All due respects to a dance hall, it was more or less a dilapidated dump. I doubt very much if it would burn down. On rainy nights the dance would be cancelled as there was more water in the hall than outside. I cannot vouch for the following story but it was told that at one time when the roof was in bad need of repair and there were no funds to repair it. They removed slates from the back of the building to make good the front.

Whenever we felt amorous a bottle of cheap hair oil called *'Brillantine'* would be purchased from Woolworth's from the proceeds of a collection made between the gang and shared. Others would slip into *Todds* for a squirt of a free sample from a bottle of perfume behind their ears. A rack (Comb) would be dragged through our locks and a parting made in the side. Others more ambitious would get their sisters or mothers to warm the curling tongs and put waves in their hair. There was the occasional accident when the tongs were applied when too hot. A scorch mark would be visible along the forelocks. With a few deft strokes between the fingers a quif (Wave) or *Cow's lick* would be made to ones forelocks. Like peacocks we would strut into the hall and stand against the wall smiling and sizing up the eagerly waiting moths.

The floor surrounding the edges of the hall would be covered in a smothering of sawdust from the local timber merchants and smelt like *Griffins* funeral premises in John's Square. The centre would be sprinkled with *Lux* soap flakes. It was rumoured that these were mixed with the remains of the burnt out candles from the church and the dead house or morgue at Barrington's Hospital. This came about because one of the ticket collectors was a morgue attendant at the hospital. We used to call him the *Ghoul or Frankenstein,* not very charitable I admit. All in all a lethal combination of combustible materials

On rare occasions we would have a three piece band, belting out waltz music but not too often. Most nights it was a one piece band playing the music on a leaking accordion. Occasionally the musician would break into a sentimental song just to add to the monotony. One old boy fancied himself as a Count John McCormack and took to singing only his songs. It was pathetic to hear him trying between coughs to give us a rendering of *Mother Machree.* When he came to the refrain.....

'Shure I love the dear silver that shines in your hair,
And the brow that's all furrowed and wrinkled with care.
I kiss the dear fingers so toil worn for me
Oh! God", cough ! splutter! cough , spit.
Then taking a deep breath he would scream........ '
"Bless you and keep you mother Machree."

We would let out a cheer as he struggled through the last line that could be heard by the nuns in the Good Shepherd's on Lough Key. Replacing the woodbine butt back in his mouth he would smile and wave to the rabble.

"Give up the *Coffin Nails* (Woodbine cigarettes) Mick or you'll be joining Mother Machree in Mount St Lawrence's," (*The General Cemetery)* would come the uncharitable comment.

It was the only dance hall where I ever saw bare footed dancing. That is apart from the Indian war dances in the cinema. It must be appreciated, that if a boy couldn't afford a pair of boots to go to school in, he would hardly be expected to have a pair to dance in.

The real highlight of the night would be the call for the *Siege of Ennis.*

This is a dance where the couples line up across the floor facing each other.

Row upon row would cram onto the floor. They would fight like cats and dogs for a place beside a Moth of their liking. When peace and order was restored the dance would commence. Nice and steady at first, then would come the swinging.

The whole building would rock and shake. We would scream and shout like savages as we twirled the moth around the floor. With their knickers exposed for all to see we twirled them faster and faster. Most of the knickers were made from *Ranks* flour sacks.

"Could I have a stone of flour from your knickers." Would come an uncharitable or similar comment as a girl was swung around the hall with her knickers exposed.

I was sure that the girls enjoyed it as much as we did for they screamed louder than us. The Priests were tired of condemning the patrons to Hell fire without success. There was no need to participate in the dance. We were automatically bounced round the floor as the building moved.

Many of the boys had second hand boots that were far too big for them. To make them comfortable the toes were stuffed with paper. If a lace broke or came undone during the swinging, one could be floored as the missile of a boot came flying across the floor. It must be appreciated that these boots were fitted with steel heels and shamrock studs also made from iron. The volunteers from the L.D.F. stood out like sore thumbs with their ruby army issue boots.

Like wild savages we would hop, dance, scream and swing the girls. Sometimes like eels they would slip from our grasp and wind up in a heap in the far corner. This was all very well until some girl's brother accused you of throwing her on purpose. It was then a matter of honour that was usually settled outside in the lane, resulting in bloody noses. At times the moth would let out a yell and slap her partner across the face.

"Dirty randy little Git, more hands than an octopus." She would complain.

"Come here you. What were you doing to my sister?" A knight in the form of her brother would step forward to defend his sister's honour.

"Nothing, nothing at all. Why?" The combatants would face each other like two fighting cocks.

"I'll give you why. Did you stick your dirty paws up her skirt? You dirty pervert."

"Me a pervert, whatever that is. I've better things to do that maul your sister. Look at yourself will you?"

"What do you mean? Come on out with it."

"I saw you rubbing yourself against the queer one."

"Right, that settles it. Come outside."

Before the combatants could leave the hall, relatives and friends would take sides. Who was fighting that did not matter. Order would be restored when both parties acknowledged that it was all a misunderstanding. Honour would be restored.

On one such occasion we were trying to dance to the waltz *'That's an Irish Lullaby.'* On the stage stood a local girl singing and trying to keeping in time with the accordion player. Like *Peacocks* we vainly waltzed or should I say dragged the moths (Girls) around the darkened floor. I apologised more often than not as I spent more time threading on her toes than on the floor. Some uncouth louts would let off a fart which forced us to move quicker in order to get away from the smell. When this happened it distracted my concentration and I lost the rhythm.

I continued moving gracefully like Gene Kelly around the floor and showing off my prowess to the girl. Then from the corner of my eye I saw a friend of mine from the *Ranch (The Island Field)* in the corner hopping about in his bare feet. The more upbeat called it *St Mary's Park*. We had slang names for everything and there was no disrespect meant.

As I was aware that this lad was of sound mind I was more than puzzled by his unorthodox behaviour. The only other excuse that I could make for his conduct was that he got hold of a flagon of cider and was drunk.

"You're doing fine" I thought I heard him shout to me as I gracefully waltzed past him and swung the moth around the floor.

We called them *moths* because they were forever fluttering between fellows.

I waved to him in acknowledgement of this compliment. Yet I could not understand why he was dancing to the *'Siege of Ennis'* when the one man band was playing a waltz.

As I came round for the second time he shouted once again and waved to me as he hopped from one foot to the other.

"You're doing fine." I thought I heard him again compliment me.

"You'd better see what your friend wants." The girl advised me.

"Don't worry about him. It's alright he knows that I'm a good dancer." I boasted.

"I'm glad that you think so, my feet are suffering something awful." Not a very nice compliment from the moth.

Next time round I waltzed the girl over to where he was dancing and stood looking bemused at him.

"The bloody place is on fire. Are you deaf? I'm trying to put it out." He shouted at us as he danced up and down on the smouldering sawdust.

"I thought you said that I was doing fine." At this point the moth saw the smouldering sawdust. Tearing herself from my amorous embrace she held her hands to her face and let out a scream that would do justice to the Bean-Ó-Sidhe. All eyes turned towards me thinking that I had molested the girl.

A knight in ragged ganzie came tearing across the floor and confronted me.

"Fire! Fire! The bloody place is on fire." She ran past him screaming, heading for the only exit.

"Sorry mate," the spectre on hearing her scream *'Fire'* vanished through the only exit. Knocking over the fair damsel in his panic to get out before her. Like all brave heroes it was a case of every man and woman for themselves as hysteria set in. They forgot about women and children first. It was survival of the fittest and leave the rest to God's mercy. They prayed, screamed, cursed and scrambled for the only exit. We turned our attention to the fire and stamping on it put it out. It was not a big fire, some idiot dropped a fag end in the sawdust. Soon order was restored and the dance continued.

Before our time I was told that the dancers would go and seek out the *'Eel Woman'*. What she sold were *'Elves'*. These were young eels that were boiled in milk to which butter and nutmeg was added. Uncle Gerald told me that they were considered a delicacy in London and very expensive there. Crubeens from the stall of Mary Anne Walshe were always a welcome treat. On her retirement from the trade she stuck a notice of closure in her window *'NO MORE TOES.'* Nostalgic memories flood back now and again.

There were many first class dance halls in the city. We would rather go to the two penny hop. At least we could manage this now and again.

Then again we as children would not be allowed into the posh dance halls.

The *Wembley* dance hall like It's counterpart *China Town* are now all but fading memories to the folk of my generation. Yet we spent many hours of innocent enjoyment inside their portal walls. I'm sure that every town and city in Ireland had its own *Wembley's* and *China Towns*. I know that many happy marriages started within their old walls.

I doubt if the *Stella Ballroom* or *The number 9 (Sarsfield band Room)* would appreciate being invaded by the gangs from the north side of the city.

BALLY NANTY FAIRY FORT AND THE FREE ALLOTMENTS

The war was still raging in Europe and the Far East and the poor of the city were suffering a lot of hardship. To the credit of the corporation, they tried to alleviate as much of the hardship as they could with what little resources they had.

There was little work, if any, to be had. The workforce, were leaving the city in droves for England where work was plentiful. Something would have to be done to alleviate the situation.

One scheme was to plough up the fields at Ballynanty Beag and mark them out in allotments. There was one problem with the chosen area and that was the fairy fort. This fort stood on the crest of a field and had remained undisturbed for as long as anyone could remember. It was finally decided that the fort would be preserved in its entirety. A wise decision by the city fathers of the time. One may call it superstitious nonsense but nobody was willing to interfere with the fairy fort. A psychic by the name of *Irene Aherne* told of her many encounters with the fairies of Ballynanty Beag fort. I feel she could tell more about the fairy fort than my humble pen could. I hope her family will excuse me for mentioning her name here.

I knew this fort well and its association with Saint Bridget and Saint Lelia's graveyards. I have referred to both of these in *Dare You Ripple My Pond*. Saint Bridget's is where the poor of the workhouse and the great hunger victims are buried in common graves. Saint Lelia's is where we walked in procession and recited the rosary for the dead on Good Friday. It is unknown by many that beneath this little graveyard lies the forgotten oratory of Saint Lelia. The three were linked to the ghostly apparitions at the Long Pavement. Perhaps she still roams its crumbling halls praying for the people of Limerick. I have told the story of *The Bridal Bride* who was taken by the fairies of Ballynanty Beag fort in *Ancient Stories of Ireland Book Two*. The stories relating to Killeely and the surrounding townlands would fill an encyclopaedia. Yet the whole area has been vandalised by Limerick City Corporation.

In the 1950's this historical and famous fairy fort was desecrated and destroyed by The Ancient Monuments Section of the Board of Works and Limerick Corporation. They were of the opinion that the fort contained archaeological treasure. When nothing was found they systematically obliterated it. How ignorant they were regarding the history of forts. It would be like digging up Stonehenge looking for buried treasure.

They should have known that the treasure was the fort itself and should have been left intact as a national monument. To this day the city fathers continue to destroy the ancient history of Limerick and the surrounding countryside. On a recent visit to my city I was disgusted to see the state of its scenic riverside walks.

(Going out the panoramic bank at Watchhouse Cross I was forced to turn back in disgust. A stinking dump overrun by vermin had been opened at the Long Pavement by the city fathers. Out on the Wexford road as one enters the city from the south east, another camp had been opened presumably for the travelling people. These areas, are all advertised, by the tourist board as scenic routes aimed at attracting tourists to the city and surrounding countryside. I witnessed poachers on the Shannon and Blackwater rivers openly stealing salmon in broad daylight. I wondered at this open defiance of the law. From what I can learn, the fisheries board, spend thousands of pounds stocking the rivers encouraging the fish to multiply and at the same time ignore the poachers. The banks retaining the rivers are crumbling and I fear that if no action is taken then at some time the rivers will break their banks.)

Families were invited to take over the allotments and as a further inducement were given, seed potatoes, vegetable seeds, cabbage plants and a spade and fork free. One allotment was allocated to each family. This was indeed a God sent gift to most families. Beside each allotment was a pile of manure and should you require more then this was available freely from the corporation yard in *Ball Alley* lane. We were also supplied with a hundred weight of fertiliser. Those who got there first were lucky for they got the ones nearest to the stream. We had to go to the corporation yard to collect our spades and seeds. Should we break a handle when digging then it would be replaced free on condition that you brought in the two pieces and not used them as firewood.

Some were of the opinion when they collected their seed potatoes that the corporation had grown them for them and so cooked and ate them. Others who got to the yard early enough were given a fresh supply and a type written sheet explaining how to plant potatoes. Those who were unlucky when the supply was exhausted were told to go to *Boyds, The Standard Stores* or other seed merchants in the city and buy their own.

Some not knowing how to plant the potatoes, peeled them and cooked them. The skins they saved and planted in their allotments. They could see no sense in digging up potatoes only to replant them again. Others planted the vegetable seeds in one small hole. These of course were the exceptional cases. Most families soon adapted to the management of the allotments. Those who were not conversed in the knowledge of farming were guided by the more knowledgeable.

There was one failing in the system, the only water available was from a stream running along the road between Killeely and Ballynanty. This was known as the Fairy stream. Locals believed that it was fed from the fort further up the hill. It was believed that water from this stream would never boil.

Out towards the *Famine Graveyard* there was a small holy well known as St Lelia's well and believed to have miraculous powers. Alas, like the Fairy Fort and the Fairy King's hawthorn of Ballynanty Beag it has now disappeared under the tarmac.

The allotments became a great attraction at weekends when whole families would converge on them to have a picnic. We would light a fire, and roast freshly dug potatoes in its embers. In between eating, we hoed between the neat rows of vegetables. As our allotment was on the crest of the hill, that meant we had to carry water to the allotment for a quarter of a mile.

Carrying buckets of water over several fields was no mean task. As the rewards were good we seldom complained.

As the war continued, Britain called up more and more of her men. This called for their places in the factories to be filled and where else to find surplus man power than across the sea in neutral Ireland. The men on the dole could not be blamed for taking advantage of the situation. Their wives saw other households improve their living standards as the telegram boy delivered the weekly money.

Slowly the novelty of the allotments began to wear off as families left the city to better themselves overseas. Gradually the once well kept allotments began to fall into disuse. We took over first one allotment, then two, finally we had four allotments, this was about as much as we could manage. I took to growing most of the produce. What surplus there was I sold and gave the proceeds to my mother.

This arrangement continued for some time. As more and more men left the city the allotments were deserted. Those left were surrounded by dereliction. Weed covered scrub became a vandals paradise. I was forced to abandon my plots when I found that someone else was profiting by my labour. I went one day to gather cabbages only to find that someone else had helped themselves to my hard work by taking the lot. I appreciate that I when younger I often stole the odd head of cabbage but I never cleaned out the whole field.

As the land was no longer being cultivated the corporation abandoned the allotments. Finally, they were closed down and the land left fallow. In later years it was used to build a new housing estate now known as *Ballynanty Beag.*

THE WIDOW'S MITE

The migratory birds returned to their watering holes in the wet lands surrounding the city. The fish had returned to their spawning grounds on the gravel beds of the rivers. Spring had again returned to Ireland as we knew it would. Mother looked out of the window and rubbing her hands together remarked that the weather would soon warm up and we would have no need of a fire in the grate. God had been really good to us, we had survived yet another winter. Although the cold bleak winds from the Clare hills blew their biting breath over the tombstones of old Killeely graveyard, mother, the eternal optimist, looked forward to an early spring. There was no fire in the grate and no fire in our stomachs. I sat looking into the empty grate wondering what exactly I had to be thankful for. Returning to her seat she looked up at the mantle piece.

"Tomorrow morning make sure that you are out early. There will be others there too, you know." It was Tuesday evening. There would be no chance of any relief until Thursday when we visited the dispensary and threw ourselves on the mercy of Mr Keane or Mr Coffee. There we would stand with the rest of the poor hoping and waiting for a few shillings. On the mantle piece that frosty evening lay our worldly monetary possessions, our salvation. One threepence piece, *The Widow's Mite*. It would be my turn to rise early and go to *Daly's* bakery in Sarsfield Street. With my flour sack over my shoulder I would try to get there first and buy the stale bread, skinnings or crusty loaves. The skinnings were loaves from the batch which when separated parts or skinnings as we called them of one loaf was left on another. These loaves could not be sold to the general public as they were underweight. I liked going to the bakery. On most occasions I got a squashed cake or a few stale buns thrown in. There were also the bins outside and in them were the chocolate, coffee and cream piping bags with scrapings of cream in them. The night was drawing in and I was becoming restless. I knew that Old faithful, my chilblains were about to return.

When digging in the back garden I had dug up two human skulls and some bones. This was nothing new for our house was built on the famine graveyard. I put them in a cardboard box ready for internment in a vault in the old graveyard behind the house next morning.

"There will be no callers this evening." Mother interrupted my fears of the anticipated nights agony. She removed her well worn Rosary beads from the back of the chair and knelt on the cold floor. There was no need to tell us what to do. With the praying brought to a satisfactory conclusion she rose and left the room.

"Come on, there is no satisfaction in you sitting there in the cold." She hesitated at the door and looked back at us. I was not sure that sitting in the cold kitchen or lying in a cold bed waiting for my chilblains to return made any difference. Reluctantly I rose from my seat and having seen to my cat and dog, I followed her up the stairs. As we entered our respective rooms there was a loud knocking on the door.

"Who in God's name is that at this hour? Mother retreated down the stairs and challenged.

"Who's there? What do you want?

"It's me Ma'am. Your parish Priest." Came the reply from the other side of the door.

"Quick light the lamp, it's the priest." She ordered as she made a hasty retreat down the stairs. We had a gas mantle but the mantle was broken and we couldn't afford a new one.

"God bless you all." Entering the kitchen he removed his black hat. Removing his leather gloves he rubbed his hands together.

"It's a cold night, thanks be to God." He tightened his heavy woollen scarf around his neck. I noticed the shiny goulashes over his patent shoes to keep him dry and comfortable and the heavy *Cromby* topcoat that kept his back warm. There was little need to tell us it was cold outside. It was far colder in the house than it was outside.

"I'd like to offer you a cup of tea, father. The truth of the matter is that I forgot to buy some when I went shopping in the city. Sorry!"

"That's alright Ma'am, no problem. I had a cup not too long ago." Again he rubbed his hands and stamped his feet on the bare concrete floor. I could see that he was in a hurry to get away from the cold house. "You know it's Easter and that I try to visit as many parishioners as I can." He paused to let his message sink home. Come to visit indeed. We knew that he had come to collect his Easter dues. Mother, having no money to give him was in a fluster. Not thinking straight and worried because she had nothing to offer him she went into the scullery and returned with a bottle of holy water. I thought for a moment that she was about to give it to the priest as her Easter offering.

"Would you bless the house, Father?" She handed him the bottle.

"Of course, but you know they were blessed when they built them." He dipped his finger in the bottle and having uttered a few words in Latin he made the sign of the cross and gave her back the bottle.

"Oh thank you father, I feel better now. Leaving the kitchen she went out the back door and returned carrying the cardboard box. This she placed on the table in front of the Priest.

"A present for me, how nice." He opened the box and blessing himself stood back horrified.

"Good God woman, this is a box of human skulls. What do you expect me to do with those."

"There's only two this time and they're not for you father, I want you to bless them. You see he keeps digging up skulls and bones whenever he digs in the back garden."

"Who, the dog?" He looked at Bruno. My dog looked suspiciously at him.

"No father, not the dog, him!" The dog looked at me as if to confirm that she was speaking about me and not him on this occasion.

"Are you telling me that there are bodies buried in your garden."

"Of course father but they're no trouble, they are all dead. The boys take them and put them inside the vaults." He looked at her open mouthed for a few moments. It's not too often that a Priest is presented with a box of skulls and bones as offerings.

"I suppose it is only to be expected. You do know that the victims of the great famine were buried in these grounds."

"Don't we know that father, there's two of them in the box there right in front of you, See." Mother took one of the skulls out and held it up to his face. We had collected enough rosaries, bones, skulls and crosses in our garden to fill Mount St Lawrence cemetery.

"Put it away, please! Now tell me why does he dig up the bones?" The priest looked from me to mother in the most peculiar way.

"He cannot help digging them up, father. Sure the garden is full of them. I make sure he takes them to the graveyard and puts them in the vaults." A strange silence followed, as the priest scratched his head and studied me.

"I bless them first with holy water. Do you think that they were all Catholics? It's hard to tell one from the others. The Protestants I mean." Whatever was she talking about I wondered.

"I'm sure that they are. He'll get his reward in heaven I have no doubt." Scratching his chin he again looked from me to the dog. Did he think that my dog had fleas or had eaten some of the bones I wondered.

"I have a lot of calls to make nice meeting you all." Again he shuffled from one foot to the other.

"I suppose if need be, you must. Don't forget to bless the skulls, will you father." Mother remained standing beside the box of skulls and bones.

The priest approached the box and tentatively lifted the lid and looked inside. Making the sign of the cross he quickly closed the lid.

The priest seemed to be on edge and anxious to get out of the house. Looking up at the mantle-piece he saw the three penny piece, *the widow's mite*. Placing his hand on the mantle piece he removed it. Having tossed it in his hand a couple of times he looked at it and then at us.

"It's not a lot ma'am, but then I suppose it's the *Widows Mite.*" He looked at the coin. He again tossed it in his hand and smiled before putting it in his pocket.

He hesitated hoping perhaps for a little more. With no response from mother he replaced his gloves and hat and he turning on his heel left the house.

"God whatever will I do." She questioned herself after he had left.

She placed her fingers in her mouth and looked up at the picture of the Sacred Heart.

"What can you do now, ma?" I asked.

"Do! Do about what?" She asked as if in a dream.

"About the bread for the rest of the week." I reminded her.

"It's not the bread I'm worried about. I lied to the priest when I told him I forgot the tea. I wonder did he know?" I looked at her in disbelief.

"Ma! He took the bread money." I reminded her.

"Don't worry about that. God will provide." She remarked as if in a trance. Returning to the window she looked out after the priest. Having wiped the frost from the window she remarked. "I'll have to go to confession tomorrow and confess that I lied.

"But you didn't lie Ma. Did you?"

"Of course I lied. Didn't I tell him I forgot the tea when I knew I had no money to buy any with. Still the dead will be happy now that the Priest blessed them." What was more important to her I wondered, the family going hungry or her empty pride. The priest couldn't but notice that we were cold and hungry. By taking the three pence from us he condemned us to two days of hunger.

I was instructed to take the box of skulls and bones out into the yard ready for internment next day.

BALDLY MICK

Thomondgate, A was quiet respectable suburb of Limerick. A place where one went to while away a few nostalgic hours. A brisk walk, along the long bank which led to Parteen village and on to Killaloe. There were the haunted woods of Cratlow and the Tail Race. One could stop at Hassets Cross and whet their whistle or swim at the point. All that seemed to change when the corporation in their wisdom decided to dig up the famine burial fields in the haunted glen of Killeely and build an estate. For one old lady it was to become a nightmare.

At the head of the high road in Thomondgate where it joined the haunted glen there lived in a small cottage an eccentric old lady. For the sufferings we inflicted on that poor woman I feel ashamed of now.

Baldy drew attention to herself by castigating the new residents at every available opportunity. She had no intention of giving a *Cead Mile Failte* to the rabble from the crumbling tenements of the city and their long tailed families. Her life had been one of serene bliss until we arrived on her doorstep. Looking back I suppose she had good reason to be wary of us.

We took every available opportunity to make her life as miserable as possible. It was little wonder that she had little hair left at all. She spent most of her time pulling it out by the roots in frustration. The pranks we played on the poor woman knew no bounds.

Baldly, it was said, had been abandoned at the altar rails on her wedding day and from that day on she became a changed person. How true the story was we never knew, nor did we care.

The cottages in the high road had half doors. Most would be open all day. That is with the exception of Baldy's. Her door was kept tightly locked and for a good reason.

We would collect as many cats as possible and put them into a large cardboard box and having tied the box with string we would deposit it over the stone wall into her backyard. Baldy would come from the house and take the box inside. It would not be too long before the cats and box came flying over the wall followed by profane swearing.

Other times would enter her small back yard, and climb on to the water butt, to gain access to her roof. There we would place a slate on her chimney pot and return to the comparative safety of the street. Soon smoke would be seen belching out from the gaps in the door. Inside the cottage one could hear the sound of coughing and spluttering.

The door would be flung open from inside. Clouds of smoke would bellow across the street. Then Baldly would appear, smoke bellowing from her sparse hair, her eyes red and watering. To us she looked like *Medea*, the sorceress of ancient Greece.

Jumping up and down in the sack apron that she always wore, she would call down all the obscenities she could think of on the people of Killeely.

"Look! Will you look up there? We never had this conduct before. Not until the corporation inflicted them blocked f****** arse holes on us." She would point at the obstruction on the top of her chimney.

"Catching them is impossible. They breed like rabbits. Nothing to do all day long but lie in bed, making more babies. What for, I ask? What for but to scourge the likes of me!" She would ask questions and answer them herself at the same time. Poor Baldly would call on the neighbours to remove the obstruction.

I suppose we pestered the poor woman more than anyone else. Because of the simple fact that she was a good rise.

On other occasions we would fill a tin with water and leave it on her half door. Then we would knock on the door and make a beeline for the nearest corner.

"Hold on. Who's there? I'll be out in a minute." We would hear Baldly trotting to the door in her hob nailed boots.

There we would wait to hear the usual stream of curses and obscenities. The tin would be pelted down the street. God help anyone who got in its way.

Calling on all the saints in Heaven to punish us. She would run up and down the road.

"Did you see them the dirty f*** Gits the skuts!" Did you?" She would stop passers by.

"See who Ma'am? Sure I saw no one. What's wrong anyway?" Baffled as to the reason for her conduct the passer by would try to pacify the woman. Others knowing that Baldy was an eccentric old woman would ignore her and pass on.

Baldly would cling to her captive until she had explained what had happened to her.

"I'll tell you what the little buggers done. They pissed in a tin and threw it in my door, so they did. What do you make of that in so called Holy Ireland?" The captive would try to get away from Baldly, but without success.

"Where are you going to? I've not finished yet if you must you know. It's all Dev's fault you know. (*De Valera being Prime Minister at the time*) Him and his *Dickey Money*. [Children's allowance] Breeding fodder for John Bulls army, no doubt." Finally Baldly would release her captive and return to her cottage.

Having waited for the situation to cool down. One of us would return to her cottage and knock at her door.

"Now who the blazes is it? I've only just closed the damn door." Once again we would hear Baldly march across the stone floor. Opening the half door she would look at the boy standing before her door looking the picture of innocence.

"You're not one of them blackguards that threw piss into my kitchen. Are you"?

"Of course not. Would I do that?" Would come the innocuous reply.

"Well! Out with it why are you here then? What do you want anyway?"

"I only wanted to know how far it went in," Would come the cheeky reply.

I was to learn later that when children behave with such bad manners the best results can be obtained by ignoring them. If she had not gone to so much trouble to chase us then we would have soon tired of the whole exercise and left her in peace. I am not making excuses for our conduct.

THE LONG CANS

During the war years the country was denuded of her men and girls to take advantage of the high earnings for their labour across the water in Britain.

The money they sent home to their families was eagerly waited for and much appreciated. No sweeter sound than that of the voice of the telegram boy was heard in the halls of the tenement houses.

"Telegram! Telegram for........."

The many doors of the tenement rooms would open and the occupants all attentive awaited, what names or names would be called out.

Most of these houses were relics from the past, with no sanitation and no running water. The exception being the water running down the walls when it rained.

Most households had a long can. This was a galvanised bucket, shaped at the top to fit the average bottom. When not in use it was fitted with a tight fitting lid for obvious reasons.

Many the child had to be rescued as they sank deeper and deeper into the bucket.

Many the backside had to be released with Vaseline. More had the round red ring on their bottoms for days after. I should know for I had an inbuilt fear of the contraptions. I was trapped in them far too often.

It was known for children to approach them in fear and trepidation. Some refused to use them and had to be given a poe.

In most homes or should I say rooms, the long can was left discretely outside in the hallway.

As the bucket filled it was taken to the river wall and its contents disposed of usually after night fall.

There was no electric lighting in the tenements; nor for that matter lighting of any sort in the halls. One had to be careful.

It required a lot of dexterity to manipulate a full can of slops from the top floor of a four story house to the river wall outside. The only light coming from a flickering candle held in your free hand.

Many the person had a slip on the stairs and found the bucket emptied for them down the stairs. When this accident occurred it called for more than a few buckets of water containing *Jeyes Fluid* or similar disinfectant to clean up the mess and neutralise the odour.

We would approach a tenement house in the evenings usually around Broad Street/ Carey's Road area and go to the top landings. Silently we would move the buckets from the safety of the doorway and place them in the centre of the first step. Each full and partly full bucket would be left in this position all the way down to the ground floor.

Knowing who lived in the top room, we would yell from the safety of the bottom hall.

"Mrs O Connor! Mrs O'Connor," we would call out the name. "Are you in Mrs O' Connor?"

"Is it me you want? I'm Mrs O'Connor." A woman's voice would echo down the stairs and along the hall.

"It's the telegram boy. I've got a telegram from England for you. You've got to sign for it. Can you come down?"

"Hold on there. I won't be two shakes of a Lambs tail. It's about time too."

It did not take too many minutes before there was the clatter of buckets down the stairs.

Buckets were knocked off the edge of the stairs and fell like dominoes. Some of the empty ones would bounce to the height of the ceiling before crashing down into the hall below. To be caught brought the ultimate chastisement. Not alone were you belted from pillar to post, but whenever you were seen in the street afterwards you were chased like a fox.

"Do you know, I'm fit to be tied. I nearly had a canary, the other night." Mrs O'Connor or another related her encounter to her closest friend.

"These couple of *cafflers* from Killeely arsed their way into our house if you don't be minding. Pretending to have the money from my son in England they were. Money be damned it was devilment they were after." Mrs O'Connor was more than upset.

"There's no use in being ignorant if you can't show it. Did you find out who they were at all?"

"No not really. Alice from the turf store saw them. I'll tell you this though, they are lively on their feet. They were out our hallway quicker than a dose of castor oil. If I lay my hands on them they'll need more than a Doctor when I've finished with them. I can assure you."

Most of the tenements are now gone and those that remain are waiting for the demolition men.

Within their dark recesses I have no doubt wander the ghosts of an age long past.

THE METAL BRIDGE

The metal Railway Bridge crosses the Shannon at Corbally and joins the Long Pavement on the opposite bank. Below the bridge on the Clare side is situated a small sandy secluded swimming bay on the river Shannon. It was the ideal place for swimmers and non-swimmers alike. The corporation did not include a bathroom when they built the new houses and so the Shannon was our swimming pool and baths. Here with the help of a bar of lifebuoy soap we could perform our ablution. We were also exhibitionists and shameless as we swam the old river in the nude.

One of our most daring and dangerous escapades we carried out when we went swimming at the Point out on the Long Pavement was diving off the top rail of the bridge. When we knew the *West Clare Express,* as we called the little train was due over the Metal Railway Bridge, we would run on to the bridge and climb onto the supports. Standing on the uppermost edge of the balustrade we would wait until it was about half way across. Then with a cheeky wave to the passengers and crew, we would dive off the bridge into the river far below. The women and girls on the train would giggle behind their shawls at our brinkmanship and nudity. Some mothers would hide their Daughters faces under their shawls. We saw no harm in what we were doing and never intended to offend anyone. Most of us could not afford the price of a pair of trunks. Those unwilling to tempt the dive from this height would content themselves with diving from the edge of the track. I'm sure that there are many reader's who will remember the *Dive.*

The guards had a habit of hiding at each end of the river hoping to ensnare the unwary and charge them with trespassing. Whenever we saw the guards approaching we would dive into the Shannon, leaving them empty handed.

Another dare was to lie between the sleepers as the train passed over you. Lying face down we hoped and prayed that the fireman did not decide to clean out the firebox. I doubt if this was necessary as during the war the trains were run on turf. We looked on these escapades as daring feats others, perhaps rightly so called them feats of madness.

There was the occasion when one of the men from The Parish went swimming alone at the point. Using the metal bridge as a diving board he dived into the Shannon. When he failed to return home a search was made for him. Soon his body was recovered from a discarded rusting milk churn from the bottom of the river. He had dived straight into the churn from which the bottom had rusted and drowned. The metal bridge is now silent and deserted. The trains have long since stopped running and the young men of the city no longer find any need to visit the Point.

MINOR AILMENTS

Not only were warts considered a minor problem, they were also an embarrassment to those who suffered from them. We strongly believed that you could get them from a carrier by shaking their hands. This made us very wary of anyone who was unfortunate enough to have them. Warts, we were told, were caused by the soft water in the city. Whatever did or did not cause them they were a constant irritant to those suffering from them. There were many cures on offer. Most were guaranteed to cure, at least by the quack offering the cure. I just mention a few to illustrate how gullible the people were.

One of our friends from Saint Mary's Park had warts. Not only had he warts, he had warts growing on warts. Poor Jimmy suffered a lot and had pestered mother for a cure.

"Ma! I'm telling you. If I don't get rid of these warts soon, I'll wind up in the mad house. Better still, I'll drown myself so I will."

"Jimmy! Don't be talking like that. You make me frightened. You know that you would go to hell."

"Go to Hell Ma! At least I'd get rid of my warts there."

Poor Jimmy's mother was at her wits end. She was willing to listen to anyone who could help. She would try cure after cure on him without success of any kind. On one occasion she walked into her friend Madge, on her way to the city.

"Mary! Mary my friend, sure I haven't seen sight nor hair of you in ages. How the hell are you?"

"I'm as well as can be expected in myself. It's poor Jimmy that is my problem."

"Young Jimmy. I thought he was such a nice boy. Not in trouble with the guards is he?" Strange how everyone thought the worst of the boys in the city.

"No, it's nothing like that. It's that he is crippled with warts. God! I've tried everything to help him but to no avail."

"Don't you know how to get rid of them, are you codding me?" Madge looked at Mary in disbelief.

"No I don't Madge. If I did, do you think I'd be standing here asking you?

That's the gospel truth." Mary blessed herself to confirm her sincerity.

"Well! Far be it for me to keep you in suspense. What you have to do is this.......

Now you may laugh. The proof of the pudding is in the eating. I'll swear by it." Madge adjusted her black shawl over her head before she continued.

"You know you have a young daughter. What's her name?"

"Young Theresa you mean." Mary replied.

"That's the very one. Well you must get her to *Piss'* in a pot and then get your Jimmy to wash his warts in it. That will soon shift them."

"Are you sure Madge? Sounds disgusting to me, so it does."

"Listen to me Mary. Maiden Piss that's what the doctor ordered. There's some kind of cure in it."

Mary cleaned out the pee pot that evening and got young Theresa to pee in it. She then put it into a clean basin.

When Jimmy came home from school his mother had the concoction prepared and ready. "Jimmy I want you to wash your warts in this basin and shake them dry after a good soak."

Full of apprehension he approached the basin and looked at the contents. Then he smelt it.

"What is it Ma? It smells like piss?" Suspicious of his mother's concoction he cocked his nose up at the basin.

"Never mind what it smells like. Do as you are told. It is a special disinfectant to help cure your warts." His mother dare not tell him what it was.

Needless to say the cure never worked.

The people relied heavily on the Priest for guidance and cures. Mary, still seeking a solution, went to see one of the mission Priests. The people had little confidence in the secular Priests. They didn't come over as holy as the missionary Priests. He listened to Mary's tale of woe and how troubled she was for her son.

"Mary, with a name like yours, you should have faith. If you don't then your son cannot be cured." The missionary Priest laid his hand on her shoulder.

"Father! If I didn't have faith I wouldn't be here talking to you. Now would I?" Mary looked at him full of devotion.

"Tell you what I'm going to do for you Mary. I am going to give you a special blessed candle. I had it blessed myself at Lourdes. Take it with my blessing and rub it over your sons warts."

"I will father. I will indeed." Mary was over enthusiastic.

"Mary you must wait until I finish." The Priest chided her.

"As I was saying. You will then light the candle. You will pray as it burns and as you do your sons warts should heal."

Mary handed the Priest her small donation and accepted the blessed candle from his hands.

"Remember my child, it is your faith and that of your family that are most important not the candle." Mary went home full of hope and belief that this time her Jimmy would be cured.

That night the family gathered around the candle. His father lit it and the family knelt in prayer.

They spent a long time on their knees. Finally they decided to extinguish the candle and continue next night. The whole service lasted three days. Jimmy watched and counted his warts. Instead of vanishing they seemed to be growing. Regretfully once again the cure failed.

Mary returned to the Priest and asked why the cure had failed.

"My child,! It is the will of God that Jimmy keeps his warts as a sign of his faith."

On hearing that his warts could not be cured I decided that I could offer my services. If he brought me a bag of chocolate toffees then I would cure his warts. My remedy was an old one and considered reliable. (Where did you hear that before) He should rub a sweet on a wart and return it to the wrapper. This he would give to me and I would leave in a conspicuous place for others to find. They would pick it up and eat it. The warts would then be transferred to them. The balance of the sweets would be mine in payment.

I met him some years later on my return to Limerick. The first question I asked was about his warts.

"Oh them! I went to a hospital in England and they burnt the lot off." There was not a wart to be seen on his hands.

There were many other so called cures that I knew of. One man in the city claimed that he could cure warts by buying them.

The patient would go and see this quack. He would examine his warts and ask a price to remove them.

When the deal was struck. The man would make a motion over the warts and you would hand over your few coppers. In return for his assurance that he now owned your warts.

I don't know of anyone who accepted these terms but I have no doubt that some were gullible enough to fall for it.

Then there was the meat cure. This involved going to a Butchers shop and stealing a piece of meat. It had to be stolen. The meat you then rubbed all over the warts. You then took it to a Protestant graveyard and buried it. As the meat rotted so the warts vanished.

I often wondered why these cures and burials always had to take place in Protestant graveyards. Why not in Catholic ones?

The last but not least was to boil two blue duck eggs. These had to be the bluest you could obtain. Some crafty Alec knowing that the patient wanted a real blue egg would add a blue bag to the water. This would dye the shell a real blue.

The shells were then removed from the egg and crushed to a powder and returned to the water.

The patient was obliged to wash his/her warts in the water. The warts were supposed to drop off during this process.

KEEP THE HOME FIRES BURNING

In winter we were more dead than alive. In fact we were half-dead. Mother suffered in silence from the cold and hunger. Since she had great faith and a simple heart she suffered all the more. She had, it seemed, forgotten her days of grandeur and the inequality of mans inhumanity to man. She firmly believed that as we suffered in this world so God would be good to us in the next. She lived the life of an honest and God fearing widow.

We on the other hand were doubting Thomas's and had no intention of waiting about for the promised here after. Sometimes I feared I would have to do as *Faust* had done and sell my immortal soul to the devil. Mother was always saying that I was the Devils own work.

Circumstances dictated that we go out into the country and forage for what firewood we could salvage. This excursion was invariably, led by my eldest brother Patrick. Under his arm he carried his well used saw rolled up in a sack. Before leaving home the saw had to be sharpened and greased with candle grease or suet. Every River Bank, wood and estate was searched over and over again for dead branches. Fallen branches and any other combustible materials.

As we were not the only family taking part in these forages the immediate area was soon denuded of wood. We were obliged to travel further afield and to take more and more risks. We had to venture where no one else would gamble to go. There was turf available at a price. This was sold by weight, half water, half turf.

"They have a lot to answer for so they have. Call themselves turf merchants, more like highway robbers," mother would remark time and time again as she tried to light her fire with turf oozing water. By the time the water had evaporated there was little turf left. It was said that there was more water in one cartload of turf, than in the whole river Shannon. This statement was a little exaggerated.

There were emergency dumps of turf, held in reserve, should war come to Ireland. These were stacked in strategic locations in secure compounds throughout the country. One of these being the playing field near where we lived. This supply of turf was cut and saved by an army youth Corp known as *The Construction Corp* in the *Great Bog of Allen*. The supplies were guarded by the voluntary Local Defence Force. The members of which were not always available for duty. Members of the L.D.F began helping themselves to the odd bag that they hoped would not be missed.

"It's little recompense for defending the country," many the part time soldier defended his theft as he tried to ease his conscience.

Hence the stack got smaller and smaller by the week. If the L.D.F. could help themselves then why not the local people came the challenge. They too had fires to keep burning and were not adverse to the odd bag or two.

Perhaps a blind eye was turned to these matters; It was known to happen.

Then there was the bag or two for the ould couple up the street and the widow woman with a house full of children. The reserve stock grew smaller and smaller until finally it was exhausted. The theft of the turf called for action by the military.

One day an army staff car drew up on the Cratlow Road. Out stepped an officer carrying a swagger stick and a map.

Having studied the map for some time he lifted the peak of his cap and looked all around him. Taking a pair of binoculars from round his neck he looked through them towards the Clare hills and the surrounding countryside. By now we had gathered in force and were begging the driver for chocolate.

"Excuse me. Do any of you children know where the emergency turf supply is stored?" He asked.

"It's over there Sir! But it's all gone now. Are you going to bring some more? God! I must run home and tell my Da." A scruffy boy informed him.

"Come here and explain yourself. Over where?" The officer looked puzzled.

"Over there but it's all gone now. I told you. Can't you see the place where the dust is? When will we get more? Look over there, him on the bicycle he's in the L.D.F. (Local Defence Force) He'll be able to help you" He pointed to a man with an army cape over his shoulders and a pair of army issue ruby boots and gaiters on his feet cycling towards them.

"Here! Come here I want to speak to you." The officer waived his swagger stick in the direction of the part time soldier.

The man, on seeing the regular army officer, braked and did a wheely on the bicycle and vanished up the high road at great speed. His cape flew over his shoulders like Batman's. As they were forbidden to wear their boots and uniforms to work in he had no intention of approaching the officer.

The officer looked after him and scratching his head he folded his map, returned his binoculars to his neck and entered the staff car.

As the car left and headed for the Union cross we jumped on to the bumper and got a free ride. That was until the driver put up speed and we had to get off.

Needless to say we never did get a fresh supply of turf.

In addition to the turf and log fires there were several other fires. We had the 'Sawdust Fire.' This was a great success. It was used for boiling clothes and cooking.

Having procured a five gallon drum. The top was cut off and a hole the size of a broom handle cut out of the centre of the bottom. A broom handle was then put into the drum and passed through the hole. Dry sawdust was packed tightly inside. Then the handle was removed and the drum stood on bricks. This would allow a good draught to be drawn up the chimney.

A small fire was lit under the drum. The flames from which ran up the chimney and set alight to the sawdust. Flat iron pieces or a grill were placed on the top to hold kettles and pots.

These fires when properly made could smoulder for days.

We also had the "Flash Fires." This method consisted of a steel plate standing on bricks. Over which two containers stood. Two pieces of wood were then inserted into the side of the drum at its lowest point and adjusted to act as two drip taps. One container contained waste motor oil, the other water.

A fire would be kindled under the steel plate until it was white hot and the taps opened. The mixture, I believe, consisted of one drop of water to two drops of oil... ....?

This mixture would explode on the plate and send heat up a small chimney to a grill or similar.

As most people could not be bothered to get the ratio of water and oil correct, this method was not used too often. There was also the problem of securing scarce waste oil.

One fine evening in autumn, Patrick volunteered us to go and get a supply of firewood. The trusted saw was taken from its hideaway, greased and checked by him. Then placing it inside the sack we were off on our forage. On this occasion we took the road towards the village of Parteen.

"We could do without that dog of yours. If he comes make sure he stays out of my way." Patrick warned as Bruno stayed close to me. As we crossed the old bridge at *Quinpool* he stopped and studied a number of trees on the *Roycroft estate.*

"There's what we want." He pointed to a huge tree covering at least a half acre in the middle of a meadow. We climbed on top of the wall dividing the field from the road. I looked down into the field below us.

"We'll never in a hundred years get down there. The drop is too far." I studied the drop some six feet below the wall.

"You can climb down the wall can't you? Come on stop dallying let's go." Patrick dropped the saw and sack into the meadow. There was to be no turning back now. We found hand grips in the old stone wall and were soon in the meadow. All was silent as we crept across the green sward. I looked to my left where stood a large chestnut tree. Under it I could see hundreds of russet conkers. Many still encased in their green protective horny shells peeped out invitingly.

Running over to the tree I began to fill my pockets with big conkers. These I would harden at a later date on the range. I would win many the battle with these, I thought. In my determination to secure the chestnuts I didn't see my brother standing over me.

"Just what do you think you're doing?" He stood threateningly looking down at me. Over his shoulder was the sack.

"Look at these conkers? There must be thousands of them. Give me the sack and I'll fill it." I reached out for the sack.

"I'll give you sack! You and your conkers! You're here to get firewood not conkers." He belted me from under the tree with the sack.

Finally we reached the tree of his choice. I never saw such a big tree before. Perhaps it was my imagination as I looked at it in the waxing moon. It was twice the size of the chestnut tree. It was a beautiful oak and under its spreading canopy were more than sufficient dead branches. Far in excess than we could possibly carry. Patrick had been right on this occasion.

My sister and I began to snap the wood into handy pieces and put them in to the sack. Patrick stood some distance from the tree. He seemed to be studying something deep in its mantle.

"Come here you, never mind picking up sticks. She can do that" he called me to his side. "Do you see that branch there?" He pointed into the mantle of the tree.

"What branch? There are thousands." I looked deep into the canopy.

"That long one that is nearly hanging off." He pointed to a limb about three feet thick and fourteen feet along the branch.

"You'll never get that out. It's stuck in the tree. There's enough for us on the ground without that." I pointed out the myriad of good logs on the ground.

"Good enough for the crows. Forget them. I'm going up into the tree to saw it free from where it is broken. If I manage to get it down I can cut it into lengths and carry it on my shoulder. You and Phyllis can manage the smaller branches."

There was no stopping him, as he climbed the tree like a monkey. He was half way up the tree and on his way to the branch he wanted before I saw him again. My sister and I stopped collecting the wood and stood back and watched him. He climbed higher and higher into the tree. I did not realise that the branch was so far up. He crawled precariously across the branches of the tree. We looked apprehensively at him. At the same time we were keeping a sharp look out for the gamekeepers. Patrick straddled the broken branch and began to finish what Mother Nature had started. We could hear the noise from the saw as he cut through the branch. We called up to him. We waved to him, we even threw small branches at him. He was so engrossed in his task that he was oblivious to our presence. There he sat straddled across the branch cutting to his hearts content. There was only one problem. He was cutting the branch that he was straddling. The saw went deeper and deeper into the branch. Then there was a mighty crash as the weakened branch gave way. Slowly at first it became disengaged from the main tree. Gaining momentum, the whole limb some twenty feet by fifteen landed on the ground. The branches scratching our faces.

Patrick landed with a thud in the middle of the branch, his faithful saw not far behind. Phyllis got the worst of the scratches and began to cry. Patrick, his dignity hurt got to his feet and came over to her.

"What's the matter with you anyway? There's nothing wrong with you." With that he gave her a belting.

"Now stop your bawling. The people will hear you." He looked across the field towards the mansion. Next we knew there was uproar. Charging across the seven acre field came a pack of dogs of mixed breeds. The roar from them was like the sound from the *Hounds of the Baskerville.* One quick look across the meadow and we were off. Scaling the wall was out of the question. We had to make for the river *Avondoon.* We were lucky that it was shallow water. Wading it we made the safety of the road where we stopped for breath.

The dogs stood on the other side of the wall wagging their tails and looking up at us. Bruno stood on the wall wagging his tail in acknowledgement and appeared to be counting them. I looked across at my brother. Somehow, I don't know how he had achieved it. He had his precious saw and sack under his arm. Taking off our shoes we drained the water from them. Then we took off our socks and wrung them out before again replacing them.

"Well there will be no wood to night. We had best get off home. We could have avoided all this trouble if you'd listened to me in the first place." I had given my assessment of the situation and was on my way home in disgust.

"Shut your gob before I shut it for you. Just where do you think you are off to?" My brother came after me.

"Home of course. Where else would I be going at this hour? It's late and I have homework to finish."

"Not likely. We came to get firewood and firewood we'll get by hook or by crook." He crossed the road and went on to the old railway line.

"You know that you are not supposed to be in there. Can't you read the warning?" I grumbled.

Most places we entered had notices nailed to trees which we ignored........

> *'Trespassers will be Prosecuted'*
> *'These lands are poisoned for the protection of sheep'*
> *'Dogs found on these lands will be shot on sight'*

What made this warning notice stand out above the rest was that it was issued by the Military under the emergency powers act, which of course we may or may not have understood but we knew what it meant.

"Take no notice of that. Uncle Ger is guarding the power station. They won't bother us." Patrick dismissed the warning. Why worry about the might of the Irish army? Uncle Ger, a private in the Irish army, would put everything to right, he assured us. Was this brother of mine a fool or had he a death wish?

Walking along the line he saw some heavy wooden sleepers at the side of the track. He stopped and looked at them. Then he picked one up on one end and weighed it in his hand. Surely he was not going to take the railway sleepers home?

"Look at these? Abandoned sleepers and not too heavy- ideal for the fire. I'm sure you could manage one," he sized me up.

"There's a lighter one over there. You could drag that one." He pointed to my sister. This was the height of folly. Although the old line was no longer in use it led to the power station at Ardnachrusha. The sleepers belonged to the Irish railways. There was another factor that he seemed to have forgotten. This area was considered to be of strategic importance and out of bounds to non-military personnel. There was a war on and was constantly patrolled by the Irish army and the Local Defence Force. God only knows what they would have done to us if they caught us? Not alone were we trespassing in a military zone but we were committing sabotage by stealing the sleepers. We would be sent to the penal reformatory run by the Christian Brother's and Patrick would go to jail.

"We shouldn't be here you know. Someone was picked up here the other week for taking photos. Let's get off the tracks." I tried once again to give my advice. This advice he stubbornly ignored as he once again picked up a sleeper.

"Stand still there." He ordered me as he laid it on my shoulder. What did he think I was? a donkey perhaps.

"That's not too heavy, is it?" I bent at the knees under the weight of the sleeper. I could not possibly carry it on my own.

"What a weakling. Come here you and help him." Phyllis was called forward to help.

He balanced the sleeper across both our shoulders and told us to march on home. Now I knew how Christ must have felt as he tried to carry that heavy cross.

Patrick caught up with us. On each shoulder he carried a sleeper. The sack he had tied 'round his waist with the saw trust through it like a scabbard. It was easy for him being six feet plus tall and standing like a bull. He looked like *Robinson Crusoe*. We reached home without being seen. Best of all was not being shot by an army patrol.

Next day he put the sleepers on to a home made wooden horse and cut them into small logs. Now my cat's home was in the oven of the range. It was here that he slept every night with the door open. The oven never got really hot. How could it with all the wet turf.

That evening mother filled the fire basket with the logs and set them alight. Within minutes the fire was a roaring inferno. The whole house smelt of pitch and burning oil. Burning tar dropped out of the fire basket and into the ashtray setting it alight. The roar of the fire as it tore up the chimney was like the call of the wild.

"Don't they make a lovely fire?" Mother in all her innocence looked with delight at the flames dancing round the oven and up the chimney. Soon more logs were needed to replenish the fire.

"You should try and get more of them. They give off great heat." Mother opened the palms of her hands in front of the fire.

"There are plenty more where they came from. We'll get them home before anyone else gets them." Patrick promised, pleased with his efforts. Considering that they had been there since 1924 or there about, it was unlikely anyone would want them. Cibby Eye Lashes came dashing out of the oven as if a pack of Kerry Blue dog's were after him. He had changed from jet black to a rustic brown and smoke belched from his fur.

"Will you just look at that? It just shows how good the logs are. They're better than that wet turf. That's the first time I ever saw that cat leave the oven, except when I wanted to use it for a cake. Come to think of it. Now that the oven is so hot. I think I'll make a scone or two. I have a drop of flour someplace."

Like a Chameleon the range began to change colour from jet black to red to white and back again. Mother moved her chair further away from the heat. Finally she rose from her chair and went into the kitchen to prepare her scones. Placing her hand on the chimney breast she called my brother to come and feel it.

"Now that's what I call a fire. Even the walls are heating up." We all ran over to feel the wall from which the wallpaper was slowly peeling.

A dense black smoke covered the road outside and the surrounding area. Flames came out the chimney that would do justice to the *West Clare Railway*. The scones were made and put in the oven. The heat was so intense that she left the door open. It was the first time ever that she baked scones in an open oven. Usually it was just warm and the scones took all their time to rise. The scones failed to rise and remained as flat as pancakes but were a russet brown in minutes. Mother was disappointed but assured us that they were still good wholesome food. Finally it came to bedtime. By now the range was a rosy red and even the big black kettle in the corner of the range was boiling.

What with the heat within the house and the overpowering smell of the pitch and tar from the sleepers we were left with no alternative but to sleep with all the windows open. This was the first and only time we were compelled to do this.

Mother came down late next morning and began to clean the grate before kindling the fire. As she put her hand into the fire basket she was surprised to find herself holding Cibby Eye Lashes. They both got a fright and the cat left the oven in a hurry. He might have got a fright but mother got a greater one. She found that there was no side panel between the fire and the oven. To add to the confusion, the bars in the grate and fire basket had welded themselves together. The ash pan, what was left of it was stuck to the concrete floor. The firebricks had disintegrated. She looked at her range in total disbelief. How could such a thing happen? She called on us to come and look at the range and the fire basket.

"Well! If I didn't see it with my own eyes I would not believe it." She looked with incredulity at the distorted fire.

"I heard of the fairies of Killeely but I never believed in them. Did you upset them?" She looked across at me.

"Me! I never said a word. I was here all night the same as the others." I defended myself.

"Well these things don't just happen of their own accord, there must be a good reason for it."

"What are we going to do now? We will have to tell them."

"Tell who? The fairies. How can I tell the fairies anything. I didn't damage the fire?" I defended myself.

"No not the fairies, whatever are you bladdering about, the corporation I mean. God but you'd torment a saint." She looked at me as if I were demented.

"I wouldn't worry too much about it. It's probably one of them cheap ones from Wexford. The English ones are better. They can't get them on account of the war." Patrick consoled her.

"English or Irish, they'll have to replace it. We cannot be without a range. That's for sure."

Monday morning saw mother at the town hall requesting a new range.

"What do you want a new range for? There is one in the house already. Don't tell me someone stole it? You'll have to pay for a new one." The official looked at her confused by this request.

"It may have been a new range but it melted. I cannot use a range in that state."

"Melted? The range melted did you say? Well that's one for the books. How the Hell could a range melt? Talk sense woman."

"Don't get off your high horse with me and don't you swear at me either. I know what I saw. Don't take the eyesight out of my head do you hear me?"

"Sorry Ma'am. A slip of the tongue, I apologise. No harm meant and none taken I'm sure. I'll call myself this afternoon and take a good look at it." He apologised.

"I should think so too. Whatever next? Make sure you call when I'm at home."

True to his word the official came to the house and looked the range over.

"I didn't believe you at first. Now I must really apologise. The range has indeed melted." He removed his cap and scratched his head.

"Well do you believe me now, I told you so. Seeing is believing you know?" Mother was glad that she was right after all.

"What were you burning in it? Not anthracite I hope?

"Anthracite! What in the name of all that's good and holy is that?

"It's a form of glossy coal that gives out a lot of heat. Used in furnaces"

"Where would we get coal from, glossy or black? Shure there's not an ounce of coal to be had. We had a good fire last night but that was from logs."

"Tell you what I think happened. It's the castings they must not have been fired properly."

"Fired properly! Just what do you mean? There's only one way to light a fire that I know of. What a cheek! I'll let you know that we had a fire in that grate last night that would roast an ox." Mother once again was of the opinion that she was getting the blame.

"Don't get so tight about it. I'm not blaming you. Your fire could not possibly melt the range. Firing is the way the castings are made." He went on to explain the method of casting to mother.

It all went over mother's head. She did not understand. All she wanted was a new range.

"We'll have to replace it. I'll send the yardman across with a new one this afternoon. He will fit it straight away." Mother did get her new range.

Patrick returned some days later to the railway track to collect the rest of the sleepers. Before he could remove them he was confronted by two armed soldiers. Who took him back to the temporary barracks at Arnachrusha. After being interrogated as a spy he was released. He was warned to stay off the track for the duration.

I was glad that he was caught. Perhaps now he would stop stealing the sleepers.

THE FAMINE CHICKENS.

My brother Patrick, you could like or dislike depending on what task he called on you to perform. He had a heart of gold although he never wore it on his lapel. He tried to be the father figure for as long as I could remember. He kept his concern for the family to himself. He done all that he could to ensure that we had, where possible, at least the minimum of heat and food. This was not easy during the war years. He must have taken us through every nook and cranny of Limerick and Clare in his search for firewood. On this occasion we found ourselves out past Mungret. Had we gone any further we would have arrived in county Cork. Going down a boreen (lane) leading to the river Shannon estuary he suddenly stopped.

"What's that over there?" He pointed to a small cottage with green grass growing on the thatch roof.

"What does it look like? It's an old cottage. What's so unusual about that?" I saw nothing out of the ordinary about it. County Limerick was full of abandoned cottages.

"Come on! It's worth more than a look." We vaulted the stile and crossed a long disused pathway leading to the cottage. We were left with little choice but to follow our leader. The gateway had been blocked with a hawthorn bush denying access. Its path buried under weeds and grass. A small stone wall surrounded the old cottage. Patrick climbed the wall to gain access. We followed close behind. He looked in through the small dirty window but could see nothing. He went to the front door. This was well secured from the inside. It was obvious that it had not been opened in years.

"Come on let's take a look round the back." He was determined to gain access. Why this obsession, I could not understand. The back door was clear of obstruction. He pushed the door open and looked in utter amazement into the dim interior. There in the gloom we saw several rows of perches. Roosting on them were hens of all shapes and sizes. On the ground were butter boxes lying on their sides with straw inside them. Some had hens sitting inside them contented with themselves. He, as leader surveyed the scene before us. Then he assessed the situation as he saw it.

"Aren't we lucky! These chickens are wild. Probably the descendants of chickens left behind after the famine." We knew absolutely nothing about chickens. Yet we doubted very much if these were as wild as he made them out to be. Why would anyone leave chickens behind during a famine? His logic baffled me. The layout inside the old cottage did not look as if it had been deserted since 1845 or thereabout.

"Where did you get that idea from, how can they be wild. Someone gives them fresh straw and water? They don't look after themselves. Even I know that much." I tried to explain. I was not that naïve.

"Shut up and close the door. For heaven sake keep a lookout through the crack." With that he took the sack from his shoulder. I was in shock as he grabbed the first hen from her perch and tried to force her into the sack. I looked at him in astonishment. What was he doing, had he gone mad? The hen roared at the top of her voice and resisted. She was not going to be put in the sack willingly.

"Hold the sack open for me one of you. These f****** chickens are stubborn. I told you they were wild. Now will you believe me?" He had the unfortunate hen by the neck, its wings flapping in all directions. Is it little wonder that she was mad as he choked the life from her body. Feathers flew in all directions. Some got into his mouth which he spat out. Brendan went and held the sack open, he kept his head to one side to avoid the claws and flapping wings of the chickens. The chickens were rammed into the sack one after the other. When in the sack they went quiet. Finally he grabbed a big Red Rooster who seemed to be their leader. That Rooster had talons like razors and a beak like a vulture. The roars of it could be heard beyond *Loop Head* in the County Kerry. It took two of us to persuade that rooster to join his wives in the sack. Having filled the sack he twisted the neck and hoisted it on his shoulder.

"Come on. Let's get out of here. We have all we can carry. Leave the rest for someone else."

As we opened the door the remainder of the flock in a state of panic made a concerted dash to freedom. We tried to surround the hens and get them back into the house without success. Soon as we got one in another flew out.

"Leave them. They're too noisy. They'll find their own way back." Patrick marshalled his troops and left the field. Now why did he not know that hens could not get in and out of closed doors by themselves? I was convinced that someone must surely own them. Going up the lane we heard the voice of a man and a woman as they ran across a field near to the old cottage. The man had a hay fork in his hands and held it forward as if he were on a bayonet charge. The woman in a long skirt that reached down to her ankles had what appeared to be a cudgel or worse still a *Shillelagh*. A weapon so we are told, that the women of Limerick used with devastating effect on the heads of the Dutch army during the siege of their city in 1691. The roars of the woman as she swung the shillelagh over her head would frighten the devils in hell. Seeing this onslaught we were off. There was no use in standing around waiting to explain or be butchered. As Patrick ran the neck of the sack came undone. Hens kept popping up like rabbits from a magicians hat. They ran, they flew and they rolled down the road in front of us before seeking the safety of the surrounding fields.

Finally we made it to the city boundary Our pursuers having given up the chase long since. Patrick still had the sack on his back and there seemed to be some life inside it. Taking the sack off his back he looked inside to see what he had left of his ill-gotten gains. The big red rooster looked up at him from the bottom of the sack.

"At least we goi one of them. We should be grateful for that." He seemed pleased with his days work.

"Someone owned them chickens you know! We could have been caught and sent to Glin or Danagan." I again warned him. These were the industrial schools of correction managed by the Christian Brothers. A prospect I did not relish.

"Will you shut up moaning, we got this one. Mother will be grateful." Ignoring me he looked in at the rooster sitting in the bottom of the sack.

"You say that we should be grateful, grateful that we were not killed back there is more like it." I was in no mood for his platitudes.

When we got home the rooster was taken from the sack and released into the backyard. The rooster strutted around pecking at pieces of food and grit.

"Let's keep him. Then we can have eggs for breakfast every day." Brendan looked down at the big fat bird.

"That's a rooster! Roosters don't lay eggs. We will kill him and make a fine pot of soup with him." Mother looked unsympathetically at the fat bird.

The roosters fate was determined before his very eyes. If he knew he didn't seem all that concerned as he pecked at the ground. The problem was who would kill him? Nobody wanted to take on the task.

"You took the chicken so you can kill it. It's all yours." I told my brother.

"Right then I'll kill him." He went to the cupboard under the stairs and took out the axe. He chased the rooster round the garden. The bird flew on to the graveyard wall and disappeared inside.

"Where's the rooster?" Mother asked as he came back into the house.

"He's in the graveyard. I'm going to look for him." Patrick left the house still carrying the axe.

"Oh my God! Get him out quick. I couldn't eat a morsel from a chicken that took food from a graveyard." She wrung her hands in anguish. It was getting dark when he left to look for the bird.

"Come on some of you and help me find it." He called for volunteers. We were not willing to enter the old graveyard in the dark. Patrick climbed the wall and dropped inside.

"Do any of you see him?" He called from the other side of the wall.

"How could we see him, he's in the graveyard." I called back.

"Stupid fool. Go up to the back bedroom and look into the trees." He ordered.

"Not me, what if the headless coach came." I excused myself.

"I'll go, you wait there." Mother volunteered.

The bedroom window opened and we saw mother stick her head out. "Here chucky, chucky come here." She called into the gloom.

"What are you doing?" Patrick called to her from somewhere in the graveyard.

"I'm calling the chicken, what else." Mother replied.

"What the bloody hell, that Fecking bird."

"Don't swear in the graveyard. What happened to you? Where are you?" She tried to see where Patrick was.

"I've fallen into a tomb. Don't worry I'm not hurt."

"Who's buried in it?" Mother again challenged.

"How should I know, what does it matter?"

"You'd better come out of there before you get hurt."

"I can't, I'm stuck somehow."

"Oh my God he's being pulled into the vault by the corpse." Phyllis began to panic.

"What's she shouting about, can't you shut her up?"

"She's worried for you. She thinks that the skeleton is pulling you into the vault." Mother called to him.

"She what, ouch! Bloody bones."

"Don't damage the vault it's unlucky. You're not near to the body are you."

"Does it matter they are all dead? Ouch! Blast it! My foot is stuck in a coffin."

"Are you in pain, forget the chicken and come home." Mother pleaded.

"No I'm not and when I get hold of the skuttering rooster I'll wring his bloody neck."

"You'd best get out of there and don't forget to say a prayer." Mother encouraged him.

"One of you best come in and help. There's another coffin below me that is not too safe."

"Louie, you're doing nothing. Go over the wall and help your brother." Mother ordered.

"Go in where? In there you mean?" I pointed in horror at the wall of the dark forbidding graveyard.

"Of course, you can take your dog. He'll keep the rats away from Patrick."

"Don't cut yourself on any bones or skeletons. If you do you will die," mother comforted Patrick.

"What the Hell now. Where did he come from? Get the f*** out of here you stupid coss."

"Who are you talking to, is there someone else in the graveyard?" Mother asked as Patrick continued trying to free himself.

"There's nobody here but me and that fecking dog. He's trying to open the coffin. Who sent him in here? Will someone call him out."

"I sent him in but I should have known better. Did he get the coffin open. Try and stop him taking any bones. Louie is coming over, they understand each other?" She kept up the running commentary from the open window.

"Don't send him in, he's no better than his f****** coss. I'm out. God but I'm a mess. Come here you ghoul."

"What's wrong now? Mother continued the conversation from the open bedroom window."

"It's Bruno, he's got a bone and is digging in the bottom of the vault."

"O Blessed Jesus, can't you stop him. Louie get in there quickly." Mother was in a panic and praying at the window.

"You won't be needing my help then?" I was relieved when I saw Patrick appear over the wall.

"There's no sign of the rooster. He must be in the trees someplace. We'll get him tomorrow." Patrick jumped off the wall.

"Where is that dog? pray God he hasn't got the bone, has he?" Mother pleaded

"It's alright he's here. There is no sign of a bone, thank God."

Early next morning we were awakened by the rooster crowing from the branches of a nearby tree.

"Get up will you, it's the chicken. I can see him in the graveyard." Mother came into the room and shook Patrick.

"Wha! What's wrong." Patrick came from under the blanket.

"It's the chicken. Go and get it before someone else does." Mother warned.

"Bloody bird. I'm sorry now that I ever brought it home. I'll strangle it when I catch it."

He finally managed to catch it and brought it back to the yard. Raising the axe he held the birds wings with his other hand. Somehow he managed to hold the roosters neck on the ground with his foot.

Bang! The axe landed on the neck of the rooster. His head separated from his body and landed a few inches away. Blood spattered all over the yard.

"I murdered him, the poor thing." He shouted dropping the axe. Blessing himself he let the rooster go and jumped to his feet He was not expecting this outcome. For a few moments the rooster minus his head ran round the yard. With a few spasms it convulsed and succumbed to death. He approached the corpse lying in the yard covered in blood and looked down at it. Blessing himself he ran into the house and closed the door. He wanted no more to do with the rooster.

"You murdered that poor chicken. You'll have to tell it in confession." Brendan chastised him.

"Will you shut your fecking gob before I shut it for you. That chicken is a rooster." Patrick threatened him.

"Don't you dare swear like that in my house." Mother warned.

"His ghost will haunt us forever." Phyllis moaned like the *Bean-Ó-Sidhe*.

Patrick made to attack her. She dived behind mother for safety. Calm was restored when mother went into the yard and returned with the rooster.

"Did you get his head Ma? Bruno would enjoy it." I asked. If looks could kill then the one she gave me should have killed me.

"Good God, you get worse by the day." She looked at me in horror.

She plucked and cleaned the bird and boiled it with the usual mixture of vegetables and herbs.

When cooked it smelt delicious. Patrick refused to eat any part of it. He was convinced that he had murdered it. This moral stand did not worry us at all. What he didn't eat was more for us.

It was a few days later when Brendan was digging up some carrots that he dug up the roosters head.

"Oh God! Ma! Ma help me the roosters ghost is in the garden." He screamed as he ran for the house.

"What is wrong now? For Heaven sake will you shut up. This family is driving me mad."

"It's the roosters ghost, it's coming out of the ground." He screamed. She went into the back garden and looked into the hole. There sure enough was the roosters head.

"Where is he? I'll kill him before he's much older." Mother ran her hands through her hair and looked like a demented soul.

"Where's who ma?" I came out to see what was the matter.

"You of course. God give me patience. You and that dog are more trouble than the whole family put together."

"Now what have I done?"

"It's you and that dog of yours. He didn't eat the head after all. He buried it and Brendan has gone to his bed half demented."

"Why would Brendan be mad over a chickens head?"

"I didn't say he was mad. Don't put words into my mouth. He thinks the ghost of the rooster is coming out of the ground. Oh! God what am I saying. Now pick it up and get rid of it." She gave me a belt around the head. Bruno made a run for the next door garden. She ran her hands through her hair in desperation.

"Now go! Go and get rid of it where he cannot find it, and when your at it get rid of him too, and yourself. I will, as sure as God is my judge, I'll swing for you." She stamped her foot at me. I picked up the head and pitched it over the graveyard wall. "Good God are my eyes deceiving me. Did I see you throw that head into the graveyard? Jesus, Mary and Joseph come to my aid before I strangle him. Get out and find that head and put it in the bin. Whatever next? Have you no shame throwing chicken heads on Christian graves?" She raised her hands to Heaven in prayer. I was duly despatched out the front door to search for the wayward roosters head. I tried with the help of my dog to find the head but with all the briars and trees we could not locate it. I told her that I found it and put it in a bin down the road. She must have believed me for she never mentioned it again.

AH SHURE THEY HAVE CROSSED THE STREET

There was two old saying in Limerick. "Ah! Shure they've crossed the street." Should you ask some of the older folk where this is you would have been told. "It's the place where the good, the bad, the mad and the dead' all live. These old saying baffles the stranger and I must admit many of the local citizens as well.

However come with me for a stroll through my old town and I'll give you a visual explanation. Take a stroll with me past the remnants of the old walls of the city. Past St Michael's ancient graveyard or what is left of it in Watergate, most of which is buried under a car park. Their ghosts care not as they wander past St John's gate and the Citadel pausing at the Devil's tower. Their vacant eyes look out at the Black Battery. Perhaps they still hear the cry of the defenders as the battery exploded under them so very long ago. This is their limit: They must now turn left into Sallyport. Sallyport was that not where the Williamite guns breached the walls? Was it not here that the Dutchman's murdering crew swarmed through the breach and attacked the outnumbered raparees? It was from Cromwell Tower that the gallant General Patrick Sarsfield called for the breach to be mended. There were no reinforcements to defend the gap. His gallant troops to the last man were deployed upon the city walls. The men may have been on the walls, but the women were in the streets.

Seeing the danger, they picked up stones from the breached wall and attacked the mightiest army in Europe. Slowly, step by step, they forced the Prussian army out through the breach. The women of Limerick held the sway as they fought below the city walls from night until the dawn. Many of them laid down their lives that night in defence of their beloved city.

On we go past Cromwell tower. It will be nearing dawn now. There's the Abbey River to cross, before they reach their final destination at *King's Island* and the castle of King John. Their spirits still wander the old lanes and walls of the ancient city as their bones slowly decay in the old cemetery at Watergate. How many know or care that this old cemetery is the final resting place of those who died for Limerick in 1691?

Let us leave the ghosts at King John's Castle and return to St. John's gate. Now let us turn into Upper William Street and on into Mulgrave Street. We have *crossed the street* we have left old Limerick proper.

We pass the old county hospital on our left. A relic of a bygone age, now converted into a college. Across the road from it we have Limerick Jail, known locally as *The Stone Jug* (Limerick saving bank is also known as 'The Stone Jug') with its grim foreboding stone walls. Its barbed wire and armed soldiers, it's sad inmates perhaps deserted by their God and fellow man. They hear the clock strike the hour, the voices of the citizens and the song of the bird. They turn their faces to the wall of their cells. It is not their time yet for freedom.

Passing the jail we approach the mental asylum, a further reminder of Limerick past. Within its walls many of Limerick's poor sought refuge where they tried to blot out the mental hunger of their tormented souls.

Others trapped in the confusion of battles and gases of war retreated to its safety. A war they were asked to participate in for the *'Freedom of smaller nations and liberty for old Ireland'*. The outcome they did not understand. They are still fighting the battle. There is no escape for their befuddled minds. They, too, are prisoners. Prisoners of their own conscience. Perhaps their relief lies no more than a stone wall away.

Behind that stone wall is the home of the grim reaper. For here we have Limerick's biggest cemetery, Mount St. Lawrence. Within its stone walls lie thousands of Limerick folk waiting the promised judgement day. They ask nothing of the living except that occasionally they are remembered. Perhaps the odd *Ave Maria,* or a hungry prayer to help them out of their purgatory.

They can do no harm to anyone. Yet their sleep is disturbed. Their church burnt to the ground. Their graves vandalised. Who will defend us they cry? Are we not as innocent babes? Where are those who cried in sympathy as they carried our coffins in sorrow and prayed at our graveside? Can they not now see that we are no longer at rest? Will those who torture our sleep not realise that they, too, one day, will have to come and join us. What excuse then will they offer for their present conduct and vandalism. Here we have the meaning of the old saying. The Sick, the Bad, the Mad and the Dead, all, more or less, in a row across the street.

As these places were outside the old city, they were *'Across the Street'*.

Sad perhaps to say it but one has a tendency to relate to a tragic childhood. It is as if these memories were all that were worth holding.

The sadness of our youth we tend to sweep aside. And try to bury it in our subconscious minds. Yet it does not go away. For every so often our past catches up with us.

EIRE-IRISH

Ireland was not prepared for the war and soon found herself isolated. Foreign ships that once brought their cargoes to her shores were seen no more. The situation was getting desperate. The country would soon run out of vital supplies. Drastic measures were called for. It was decided to send out buyers to the four corners of the earth to purchase ships. Ships were a precious commodity and all they could find were some rust buckets. These would have to do. Slowly they made the dangerous journey back through troubled waters to Irish ports.

The Ships engines were stripped down and overhauled. A few coats of paint applied and a new name painted on their sides. On the port and starboard sides of each ship was painted a huge Irish flag. Overprinted on it were the words Eire-Irish. Each vessel was named after Irish native trees. i.e. The Irish Ash, The Irish oak etc, to let all and sundry know that they were Irish and neutral. This they hoped would deter any submarine or gunboat from the Allies or Axis powers from sinking them. Even this did not prevent some of them and their crews from finding a watery grave.

As the war in Europe, Asia and Africa raged on, the Irish merchant seamen risked their lives running the gauntlet. German and Allied submarines and destroyers were on the lookout for any merchant ships bringing supplies to replenish their enemies. There was also the problem of mines. These would frequently sheer their moorings and float free. Having ran the gauntlet of the open oceans we would periodically see these little ships arrive at Limerick docks with badly needed supplies. They must have run a great risk both to themselves and to their ships as they sailed the waters of the Atlantic and Pacific Ocean and the seven seas seeking supplies to sustain their beleaguered country.

German killer submarines were sending American and British ships to the bottom of the ocean on a daily basis. Some of our little ships were sent to the bottom too. At times a ship would arrive from England laden with precious coal. Hardly had the coal come off the ship and into the coal yards than it was sold. We would go to the docks to watch the ships arrive and leave on the high tide. As the ships left the docks they would sound their horns. The wail echoing down the Shannon river like the wail of the Bean-Ó-Sidhe.

Mother never forgot the men who risked their lives on behalf of the Irish nation. Looking out towards the docks she would call on us to pray for their welfare.

"May God and his blessed mother protect and bless all the sailors on the high seas this night." It was just a simple prayer, what we called *The Trimmin's of the Rosary* or personal prayers in addition to the saying of the Rosary. Nothing elaborate or long winded as we would say about some prayers.

'Ah, the trimmin's that find me now my hair is turning grey,
Drifting in like painted butterflies from paddocks far away;
Dripping dainty wings in fancy- and the pictures, fading fast,
Stand again in rose and purple in the albums of the past.
But I wonder has she 'trimmin's or is the Rosary said?
But the years have crowed past us, and the fledglings all have flown,
And the nest beneath the sugarloaf no longer is their own;
For a hand has written 'Finish' and the book is closed for good-
There's a stately red-tiled mansion where the old slab dwelling stood;
There the stranger has her evenings, and the formal supper's spread,
But I wonder has she 'Trimmin's' now, or is the rosary said?
Ah, those little Irish mothers passing from us one by one!
Who will write the noble story of the good that they have done?
All their children may be scattered, and their fortunes windward hurled,
But their trimmin's of the rosary will bless them 'round the world.

(From 'Around the Boru Log')

I often wondered, if the sailors on their ships were aware that the people of Limerick were praying so earnestly for their safety. The arrival and departure of these ships did not pass without some humorous incidents at times. The ships arriving at Limerick docks were compelled to await the tides. The fishermen of the river would wait in ambush.

The fishermen had long Shannon fishing boats. These were manned by four or more men with heavy oars. Their nets stowed on the prow of the boats. Their fishing grounds were, as far as we knew, in the Shannon Estuary. As the coal boats were being unloaded at the quayside, the fishing boats would arrive alongside. The fishermen would ask the sailors standing on the deck to throw some lumps of coal into the Shannon. Great lumps of coal would be dumped into the water. Huge splashes of water would cascade over the fishing boats.

"Take it easy there. You nearly sank us." The fishermen would call to the obliging sailors.

"Have you got anything for us?" The sailors would call down to the fishermen below in their little boats.

"We have of course, pass down the basket." The rope and a basket would be slung over the side of the ship. Then the bottles of poteen, a home made spirit drink, highly potent, would be removed from the locker of the fishing boat and placed in the basket. Eggs, meat and bacon would be added to replenish their stocks. then be hauled on board by the grateful sailors. With a fond farewell the fishermen would then row away up the Shannon to their moorings at the Strand barracks or the Treaty Stone. Some would take their boats to their moorings on the Abbey river. How this supposed secret illusory trade was carried out without the customs knowing was hard to understand. The dock customs officers were not far away. Be that as it may as the ship once again left the docks and the tide receded the fishermen would return. Donning their big waders they would walk through the mud of the river. Collecting the coal from the riverbed they put it in their boats and took it to their respective homes. Some would be sold to potential customers. The money helped out when the fishing was poor.

There was also the trade in timber. This would fall off the various quays owned by the city merchants. At times it was said that it got a little assistance in the form of a gentle push. There was always some flotsam to be found in the Shannon that could be used to make a few shillings. We felt both humble and proud of our fishermen. As we sat on the river wall or looked out from our window we could see and hear the fishermen returning. As the boats came up the Shannon, their oars making ripples on the still waters we would hear the rosary being called by the man at the prow and answered by the other fishermen in their boats. Far out in the Atlantic the deep sea fishermen would trade fish, meat and vegetables for diesel oil and grease to drive and maintain their vessels. This trade was carried out with both the Axis powers and the allies.

It was wrongly misconstrued that Ireland was supplying German submarines with fuel. This rumour was encouraged by many mischief makers on the allied side, they reported seeing Irish fishing boat tied up beside German 'U' boats. They were also annoyed that they were denied access to the big gun batteries on our coast. Ireland had no oil whatsoever and was dependent on Britain, America and her own little ships. Ireland had no oil tankers of any shape or size. She sent vast quantities of food and manpower to Britain during the Second World War. Had the Germans been vindictive, they could have sunk the boats sailing between British and Irish ports and justified their action.

Our sailors who defied the elements and the war to bring badly needed supplies to our shores deserve our thanks and gratitude. Their efforts and sacrifices on our behalf deserve to be remembered.

I doubt if the old anchor that I saw stuck in a cement base on the quayside is a fitting memorial to them. It does no credit to the citizens of Limerick and to the memory of those who sacrificed their lives for us against all the odds

THE AUGUSTINIAN CHURCH

A new Augustinian church had been erected in O'Connell Street during the war on the site of an old theatre. The building cost £42,000 to erect and the people of Limerick were called upon to give generously. With the war taking its toll on the population funds were slow in coming in and so the Augustinians looked 'round for other outlets to boost their coffers

In Bedford Row were empty motor showrooms and with divine help they opened it up as a casino of sorts. So long as you were gambling in aid of the Church then it was not considered a sin. The slot machines and the push penny ate up what few coppers that were available. There was little return, the gaming machines were constipated when it came to paying out. The music and the lights were as tempting to the citizens as was the hope of gaining a place in Heaven.

Phyllis and I were detailed by mother one morning to go to Daly's bakers and purchase a bag of broken bread.

"Now there's the sixpence and here's the sack, don't dilly dally and stay away from the river. Do you hear me, then heed me." Mother warned as she gave the sixpence to Phyllis for safety. I was left with the dog.

We crossed the strand and went over the bridge into the city centre. As we came off the bridge we heard the loud music tempting us to come to the casino.

"Here, let's look in and see what's it like." I suggested.

"No! You know what mother said, get the bread and come home at once."

"It's only 'round the corner, she'll never know, come on." I nudged her.

"Ok then, but just to look and no more."

Round the walls of the showroom were rows and rows of gaming machines. All promising to give a good return for every penny spent. There were machines with little steel balls, if you could get the four into their respective holes then you would win one pound. It would be easier for a camel to get through the eye of a needle than get the ball into the winning slot. There were machines with a set of three wheels with various emblems on them. Get three in a row and you could also win one pound. Most citizens put their losses down to a donation to the Augustinian's and a step nearer Heaven.

"Do you know something, if we said a novena to Saint Anthony and put a penny in one of them machines we might win the pound." I suggested.

"A penny! Where would we get a penny. Mother told me to watch you."

"We have the sixpence that mother gave to you." I reminded her.

"God, we mustn't touch that, lets get out of here." She was out the door like a bat out of Hell.

"Look there's the Franciscans over there. Come on, Saint Anthony won't let us down. He helped me in the past, you know." I again tempted her.

"Well, alright then but just the one penny and no more." She weakened under the temptation.

We knelt in that church and prayed as we never prayed before. As we left the church Phyllis collected holy water from the font.

Returning to the casino she went to the cash desk and changed the sixpence into pennies. She stood before one of the machines and taking a penny from her hand she dipped it in the holy water. Then she reminded Saint Anthony of her prayers.

"Now let us say a prayer." She dropped the penny into the slot and again blessed herself before pulling the handle.

Round and round the wheels spun. The first stopped at a lemon, then the second stopped at another lemon.

"Hail Mary, come on pray." She called to me as she closed her eyes. The wheel stopped and she waited with her eyes still closed. There was no clatter of money, the wheel stopped at a bunch of grapes.

"Oh God! What happened? I've lost my penny. Are you sure that you were praying?"

"Don't worry, the next time it will pay out. He's just testing your faith." I assured her.

"The next time, do you think we should?" She had the penny in her hand.

All too soon we were down to the last penny without any return.

"You may as well try the last one, we'll get nothing for a penny." Once again the machine consumed the penny.

"I'll be killed and it will be all your fault, I won't be able to go home now. I thought you told me that saint Anthony knew you?" Phyllis was distraught and who could blame her.

"You wait here, I'll have a look 'round and see what I can find. I'll try and get the bread for nothing." I promised.

There was no luck at the bakery and I went deeper into the city. Outside Barry's Butcher shop I saw several carcasses of sheep on long rows. The heads with the wool still on, and snots coming from the mouths and nose. The sides were cut in decorative patterns. Next to them, was a long line of sausages and black and white puddings hanging on 'S' hooks. In the laneway was a wooden slatted box. I removed one of the slats and sticking a nail in the end I reached out and slipped the row of sausages off the rail. The sausages were in one long string and when removed trailed along the ground like a skipping rope. Bruno seeing the sausages ran out of the laneway and grabbed them. I ran down the laneway with Bruno holding on to one end of the sausages and me the other in a long skipping rope. I tried to take the sausages from Bruno's mouth. He growled and was reluctant to give them to me.

"There's a good dog, I'll let you have one." I forced his jaws open and retrieved the sausages that were half way down his throat. I was glad that mother did not witness him disobeying me. Returning to the casino I saw Phyllis standing in a corner with a worried look on her face.

"You're back then, how did you get on. Oh God help me, Ill be sent to the Magdalene and it will be all your fault." She jumped up and down.

"They wouldn't give me the bread for nothing but I got these." I opened the bag to her.

"Sausages! Who gave them to you? We can't tell our mother that we bought sausages. You didn't steal them? I wouldn't put it past you."

"Of course not, they were going off and the butcher let me have them for the dog." I lied.

"For the dog, rotting sausages, God! But you get worse. I should never have listened to you. Mother is right you are a devil." She stamped the ground.

"Stay there, I have another plan, a better one. Here hold on to Bruno, I won't be too long."

Returning to our home in the barracks I got in without mother seeing me.

I lifted a loose floorboard and retrieved my Oxo box and removed three of my filed down penny sized medals and ran back to the casino.

I went to one of the machines and tested to see if the medal would fit. It fitted like a glove. I pulled the handle and the coin dropped out, rejected!

"Come over here and cover for me." I called to Phyllis.

"What are you up to, where did you get the money from. Oh God help me, I feel like a criminal?" She was in an agitated state and blamed it on me.

"Never mind where I got it, warn me if anyone comes over." Again I put a medal in the machine and pulled the handle. This time it accepted it but did not pay out. I put the second medal into the machine and again the wheels spun round and again failed to pay out.

"This is the last penny I've got. Say a prayer and wish me luck." Not thinking I held the medal up but quickly realised what I'd done and pulled it back. I fed the medal into the machine and watched the wheels spin round and round. "That's it then." I began to walk away.

Clank! Clink! Clang! The wheels stopped, I turned and looked. The machine came to life and vomited out 240 pennies one after the other. Soon, we were surrounded by other customers. Congratulating us. One would have thought that I won the Irish Sweepstake.

"Thank you, Saint Anthony, thank you!" Phyllis wrung her hands in prayer and began to cry. I went to the teller and changed the pennies into a crisp one pound note.

We went down to Dalys bakery and purchased our bag of bread and a cream horn each. Mother was delighted with the money I told her that I found a penny and put it in the machine and won. She said that it was all due to the intercession of Saint Anthony. What she would have said if she found out that I was filing down her holy medals is another story.

She took the sausages from the bag and smelt them. "These are not going off, whoever said they were?"

"He did! He got them from the butcher for the dog." Phyllis disclosed.

"Louie, you mean? Oh well then, that's it then isn't it." She placed the sausages on the table.

"Were you begging again? God but you are shameless. Instead of putting a lead on the dog it should be put on you." Now there was gratitude, I thought.

The sausages were boiled in a pot with potatoes and vegetables. I forgot to cut off the ones that Bruno had bitten through and half swallowed. Still nobody noticed and Bruno got his share of the pot.

Phyllis was all for thanking Saint Anthony and how could I dampen her faith by telling her the truth.

She never did tell mother what I had done and for that I was thankful.

THE TURF STACKERS.

It was on a hazy autumn day when Brendan, Bruno and myself were out past the other side of *St Patrick's Well* in *Mungret'*. Passing a gentleman's detached residence, we came upon a priest standing outside the gate.

"Good day Father." We saluted the Priest as was the custom at the time.

"Well now you look like a fine healthy pair of boys. Would you ever do a little job for me?" He knew that we could not refuse, nobody refused a Priest.

"Of course Father. It won't take too long we hope."

"Not at all. It's just a creel of turf I want stacking. It should be here soon." He looked up and down the road.

"I'll leave you lads to it. I have an appointment. Just throw it into the outhouse, there's good boys." With that he left us standing by the roadside.

"What are you two doing here?" Our friend Josie came along the road.

"We're waiting for a creel of turf. The Priest gave us the job of stacking it. Do you want to share?"

"How much is he giving you, Priest's aren't too generous, you know?"

"We don't know yet. At least a couple of bob each I hope."

Up the road came an ancient tractor and behind it the longest trailer I ever saw. It was stacked so high that every time he hit a bump a few sods fell off.

"I hope that's not his creel, If it is I'm off." Brendan grumbled. Sure enough the tractor stopped at the gate and reversed inside.

"Are you boys working for the Priest?" He asked as he removed the pins from the trailer.

"We're here to stack the turf. How much of it is for him?" I asked.

"It's all his, good luck to you." Picking up the turf fork he pitched several forks full into the yard.

"Come on now lads that should do it. Give me a hand to tip the rest." With superhuman strength we tipped the remainder into the yard. There was not a breath of space left when we finished.

"God! We'll never get this lot finished. We should go and forget it." Josie suggested.

"Look here, there are three of us. We should get it finished in next to no time. There should be a good few bob in it for us." I encouraged them. Looking back I wish that I had taken Josie's advice.

The priest returned some time later and encouraged us with the task. He did not see Josie inside the outhouse.

Meantime his servant girl came out with two mugs of soup.

"I didn't know there were three of you." The girl looked surprised when she saw Josie appear from deep inside the shed.

"What's the matter Bridget?" The Priest came to the door and looked at the servant still holding the mugs.

"There's three of them Father. I don't have that much soup."

"I found it a bit on the thick side myself. Take it back and add a little stock."

"Talk about the water into wine." I whispered .

Bridget returned with the watered down soup in three mugs.

We worked hard throwing and stacking his turf. By the end of the day we were exhausted. I went to the door and knocked. The door was opened by the Priest.

"That's a grand job. I notice you swept the yard too. Wait there a minute." He seemed pleased with our work.

"I told you so, he's going to see us right." I looked at Brendan and Josie. Both looked like minstrels with their black faces. He returned and told us to hold out our hands. Anxiously we stood in a row with our hands extended. Into each palm he placed three pennies and a medal.

"There now boys, you earned that. In Nomine Patris, et Filii, et Spiritus Sancti. Amen." He blessed us and closing the door left us standing on the step.

With our black faces and mouth fully opened. We looked like three minstrels singing. I wouldn't have minded too much but for the fact that the medals were small ones and could not be filed down.

Josie, was not too pleased and called me all the names under the sun. It was lucky for me that I had the Priest's blessing under my belt.

THE BICYCLE

My sister Mary, always wanted to own a bicycle, ever since she learnt to ride one. This skill she mastered on a man's dilapidated bicycle. It was no easy task. She had to learn by getting her leg through the cross bar to reach the pedal on the other side of the bicycle. She fell off it so many times and scratched herself in so many places that there were not too many places left to scratch or scar. Yet through her perseverance, she finally mastered it.

'If only I could get a bicycle of my very own.' She would wish. She spent so much time between churches praying for the bicycle that she had worn out the pavements. Like all other dreams and aspirations this was only a pipe dream. There was little enough money for food. She could forget the luxury of a bicycle unless she could find a generous benefactor. She pestered mother day and night to buy her a bicycle on hire purchase without success.

"If I cannot afford to pay for one now. How do you expect me to pay in the future? No there will be no bicycle. If you got one then Patrick would want one. Where would it all end, go on tell me? There will be no bicycle, you can be assured of that." That so far as mother was concerned was the end of the matter. Still she craved for that bicycle and nothing would quell her heart felt desire for one. Then a generous Father Christmas the guise of Uncle Gerald arrived.

"Don't worry about the bicycle. You want a bicycle and a bicycle you shall have." He was a bit under the weather when he made this promise.

"Now don't you go making promises you cannot keep. It's not fair if you must you know." Mother chided her brother.

"Who said I won't keep my promise? I promised her a bicycle and a bicycle she shall have," he retorted rather hurt.

"Will you take no notice of him, it's the drink talking." Mother reminded Mary after he left. The matter was left to rest for several days. She had given up all hope of getting the bicycle. Then one evening to her surprise Uncle Gerald came to the door. Over his shoulder he carried a brand new girl's bicycle.

"Here you are. True to my word. I hope you like it?"

"Like it, I love it. Oh you are so good. Ma look! It's my new bicycle."

Mary was over the moon and wanted to take the bicycle on the road before the wrappers were completely off it.

"Hold on now until I adjust the saddle and show you where everything is." He stopped her rushing out of the room with it. When all was ship shape, she took it down the stairs and on to the street. Up and down the road she rode it. Ringing the bell to let the neighbours know that she had a new bicycle. Uncle Gerald came round to the house periodically to check on her progress.

"How is it going? Have you been to many places on it?" He would ask.

"Not yet. I'm hoping Ma will let me go to Corbally on it next Sunday after Mass." Gerald went into the house. Mary parked the bicycle in the hall.

On her return Gerald and mother were in discussion about the bicycle.

"Tell me, where did you get that bicycle from, If that's not asking too much of you?" Mother was not happy with the situation.

"You should know that doing this only makes the other children jealous. Can't you see that?" Mother tried to make him see some sense.

"Don't worry about the bicycle Kate. It's all right. I got it from Miles if you must know." He awaited her reaction which was not too long in coming.

"Oh my God! Anyone but him. The *Gombeen* man, don't you know his reputation?" She held her hand to her mouth in disbelief. Miles, to use his full name which was Miles Nagalopas was of Greek origin. He was a dealer in all kinds of hire purchase. During the famine years they were known as *Gombeen* men. Only the desperate or the foolish went next or near him for credit.

Money, radios, prams, bicycles- you name it, Miles could get it for you at a price. The problem was repaying him. By the time Gerald would have finished paying for the bicycle he could have bought bicycles for the whole family. Gerald continued to pay for the bicycle for some time. The more he paid the more he seemed to owe. It appeared that the bicycle would never be paid for.

Then one day there was a knock on our door. Mother answered it. There in the casement stood Mr Miles. He was anxious to have words with Gerald.

"He does not live here. Can I give him a message?" Mother asked.

"Just tell him that Mr Miles called. He will know what it is all about." With that he left. She now knew that the exorbitant payments on the bicycle were no longer being paid. That evening Uncle Gerald called at our house with an old war comrade. Both felt better after a few jars of drink.

"Kate would you ever be so obliging and make us both something salty." For some peculiar reason he always wanted something salty after a few drinks.

As mother made the sandwiches of salty bacon and mustard she reminded him of the visit by Mr Miles.

"Mr Miles was here to see you. Is it about the bicycle? Surely it's paid for by now."

"He shouldn't have come troubling you Kate. This is between me and him. What did he have to say? The miserable skin flint" Gerald asked.

"All he said was that you knew what it was about. You did not answer my question. Is it about that bicycle?"

"Yes and no. You see Kate, I hit a bad patch and missed a few payments. Nothing to worry about." He shuffled, uncomfortable in his seat.

"Well you had best settle it with him one way or the other. I don't want the likes of him at my door. I knew from the beginning that this would end in tears. Now my words are about to come true."

"I told you Kate not to worry. I'll see to it."

Next day Mr Miles again called to ask if Uncle Gerald was in.

"I told you before that he does not live here. Would you please stop pestering us?" Mother disliked the man intently.

"You tell him from me that I'll be back, to collect my bicycle that he never finished paying for. You make sure that he is here. I'm not a charity." With these words he left.

When Mary returned with her bicycle mother dispatched her to Spaight's the builders merchants in the city where uncle Ger worked.

"What brings you here?" He asked Mary as she dismounted from her bicycle.

"Mother said that Mr Miles called and says that you must meet him at our house." She relayed the message to him.

"I hate to have to do this to you. Would you leave the bicycle here and walk home. Tell your mother that I'll call round to night." Mary reluctantly handed it over to him and left the yard.

"Where is your bicycle? Did you leave it someplace?" Mother asked as she entered the house.

"No I didn't leave it anyplace. It has to go back to that rotten Mr Miles." She kicked the floor in a temper.

"I knew, I told him so. He would not listen? Oh no! I am really sorry for you," she consoled Mary.

That evening Uncle Gerald called. He was still in his working clothes. This was unusual for him. He would always dress up before coming to our house. In his hand he had a sack which rattled when he let it down.

"Whatever brings you here this early? You must be going someplace in a hurry?" Mother looked at the sack sitting at his feet.

"Has that skin flint come bothering you yet again, Kate? I have a present for him." Uncle Gerald looked down at the sack and smiled.

"If you mean that Mr Miles? He has not and I don't want him calling here. Do you understand?"

"I don't think he will bother you again after to night. I'll have a cup of tea when I'm waiting. That is if you are making one." He pushed the sack under the chair.

Mother gave him the cup of tea and he settled back waiting and watching the door. After some time there was a knocking at the door. Mother opened it to be confronted by Mr Miles.

"Oh! So it's you again. Don't you ever get the message?" She looked him up and down her contempt for him showing.

"Never mind all that. Did he call or not?" He pushed the door open.

"Is it me you want to see?" Uncle Gerald rose from his seat and came to the door.

"Of course it is. Didn't you get my message? I want my money or my bicycle right now." He tried to outstare our uncle.

"Look you know well that I paid for that bicycle over and over again. I owe you no money."

"Well if you cannot pay me the money you owe then I'll take the bicycle. Have you got it?" He demanded.

"I've got the bicycle for you alright, have no fear. Hold on a minute and I'll fetch it." Uncle Gerald smiled.

"I'm not going anyplace without the bicycle or money."

"Hold on a tick. Don't get your hackles up and don't go away now." He returned to the house and picked up the sack.

"Here it is." He handed the sack to Mr Miles.

"Is this some kind of a joke?" Mr Miles took the sack and looked at it.

"It's no joke I can assure you. Look inside."

He opened the sack and looked. Then he reached in and took out a piece of tubular steel six inches long.

"Good God! What have you done man?" He reached into the sack again and took out more pieces of steel. It was obvious from the colouring and the name that these pieces were once part of a bicycle.

"If this is what I think it is then you are in very serious trouble my man." He dumped the sack on the doorstep and left fuming and cursing under his breath. Uncle Gerald picked up the sack and brought it back into the house closing the door behind him

"Just what was all that about? He sure left in a huff." Mother looked at the sack again. Uncle Gerald sat in the chair the sack between his legs and laughed. Then he opened the neck of the sack.

"You see Kate, he wanted to take the bicycle back from the child. He would resell it at a greater profit. So I let him have it."

Mother looked into the sack and took out some of the pieces.

"But you cut it into pieces. It's no use to anyone."

Miles never took any further action about the bicycle. Had he taken the matter to court I expect the judge would have seen that he was well paid for the bicycle.

Perhaps he did not relish the thought of all the adverse publicity in the local press.

CAPTURED BY GUARD WHITE

I awakened one morning with a severe pain in my stomach and told my mother that I was feeling unwell. To add to my misery I had suffered a long restless night of agony with '*Old Faithful*' my chilblains.

"Come here let's have a look at you." Placing her hand on my forehead she looked deep into my eyes.

"You're not fibbing this time, you don't look all that well. Best stay at home from school to day." For once she agreed with me and I was pleased. As the morning wore on I was beginning to feel much better and told her so.

"Pleased to hear it, still it's too late to go to school now. Tell you what, we'll go into town and do a bit of shopping."

On reaching the city centre she decided that we should go to the Franciscan Church and say a little prayer. As we took our place in inside I noticed an acolyte coming out from the sacristy carrying a pole with a lit taper on the end. I knew that a low mass was about to be celebrated and that mother would attend. Having lit the two side candles on the high altar he retired to the sacristy. Some moments later a bell tinkled and the door opened and a friar carrying a chalice with the acolyte in tow came out and mounted the steps leading to the high altar.

"In Nomine Patris, et Filii, et Spiritus Sancti. Amen. Introicbo ad altare Dei." The friar faced the congregation and blessed us one and all as he introduced us to the Mass in latin.

"Ad Deum Qui Laetificat Juventutem Meam." Replied the acolyte. Low mass had begun.

When Mass finished we adjourned to the city centre.

"Is that the time?" Mother looked up at *Cannock's* clock. "I have to get to the town hall before noon, be a good boy and go to the dispensary for me."

"Of course, what do you want from there?"

"I'm hoping to get a few bob from Mr Keane. You don't mind, do you?"

"That's Ok Ma, I'll meet you later outside '*Boyd's*' in William Street.

I reached the dispensary as Mr Keane was about to call out the names. Standing in the well of the building I had plenty of time to think. Then I realised why mother had allowed me to stay away from school. She did not like going to the dispensary to be humiliated. I listened and hoped as name after name was called. As the gathering slowly dwindled I realised that there was no money forthcoming for mother. I knew that she would have made a novena to Saint Anthony in the church that morning asking him to intercede.

As I strolled down William Street feeling sorry for mother I was grasped from behind.

"Got you, you little caffler." I felt a heavy hand holding on to my arm. Looking behind me I saw the huge figure of Guard White, the school guard towering over me.

"I'm not mitching guard, I was feeling sick and my mother let me stay at home. I'm going to meet her down at *Boyd's* Store." I pleaded with him.

"You're meeting no one but your teacher, come on." He held me in a vice like grip.

Arriving at the school he opened the classroom door and marched me in.

"Is this one of yours, brother?" Releasing me he pushed me into the room.

"He is indeed guard, very commendable of you. Where did you find him?"

"He was sneaking down William Street, said he was sick and going to meet his mother."

"Thank you guard. As for you come up here." Wagging his index finger he pointed to where he wanted me to stand.

"So you were sick were you? You don't look sick to me but you will be." Reaching into the hidden pocket in his cassock he withdrew the dreaded black strap.

"But Sir, I was sick and I was going to meet my mother, honest I was."

"So you still insist on lying. For not attending school you will receive six slaps, for lying six more and a further six for good measure. Now hold out your hand."

I sneaked the horsehair from my pocket and placed it in the palm of my hand. This we believed would absorb the pain. I gritted my teeth and waited. Then they came landing accurately on my fingers. Slowly and deliberately he paused between beatings. As my hands had been previously injured by the black strap it was not too long before the old wounds became red raw. Then it happened, a trickle of blood appeared. I looked from my injured hand to the brother hoping that he would realise that I was injured and stop. I knew that pleading with him would only result in more brutal treatment. There would be no stopping, the punishment would have to run its full course. I knew by the way that he looked at me that he wanted me to cry out for clemency, but I stubbornly refused to be cowed down. I must admit that I was stubborn and perhaps stupid but |I would not yield. I was leader of the gang and if I cried out then my position as gang leader would be in jeopardy.

"Now the other one." He demanded. I dropped my injured hand to my side and replaced it with my good hand. There was no sign of the horsehair, I wondered where it had got to. Then as he raised the strap I saw it sticking to it. It must have got caught up in my blood. Again the strap landed on my outstretched hand, one, two, three I counted as I tried to mentally deaden the pain. But the pain would not go away and I knew that I had many more slaps coming to me. It took a lot of courage to stand up to the beatings. Finally my punishment was completed and I was despatched outside the classroom to cool down.

Alone now I had plenty of time to let the anger and sorrow building up within me escape. There was nobody to see me now as I felt my lower lip quiver and a tear run down my face and drop off the end of my nose. I looked at my bloodied hand and then it happened, the floodgates opened. I cried, I cursed the brother and stamped my feet. It might have taken courage to accept the unjust punishment before the class but it took real courage to show ones emotions. After some time when all my emotions had drained the door opened and the pupils came out from the classroom. They looked at me as they passed by in ones and twos. Then the good brother came out and looked down at me. I knew that they were going for the bun and bottle of milk.

"You can go back inside now and get on with your reading. There will be no milk for you this day." He held on to the brass latch of the door. I walked through the door and heard it close behind me.

That evening as I took the road home I wondered what mother would say to me. She would be waiting patiently for me to return with the money. As I had no money to give her, would she believe me? Why did she not go herself to plead with Mr Keane? Saint Anthony would have listened to her prayers, he was always out when I called. Would she believe me when I told her that I was captured by the school guard and had been beaten by the brother?

She listened as I related what happened to me and sympathised with me when I showed her my hands.

"I should have given you a note and this would never have happened. I am sorry but time will heal your hands, you'll see." I was grateful that she at least believed that I was telling the truth. Would time heal my mind I wondered?

That night as lay on my sparse pillow I had plenty time to concentrate on my wounds. As if I had not suffered enough punishment that day 'Old Faithful' inflicted burning itching pain to my feet and ears. Again in my frustration I bit my lip and shed tears of anger and sorrow into my pillow. My mind was filled with self pity, Who could I turn to? Not God, he was always out when I called.

As God had little time for me or so it seemed I turned again to the Goddess Myosotis for help. She would on hearing my crying come with a jar of healing balm. This she would spread on my hands and my chilblains.

I listened to the night winds and then I heard her call, Louie, Louie. In her hand she held a jar of sweet smelling balm. She wafted cool air on my blistered feet with her delicate wings. They were as transparent as crystal and sent out healing rays. Then she flew high above me and looking down at me smiled. She shook her wings and once again delicate gold pieces landed all around my huge bed. Then she sent down layer upon layer of finest silk. I found myself sinking deeper and deeper into the mantle of silk. I was free of pain and sorrow.

TEMPTATION IN THE GRADEN OF EDEN

Pupils attending the secondary college were under an obligation to attend a weeklong retreat once each year. The purpose of which we were told in no uncertain terms was to cleanse our souls of any sins that may have escaped our attention or that we inadvertently omitted to confess in our confessions.

One would have thought however that this was nigh impossible. With confraternity once each week. Prayers on the hour in the class rooms. Benediction at least twice each week, Mass on Sunday, Rosary every night in the home and a blood and thunder retreat by the Redemptorist Priests every year. This should be more than sufficient religion for any boy to absorb.

Not so, the good brothers had their own retreat in the monastery for the redemption of the souls of their pupils. This retreat was held one autumn in the monastery grounds and was supposed to last for a whole week. Culminating with high mass in the chapel.

The good brothers answered their calling to celebrate the most magnificent cult of adoration to Christ and his Blessed Mother. Each also brought with them all their skills and knowledge which God had provided him with. These skills they would pass on to us ungrateful as we were. Many devoted their skills to writing books and drawings. Their rules of humility, prudence, retirement, respect, virginity and obedience were strictly observed. The problem was that some of them believed that we should follow their example. They would speak of *The Virgin of the Moon, The Fountain of all Holiness, The Well of Living Water*. These and many more images of the *Virgin Mary* were meant to instil into our souls her all powerful intercession for our salvation. She was the *Queen Of Heaven* and they looked forward to so great a challenge in her praise hoping for their reward in the hereafter. Many I fear fell by the wayside lamenting when confronted by our ignorance and reluctance to comprehend the meaning of knowledge. I fear that some in despair were driven to the very gates of Hell. My mother was of the opinion that I was one of the little devils driving them to despair.

During the retreat there would not be any lessons in the classrooms. Apart from the time spent on our knees in the church, most of the time we spent walking round the grounds and orchard with our rosary beads in our hands or our missals open in prayer.

We were forbidden to speak at any time within the walls of the monastery. It was funny to see boys stick their hands in the air and point towards where the toilets were.

The brother would acknowledge the silent signal and would nod his head in agreement or shake his head and wag his finger at a persistent pupil.

It did not matter if the pupil had a weak bladder or not. The brother decided on how often one needed to go to the toilet. Then there were those who needed a crafty smoke badly. The brother would let them go and on their return call them over to him.

Then not unlike a semaphore. He would signal for the boy to firstly show his hands. These he would examine minutely back and front paying special attention to his thumbs for the tell tale traces of nicotine stains.

Some brothers would order us to open our mouth and breath out. He would then sniff our breath for the tell tale smell of tobacco fumes. This was not very hygienic when one took into consideration the amount of consumption and other related illnesses that were abroad in the city at the time.

Having established that the boy had gone for a crafty smoke under false pretences, he was duly escorted away for punishment with the brother holding firmly on to his ear. When he was brought back to the fold he would have his rosary round his neck and his hands tucked under his armpits. You knew that he had got at least five of the best on each hand from the dreaded black strap. After that beating he would find it impossible to hold his rosary beads for some time at least. We were under constant supervision of the brothers at all times. Yet somehow we still managed to fool them.

Outsiders looking into the school grounds at us marching round and round the grounds in pairs with our missals and rosary beads in our hands would have thought that we were angels. That butter would not melt in our mouths. I can assure the reader that this was far from the true picture. Within the covers of the missals and prayer books were concealed other books unknown to the brothers.

Our minds were far from God and prayer, as we became engrossed in the heroic deeds of *Dan Dare*. Of *Flash Gordon* as he fought to save the earth from the clay men from Mars. Of *Tom Sawyer* and *Huckleberry Finn* in the swamps of America's deep south.

The list was endless. As we finished one miniature book we exchanged it with the next boy with a sleight of hands. Our performance would do credit to a conjuror even under the watchful eye of the brother.

The only sound that disturbed our meditation was the singing of the blackbirds and robins.

That was until one of the brothers broke into a hymn. There were all the old favourites: *Stabat Mater, Soul of my Saviour, Sweet Heart of Jesus* and of course *Ave Maria.*

As the brother's voice rang out in praise to the Lord or the Blessed Virgin, we were obliged to join in.

Some boys who were so engrossed in their comics would need a belt around the ear. This to arouse them as to what was going on around them and to get them singing.

As the last notes of the hymn died away we would return to our prayers or comics. The *Holy Joe's* and *Craw Thumpers*, a nickname we called the holy ones returned to their prayers.

As this was our first and only retreat in the grounds we felt privileged. We were glad to get away from all the lessons. The shouting and the beatings.

We were content strolling round the grounds reading our comics tucked inside our missals.

It was irritating when one of the brother's would begin the rosary out loud and we had to answer. We would have to put away our missals and take out our rosary beads. This was not considered a breach of the rule of silence.

We would still be talking to God. Only this time we would be speaking to him in one voice.

All went well for the first half of the week. There was no reason for the brothers to suspect that we were doing anything amiss. The beads were to be seen swinging from our hands and the pages of the missals turned to a new page.

That was until mid week, it was on a Wednesday to be exact. In the afternoon, for some reason best known to themselves the brothers retreated to their chapel and left us unsupervised.

Was this a test of our obedience or were they so naïve as to trust us? I peered after them retreating into the chapel. Either way they were tempting providence.

Although we were honour bound to keep strict silence and continue with our prayers there was always that one bad apple in the barrel. If Adam could be tempted in the orchard in the presence of God. What hope was there for us in the brother's orchard.

It began with one boy leaving the ranks and going to the nearest apple tree and plucking an apple from the branch and eating it. This show of bravado brought sniggers from the rest of us who soon broke ranks and began to skin the orchard.

The rosary beads and the missals were discarded as we ran through the orchard. Like Adam and Eve we were not content with the apples on the ground: There were bigger and better ones on the trees.

We shook the ripe fruit from the branches and laughed as it rained down on us. Others climbed into the branches and jumped up and down sending more and more fruit tumbling to the ground.

Then some boys started throwing the fruit at each other and we all joined in the mayhem. Boy's ran across neat flower beds to escape the apple throwers as others tried to hide behind the statues. Boy's heads popped out from the highest branches and vanished as they were met with a well placed shot from an apple. With all the noise and playing we failed to notice the return of the brother's until it was too late.

Drawing their dreaded black straps like sabres. They lifted the hems of their cassocks and charged into us. It was reminiscent of the *Charge of the Light Brigade*. We were like cattle in a stampede as the brothers tried to round us up. Boys fell out of the trees and tried unsuccessfully to make a dash for freedom only to be captured by the irate brothers. All the strict rules of the retreat were forgotten as they lashed out at the boys. Perhaps they were thinking of the three days retreat time wasted. Whatever they were thinking they were not at all amused.

Some boys hid in the upper branches and kept quiet hoping they would not be found. This was like the ostrich burying his head in the sand. They were searching every tree and shrub. There seemed to be more brothers than pupils or was it the speed that they moved at.

"Come down from that tree at once," a brother shouted into the branches.

"I'm coming Sir. It wasn't me, it was him, it's all his fault you know." The boy pointed further into the tree. Hoping against hope that his betrayal would ease the blows he expected and got. As he landed on the ground the brother began to belt him with the strap. The other boy landed and made a dash for freedom as the other was getting a beating.

"Oh God Sir, I'm sorry. We didn't mean it, really Sir"? He looked to the boy who he had betrayed for support. He had his own problems as he ran round and round the tree and was being pursued by another brother.

"Stop at once! Do you hear me?" The brother shouted at the boy as he ran faster and faster round the tree.

The other boy stood still in the one spot and every time the brother came within range of him he belted him.

"Please Sir. I won't do it ever again." He pleaded with the irate brother still pursuing the other boy. Why did he not move out of the way I could not understand. He must have been petrified with fear or plain stupid.

I had a bird's eye view of all the proceedings from my vantage point high up in a tree.

"I told you not to talk, didn't I?" He stopped and shouted at the boy who was standing in the same spot. Then he gave him another few wallops for good measure and ordered him to join those who had been rounded up.

Now what did he expect the unfortunate boy to do? Remain silent as he walloped him with the dreaded black strap.

Boys hopped and jumped as the brothers belted them on the buttocks and legs.

Apples and pears fell from the trouser pockets of the boys and from under their pullovers as they tried in vain to escape.

One brother made a mad charge after a boy who was trying to evade him and his dreaded black strap. The brother lifted his cassock hem up as high as he possibly could and was after him like *The Proverbial Hairy Man* (a very quick runner)

The brother failed to manoeuvre round some damaged apples on the ground and slipped. He landed with a crash on the path. His pride hurt more than he did.

"Come back here this instant," he called from his humiliating position on the ground.

The boy looked round and hesitated for a moment. Then thought better of it and was off. He had no intention of returning to help the brother to his feet. He knew what the folly of this act of kindness would be.

We could escape as far as the School grounds and no further. The gate leading to the city streets was firmly locked.

I was one of the last to be captured and was duly belted into line with the rest of the rabble.

Finally all the boys were rounded up and accounted for. We were then marched across the grounds to the chapel and dispersed into the seats.

There we sat for some time wondering what would happen to us.

Finally the brother superior came out on the altar and gave us a sermon on the sin of disobedience. He told us that we had condemned our very souls to hell fire. Then on his instructions we knelt and asked God's intervention as we had been tempted by the Devil in the garden.

We prayed for the redemption of our souls and asked God to forgive our iniquities.

More prayers followed before we were once again ordered back out into the grounds. We were pleased with ourselves at getting away so easily after what we had done.

When it came to the end of the day's retreat we thought that we would be kept in late. Much to our surprise we were allowed to go home.

Next day the retreat continued. There were no recriminations from the brothers. This lack of punishment was causing us a lot of anxiety. We would have been happier receiving some form of punishment as was the usual case.

On Friday evening as we were prepared to go home the superior ordered us into the chapel and wasted no time in telling us the bad news.

We would have to continue the retreat into Saturday and Sunday to atone for our sins and to compensate for the loss of the two days.

I understand that this was the first and last time that the retreat was held in the grounds.

There was a sense of satisfaction when the *Holy Joe's* and *Craw Thumpers* were also included in the punishment.

JOHNNY I HARDLY KNEW YOU

How many from the city and county have memories of *The Travelling man.*
He was a regular visitor to the many villages around the city and indeed into
the city itself. Like a ghost he would arrive in a village and vanish just as
mysteriously. They were called travelling men because they never settled in one
place. They were *Jacks of all Trades* but masters of none. They were semi-
skilled in most crafts, from mending a pot, making cans, repairing harness,
curing animals, to entertaining the people with their songs and music. Is it little
wonder that they were in such demand throughout the country?

They usually arrived on a bicycle, sometimes with a trailer attached. The
bicycle would have an attachment for sharpening knifes. Hanging from every
vantage point would be home made tin cans, funnels, milk tins with lids and a
thousand more utensils. If he had not what you required he would make it for
you before evening. He also carried cards on which were pot repair kits. These
consisted of two round pieces of tin and a cork washer. They were used to repair
holes in cans etc. In the centre was a nut and bolt. You would place the washer
and the piece of tin on the inside of the can and thread the bolt through. Then on
the outside place the other piece of tin and tighten the nut on the bolt.

There was many the wedding that started out as a dull affair until the
travelling man arrived and turned it into a real hooley, [a day and night of
entertainment]. Why it was said that when the travelling man started up with his
music and song. Not only did the very birds on the trees forget to go to roost, the
bride and groom refused to go off to the marriage bed.

There are many stories of the travelling men, I relate just the one.

My travelling man was known as '*Johnny I hardly knew you*'. Where he came
from and where he went to was of no concern to anyone but himself as he would
remind the folk.

"Tell us will you and put our minds at ease. Just where do you hail from? I'd
say you are a Galway man from your accent?" He would be prompted.

"Would you ask Jesus who he was and where he came from, if he came to
your village?" He would indignantly evade the question.

"Of course we wouldn't if we knew him. What has that to do with it?"

"You would not know Jesus and he a travelling man like myself. Now there's
the pity."

"Why should we know him no more than we know you?" There were more
questions asked by the travelling man than were answered.

"Of course you would know him. His image is in all your Churches." With
this remark and his raucous laughter he would kill the conversation.

Johnny was not a handsome man but that did not worry him unduly. He lived
a life style that showed he was in easy circumstances. His requirements were

simple, a drink, a shake down for the night and good company. All of which he had an abundance of. He had no wealth to speak of but he had a God given talent in his hands. There was nothing more that he craved for. These men knew more about hardship and hunger than was appreciated by the majority of the people.

'*Johnny I hardly knew you*' was more than a travelling man. He was also blessed with the cure. Better known in other lands as the laying of hands.

With the laying of hands and passing the patient under the belly of an ass he could cure mumps, small pox and many other ailments.

In one village a young farmer by the name of Paul caught the mumps which led to further complications. This was disaster to Paul and his young wife Nora. Not only had she a baby and young son to look after, but being a city girl she was unable as yet to milk the two milch cows and knew absolutely nothing about farming.

Paul had a small farm. About twenty five Irish acres of mixed land. More a small holding than a farm. This he had inherited from his widowed mother after she passed away.

Though small, it was sufficient to support him his wife and two children. Paul's neighbours rallied round to help with the chores and the running of the small farm during Paul's illness.

There was nothing out of the ordinary in this. It was customary for the neighbours to rally round in the time of need in the villages of Ireland.

Poor Paul was not fighting his illness too well. His throat was badly swollen and solid foods were beyond his capability. His wife resorted to feeding him beef tea, a good aphrodisiac when one was convalescing. Not enough to regain one's strength though.

Daily the doctor called. There was little help he could offer. He had done all that his skills allowed.

"How is he doing doctor? Is he getting any better?" His wife asked.

"Nora. I only wish that I could do more for him. I've done all I can. Nature will have to take its course I'm afraid." He would try and comfort her.

She was advised that there was one man who could cure him if anyone could and that was *Johnny I Hardly Knew You.*

"If you don't be minding doctor. I think that I will send for the travelling man." She looked shyly at the doctor.

"You'd be far better leaving him to God and the qualified doctors. Avoid the quacks," he closed his bag and left the kitchen.

Stopping at the front door he turned and looked back at Nora.

If you think that it will cure him any quicker. Then fetch him by all means. Sure it cannot do any harm. It may even do him some good." With that he left closing the door behind him.

Nora let it be known that she had urgent need of Johnny. The message was relayed to all the villages in the neighbouring counties.

It did not take too long for the call for help to reach the ears of Johnny himself. He was repairing the thatch on a cottage in another village at the time.

"I'll have to leave the thatching for a day or two. I must go and see to this poor sick man." He apologised to the owner of the cottage.

Being a charitable man he wasted no time in making his way to the village where Paul and Nora lived.

"Paul love, I have great news. Johnny the travelling man will be here by this evening or tomorrow at the latest." Unable to speak Paul smiled weakly and reached out and took her hand in gratitude.

All day and late into the evening the neighbours watched the road leading into the village anxiously awaiting Johnny.

"We'll go to our beds. He'll not make it this night." With that the neighbours dispersed.

Next morning as the cocks were hailing the early morning and the cows were calling to be milked, Johnny came over the brow of the hill, all his worldly possessions strapped on his back.

"Are my eyes deceiving me? Is that himself that I see coming over the hump backed bridge?" an early riser called to her neighbour.

Both women ran into the centre of the road and shielding their eyes from the morning sun looked down the road.

"It is, It is indeed. It's himself as good as his word. Will you ever run and tell Nora to get Paul ready."

In such a small community it did not take long for the news to spread that Johnny had arrived.

Johnny walked down the Village Street like the *Pied Piper* followed by the whole population and entered the house of Paul and his wife.

He went at once to the sick bed of Paul and established that he had indeed a bad case of the mumps. Leaving his patient he returned to the kitchen where breakfast had been prepared for him. Breakfast over, he called on Paul to leave his sick bed and prepare for the cure.

Though weak and hardly able to walk he got dressed with the aid of Nora.

Johnny called him out of the house and into the stable not far away. He was helped on the short journey by one of the neighbours.

In the stable Johnny took down a set of donkey blinkers. These he put on Paul. Then he led him by the halter to the banks of the stream below the bridge. A donkey had been tied in the middle of the stream on Johnny's instructions.

Halting at the bank of the stream he called on the neighbours to pray. There was no prompting needed. The people had already started the rosary.

Johnny walked into the stream pulling on the halter attached to the blinkers round Paul's face.

The neighbour was still helping Paul. The travelling man ordered him to return to the bank.

Approaching the donkey he passed under his belly still dragging Paul behind him.

As he passed under the donkey he made the sign of the cross and called on Paul to do likewise.

As they emerged out on the other side of the donkey he stroked Paul's head and face several times with his hands. Three times he carried out this operation. Finally he returned to the house followed by the people.

There he removed the blinkers and ordered Paul to dry his feet and return to his sick bed.

The putting on of the blinkers and passing under the belly of the donkey was for the benefit of the neighbours. The cure lay in his hands. The rest was bravado or showmanship.

Whatever one may think or doubt the laying on of hands is a cure as old as time itself. It is practised more to day than it was when I was a boy.

Time passed and the curing of Paul and many others by Johnny was forgotten as were the other skills that he had performed.

One evening as the neighbours were assembled at the cross roads for the harvest dance. A woman sitting on the stone wall of the bridge remarked.

"We have not seen sight or sound of *Johnny I hardly knew you* these past two seasons. I wonder where he got to?" She addressed the folk around her.

"Come to think of it, neither have I." Another remarked.

It was then that they began to wonder what had become of Johnny.

"We did not need his help so we forgot all about him," remarked one old man.

The news soon spread that Johnny had not been seen in the counties for some considerable time.

Time passed and again Johnny was forgotten, that was until a stranger came to the village.

As was the custom the folks were curious to know who he was. What he was doing in their village.

"There is little or no need to worry about me. Sure I'm just passing through," replied the stranger when prompted as to his business.

"Did you ever come across or hear of a travelling man better known as *Johnny I hardly knew you?* He was asked in the course of a conversation over a glass of stout.

"Oh him! You could say that he was known throughout the length and breadth of the land. God rest his soul." The stranger lifted his caubeen [cap] in respect.

"You don't mean to say that he is dead." The glasses were laid back on the counter.

"He is dead alright poor soul." He was found stiff as an ash plant under a blackthorn bush near Clonmacnoise."

"God be with himself. If ever there was a gentleman he was one. I owe a lot to that man." Paul shook his head.

"Well! You'll not need to repay him now. He has got his reward." The stranger looked across at Paul.

"Whatever do you mean he got his reward?" The men were anxious for a full explanation.

He was buried in the old churchyard at Clonmacnoise with the saints and kings of Ireland. A fitting end for such a fine gentleman wouldn't you agree?"

"We'll all drink to that. There was no finer man than *Johnny I hardly knew you*. The glasses were raised in a final salute to Johnny.

"Seeing that you know so much about him. Would there be any harm in asking just what was his real name? Where did he come from?"

"His name is it? Sure I was of the impression all along that you knew his name."

Stories like these were told around the turf fires during the long winters' evenings in my young days. This story is true as are the other stories I tell in my books.

Yet in parts they are like the stories and legends of Ireland. Half truth and half compliment to others.

People today may wonder what need was there for the travelling men. To the farming communities they were a God send and a necessity.

These people did not have a lot to give. Yet they were generous to a fault when it came to being charitable to others. They were not wretched souls as some may imagine. They owned the highways and byways and were beholding to no one.

Johnny had a silver tongue that could tell a tale or sing a song that seemed to go on forever. He was not one from the learning class but he had more stories and knowledge in his old head than many the Jesuit scholar.

In all the wonderful yarns and tales he told he never lied or so he claimed.

"It's as true as I'm sitting here. Would I lie to you?" he would open his hands in mock innocence and smile.

Johnny I hardly knew you Could cure others yet he could not cure himself'.

BLESS ME FATHER FOR I HAVE SINNED

It is said that idle hands are the Devils own workshop. Would this apply in the house of God I wonder?

One afternoon as the Gang sat on the river wall outside the parish church awaiting afternoon confessions. The debate turned to the role of the Priest. We discussed the Priests power in the matter of Birth, Marriage and Death. Then in the course of the conversation we turned our attention to the Priest's role in the confessional.

"I for one think that the Priest just sits in his box half asleep. He dishes out punishment according to his mood." I told them.

"What a thing to say about the Priest. You should wash your mouth out." Came a quick retort.

"The Priest is guided by God. That is why he always wears the sacred scroll around his neck when he is hearing confessions," another contradicted.

"If I were a Priest I would make all you blackguards suffer. I'd punish you all by making you to go to Mass every morning for a week at seven o'clock sharp and no messing about," I warned them.

"How many would be seen at your confessional if you done that, tell us? You're talking a lot of Cods wallop and you know it." The conversation was getting deeper and more intense by the minute. It was a true saying that politics and religion should never be discussed as it only leads to arguments.

"By the way you talk, nobody would go next or near to you for Mass, let alone confession. Then what would you do?"

"The Irish are not like that. They would accept whatever punishment that I gave them because it was given by God through me to them." I stuck to my convictions.

"In a bull's foot they would. If you are all that positive why don't you prove it then?" My pals were getting irate.

"Don't talk daft. How can I prove anything? I'm not a Priest in case you haven't noticed."

"Well there is the Church and inside are the confessionals boxes. You go in and see how far you will get."

"You are not suggesting that I go into the Church and hear confessions? Not in a million years. I'd get shot if they found out."

"We thought so, talk is cheap. It was you who put out the challenge not us." One lad jumped off the wall followed by the others and went towards the Church. I sat alone on the wall for a short time before I too jumped off and crossed the road and into the church. Entering the church I took the holy water and blessed myself before joining my pals in the back seat.

"Now is your chance to try it out. There's nobody about." The boy next to me nudged me and pointed to the confessional box.

"You think that I wouldn't, don't you?" We both looked at each other and giggled.

"You just watch this." I got up from my seat and crossed the floor to the confessional. Taking a good look round the church to ensure that it was empty, apart that is from my mates. I entered the Priest's section in the centre. Closing the door behind me I sat down on the red plush seat. When I had settled down I opened the curtain slightly and looked out at my mate and waved to him. He waved back and giggled. Then he got up from his seat and came across and entered the right hand confessional. I opened the slide covering the grill dividing us from each other and looked out at him. I was always of the impression that the Priest could not identify the person in the box. To my utter surprise I could see him and recognise him clearly. After a few moments of play acting between us he got up and left the box. I got up from the priest's seat and came out of the box as fast as my legs could carry me.

"I bet that you were frightened to death in there." My pal nudged me. We thought it was a great spoof. To be honest I felt like a real hero having carried out such a daring challenge.

"Don't be so stupid. I had you sussed all the time. I knew that it was just a game." I did not want to let him know just how scared I really was.

"What do you mean a game? I was as scared as you." He looked at me amazed.

"Go on pull the other one. It has bells on it," I told him. I reached out my leg to him.

If I had thought that this was the end of my little escapade then I had a surprise coming to me. The rumour went round that I had been hearing confessions all over the place. Like all rumours it started out innocently enough and finished up a major catastrophe for me. Finally the rumour reached the ears of the Brothers and from there to the Priest. On hearing the story as told they had no intention of treating it as a childish prank. It was inevitable that I would find myself before my ecclesiastical masters at some time and now was as good a time as any. Mother was none too pleased either with me when she found out just what prank I was up to.

"Oh God pity me. Only you know what I have to suffer with him." She pointed to me as she prayed.

I saw no reason for her to go to all the trouble of pointing me out to God. He must have known of me by now.

"Out of all my children. You sent me him as a punishment Are you listening to me?" She looked across at me.

"I am Ma! I am really." I replied.

"Not you. You demon. I'm talking to God. Why I don't know? With you I should be talking to the Devil. God and his blessed mother forgive me." This was a bit harsh I thought. I was not all that bad.

"Hearing confessions, rising the dead. No! No! No! I cannot, I just cannot, God forgive me but I'll kill him. Get out of my sight before I forget myself and do something that I'll regret." She pointed to the door. There was no real need for all the theatricals. I got off easy with her. She did not give me the thrashing that I had expected. I had to report to the brother. He believed that I had heard a confession. Not only had I flown in the face of God, I had committed a grievous mortal sin. No punishment would be severe enough.

The outcome was that I was called before the Brother Superior who asked me about my little escapade. I explained that it was just a prank. All I done wrong was to sit in the priests seat in the confessional. He looked at me and wondered why I had not been struck down dead for my sins. Then he proceeded to give me a good belting with the black strap.

That night I cried myself to sleep, my tears once again on my pillow. I should have considered myself lucky. I could have been sent to one of the reformatories run by the Christian Brothers. Why was the whole world against me and my poor dog. Why did everyone doubt me?

STOP THEM TWO COWS WHILE I COUNT THEM

Most of the boys in the city took it upon themselves to find the odd job that would give them the few pence needed to get into the cinema. In some cases to buy five Woodbine cigarettes better known as *Coffin Nails.*

One venue not to be missed was the weekly cattle market. It was there that the drovers would reluctantly part with a few pence to any boy willing to mind the cattle or sheep. They wanted to *wet their whistles* in the nearest public house and were only too glad of the help.

It was usually the farmer's who purchased the cattle and sheep at Fitt's or Sexton's auction. They then made a deal with a drover to deliver the animals to their respective farms.

In my young days all cattle were delivered to the farms on the hoof. That meant that they were walked from the market to the farms. On one occasion my brother and I approached a drover who had a small herd of cattle bunched in a corner. We knew from the anxious way he was looking around him that he needed help.

"Do you want the cow's looked after Mister?" I called over to him.

"I do indeed. That is if we can strike a reasonable bargain. I'm not all that flush," (meaning that he could not afford much.) We were used to them putting on the poor mouth. Tell me what farmer doesn't?

"Just how long do you want them minded for?" I asked of him.

"Oh not more than an hour or two at the most." This could mean anytime.

"Tell you what. Make it sixpence each and we will forget the time limit."

"I doubt if I'll need the two of you. They are very docile animals as you can see." He pointed his stick towards the cattle. They eyed him back suspiciously.

"Sorry Mister. It's the two of us or the deal is off." I told him.

"God, but you Limerick boys strike a hard bargain. I got two boys in Cork last week for half what you are asking."

"Far away fields are green. If the Cork boys want to work for nothing then that's up to them." I told him.

"Alright then. Mind that you take good care of them and don't lose any." He handed me the ash plant and made his way down the road.

"Leave them to us. They are as safe with us as in God's pocket," I shouted after him. He waved back to acknowledge that he had heard me. We stood guard over the cattle for some time. He was right they were no trouble at all. This was where the problem started for us.

The cattle were so quiet and docile that we relaxed our vigilance and began to chat with some of our mates who were looking after another herd.

"Here! Didn't you have more cattle than that?" It was one of our mates coming down the field having relieved himself remarked.

"Bloody hell! Where have they got to? Them scuttering cattle never stay where you put them." I replied without thinking or looking.

"Look! There they go." Brendan saw the rear end of a cow enter a pen in the yard and join other cattle.

"Come on, we had best get them back before the drover returns. Did you see exactly where they went?"

"Yea! You cannot miss them. Look at them, they're in that pen over there." He pointed to a pen some distance away.

"Right! Let's round them up with the others. The drover should be back soon, I hope."

We rounded up the two beasts in the pen and returned them to the herd that we were guarding. From then on we watched the herd diligently until we finally we saw the drover returning He staggered up the road taking both sides in his stride. We could see that he had a skin full.

"Are they alright? They were no problem were they?" He looked bleary eyed at the cattle.

"We'll have the sixpence each now Mister and be off home. It's getting late you know." I reached out my hand.

Reaching deep into the pocket of his breeches he withdrew a handful of coins and picked out two sixpence pieces and begrudgingly handed them to me. I put the two coins in my pocket and began to walk away.

"Didn't you forget something?" He called after me.

"Forget what? There are your cattle and I gave you your ash plant. What more do you want?"

"Wha! Wha what about the luck penny then?" He stuttered as he staggered and held his hand out and spat on it.

"Luck penny! What is that?" I asked as he swayed from side to side.

"Ev, Ever every one give gives a luck penny so they do, where I come from," he let off a series of farts that could be heard half way to Cork.

"Not in Limerick they don't. We'll say a prayer for you anyway." I walked away.

"Pra pray for me. Wha. What are you fecking talk talkin about. Play pray for yourselves you Fecking pair of skin flints."

He staggered back to where we had left the herd of cattle. He looked the herd up and down and then tried counting them. He stopped counting and scratched his head.

"Hi! Here hi you's two, come back you two fec feckers. Wha when oh shit where did all them cattle come from? I never left you with all them did I?" He looked befuddled at the herd of cattle.

"They are the same cows that you asked us to look after. What's the matter with you? Too much to drink, that's your problem." I looked at the herd. They looked the same to me.

"Drunk! Dri drunk Who's drunk? Will, will you for feck sake look at them, for Go Go God's sake. What bloo bloo bloody sch school do you go to." He spluttered as he pointed at the herd who by now were looking anxiously at him.

"Are you taking the eye sight out of my head? You pa pai pair of Caff caffl Gob shi shit shites. The farmer bought fi fiv five beasts. I'm sure of that. Now we have seven or eight. Where the hell did the other two, one, two, three come from?" He wiped the spittle forming on his mouth and removing his cap scratched his head.

"Did anyone of them have a calf in the meantime?" Brendan asked.

"What sort of smart ar ars ars Gob shites are you two. You'll ca caf calf if I go back there and sho shuv shove this stick up your arse? Where did you get them them feck fec feckin fecking animals from? There are no cal calvs calves here. Why don't you two frek feckers 'f' off." Taking his cap from his head he threw it on the ground and stamped on it. Brendan's suggestion brought a string of curses from the drover which I refrain from printing.

"Look Mister. Perhaps in the excitement of the moment you forgot to count them right. Ask the farmer when you get there he will know?" I suggested.

"Wha ! Wha! What do you mean ask the farmer? Wha wha what kind of a smart ars arse are you anyway? If the other tooo to two are not his then what will I do?" He spluttered.

"Well you could wait until the others return. Perhaps they will know who owns them. Cattle don't just drop out of the sky you know. Anyway we are off home."

We left the puzzled drover still scratching his head and looking befuddled at the cattle

When we got some distance down the road I stopped my brother.

"Just how many cattle did you say strayed into the auction pens?" I asked.

"I don't know. I saw the last one go in and presumed that they were all his."

"It looks as if he has two extra cows at the moment. I'm sure that someone will eventually claim them. Still that is not our problem. Is it?"

THE DEAD AROSE

Funerals and wakes were always treated with dignified respect for the bereaved and the family. It was not uncommon to see a funeral going through the city consisting of the hearse and one black carriage containing the mourners. This was a basic funeral and all that the family could afford to provide. The payment for which would be met on weekly terms. This debt they would be paying off for several years. Sometimes overlapping a new funeral. There was seldom a Priest at these funerals. There was no money available for his services. Thus the saying in the city...............

'High Money, High Mass
Low Money, Low Mass
No Money, No Mass.'

As the lonely and sparse funeral reached William Street corner men walking along the footpath on seeing the poor funeral would take it upon themselves to fall in behind the hearse. As more and more men joined the cortège, the funeral would get longer and longer. When asked why they joined the funeral of someone they never knew the answer was invariable the same.

"Just to make it a little more respectable. You know what I mean?" We all knew what this simple charitable act meant to a lonely widow.

Some doors down from where we lived a tragic accident happened to a member of the family. The person had drowned in the Shannon and his body was trapped in the Curragower Falls. Although the entire family have long since emigrated I feel it would be disrespectful even after all this time to mention names. There was the usual wake in the house. The front door was left open wide as a sign of welcome. Those wishing to pay their last respects and condolences to the family were encouraged to enter. To say a prayer in order that they may not go to their maker with only hungry prayers were appreciated.

On the table lay food and a few drinks, refreshments for the mourners.

Upstairs the corpse was laid out on the bed in the usual manner.

The four brown candles had been placed at the foot and head of the bed. This to represent four angels in mourning. Women knelt round the bed. Repeating over and over again the rosary and the prayers for the dead. Two pennies covered the dead man's eyes. It was said that the pennies from a corpse held a special cure. Every so often some of the women would get up and leave only to be replaced by others. The dead were never left alone, this was an old Irish custom to prevent evil spirits entering and stealing the soul.

It was taken and understood that all the immediate neighbours and their families would call to pay their last respects. Not to do so would be taken as an affront not easily forgiven or forgotten.

As I finished my homework I put my books in my satchel and made a move for the door.

"Just where are you off to now?" Mother looked up from unravelling an old pullover she was recycling. The best parts she would make into a pair of stockings or part of a F*airisle* pullover. The wool had been knit and unravelled and reknit so often that any warmth there had been in it had long since expired.

"Just going to see my mates. I won't be too long." I promised.

"Don't forget to call into the wake. Make sure that you are seen. We don't want anyone talking, now do we?"

"Do I really have to go? You've been and the rest of the family have been. I'll only get in the way."

"Don't ever let me hear you talk like that again. The very idea, you're getting too big for your boots my lad. Now get on with you." As she spoke she picked up the poker but only to riddle the fire.

"Leave that dog of yours here. You are going to a wake, Do you hear?"

"Alright! I'll call in on my way down. Then we're going on down the Quarry Road." I waited for her answer before I closed the door and left. I entered the front door of the house. There was no excuse for me entering the parlour. This was reserved for adults to partake of the refreshments and to offer their condolences. The purpose of my visit was to be seen and to say a prayer.

I went up the stairs to where the corpse lay on the bed. As I entered the room he appeared to be looking out the door. Two pennies covered his eyes I wondered if they buried the corpse with the pennies. I would take a look the next time there was a burial. If they did then they were bound to be brought to the surface as they opened the grave for a new burial. His hands were not crossed, they were joined as in prayer. A Rosary beads had been entwined in his fingers.

The women took little notice of me as I entered the room. Having said a few *Hail Mary's* I began to rise to my feet when I saw a white rope under the edge of the bed. Looking further I noticed that it was attached to the ring of a heavy potato weight. The rope went up under the mattress of the bed and disappeared into the bed.

This caught my interest and I held the end in my hand and pulled it. Nothing happened. I looked across at the women, they were too intent on praying to take notice of me. Sliding down the side of the bed I saw that the rope came out the other side of the bed. This end was tied to the ring of another potato weight. I crawled under the bed to where the rope was attached to the weight. Perhaps it was childish curiosity, or devilment or both. As I could not fathom out why the ropes were tied I released one end. The rope ran freely through the ring of the weight and vanished under the bedclothes.

"Oh Jesus, Mary and Joseph help us." I heard some of the women call out. Others started to scream. Hearing the commotion. I jumped up only to bang my head on one of the coach bolts holding the springs taunt. As I rubbed my head in the confined space I saw women's feet running towards the door. Coming out from under the bed I saw one woman holding the corpse down. Others were leaving the room in a hurry. Whatever was going on?

Before I could absorb all that was happening around me several men entered the room. I decided to take refuge under the bed. Something tragic must have happened. I was worried that they might blame me, as I was always swimming in troubled waters.

"Come out of there you skuttering Git"! A man's face appeared from the bedside. He looked really angry.

I sat where, I was crouched only to be pulled out by the hair of my head.

When I came out I saw two men settling the corpse back on the bed. Why would they be making the bed for a corpse, after all, he was dead? What was all the commotion about and why were they blaming me. The man drowned, I didn't kill him?

The corpse was in a sitting position on the bed. The two men and a woman were settling him back in a prone position. I did not see the pennies on his eyes. I felt frightened. I caught a glimpse of the rope across the chest of the corpse. They were covering it with a sheet. Another was under the bed adjusting the rope.

"What were you doing in there? Have you no sense?" The man held me as he pointed under the bed and at the same time clouted me around the head.

"I saw the rope and opened it. I didn't know I was doing any harm, I'm sorry." I did not understand what all the excitement was about.

"Do you know that if you had any more wit you'd be an Amadan." The man shook me like a mongrel.

"Did anyone of you see the pennies?" A woman asked.

"Don't tell me that the little caffler stole them." The man looked at me and then began searching my pockets.

"Will you take him out of here and do that elsewhere. Can't you see he's causing the widow distress." The widow was lying over the body moaning. I wondered was she moaning or was it the corpse.

I was taken down the stairs and out the door and into the house next door.

"Because you were such a *Nosy Parker* we very nearly had another death on our hands. What's wrong with you anyway?" Before I could give any explanation or excuses I was given another belting.

"You should think yourself lucky, you whelp. You were nearly the cause of the poor widows death." Another slapping followed.

"As if she hasn't enough on her plate to contend with. God I could swing for you, you little fart." Another shouted into my face before twisting my ear and slapping me in the face.

What I failed to realise at the time was that man had been drowned in the Shannon and his body was in a crouched position when they found him. It was the widow's wish that the bones should not be broken in order to straighten the corpse. Ropes were used to hold the corpse flat on the bed instead. When I released the ropes the corpse sat up in the bed. That was what mother explained later that this was the reason why the cords were around the body. Why then were they so quick to blame me, I thought.

Anyone would think that it was my fault that the corpse moved, I was told that what I had done was unforgivable. I was also accused of stealing the pennies, which I didn't. Eventually they found them in the bed but nobody apologised to me. As a matter of fact I was ostracised from the community.

When mother heard it she was not surprised but she was in shock and had no sympathy at all for me.

I told her that they beat me she said that I didn't get enough and gave me another belting. I was beginning to feel sorry for praying for the soul of the corpse.

"Where in the name of God did I get you from anyway? You can't even go to a simple wake without something happening. How in God's holy name could anything go wrong at a wake? How do you do it? Are you possessed by a Devil, or something? How in the name of Jesus can I face them at the funeral I to morrow I just don't know?" She went on and on as she looked daggers at me. I thought she was over reacting and that there was no need to take the Holy name in vain.

"Don't you dare go next or near the funeral to morrow. You'll only cause more trouble, How I don't know but I know you would. Go! Go wherever you will but keep away from that house. Do you hear me? Take you and that bloody dog out of my sight." Bruno looked up at me wondering why his name was mentioned.

That night I cried tears into my pillow because I felt that I was not understood.

The widow woman crossed the street for weeks after when she saw me coming.

What they failed to realise was that it had frightened me too. Not alone did I cry tears into my pillow that night, I also saw the dead man in my dreams.

I never did find any pennies in the graveyard, I came to the conclusion that the holy Joe's kept them themselves for their cures.

Who cared for my feelings?

THE PERFIDIOUS PAIR

At the cross roads leading to the west and north of Limerick city, the construction Corps had built Pill boxes, block houses and machine gun dugouts. The purpose of these was to defend the city should the enemy, whoever they may be, attack from the north Clare side of the city. These defences may have seemed adequate to whoever planned them. One wondered if they had ever seen a map of Limerick or had ever visited the city before they built them? Not more than fifty yards down the strand was another road leading over Thomond bridge. This also connected with the Clare road. All the potential enemy had to do was to take this road and avoid the defences.

The time came to test the defences of the city in case the need should arise. The day of the manoeuvres dawned bright and cheerful. Soldiers in full battle order took up defensive positions along the Ennis Road. The pillboxes, block houses and machine gun nests were now occupied by fully armed soldiers instead of courting couples. Sandbag traps were laid in a chicane down the centre of the road. The purpose of which was to delay the enemy advance. This upset the daily lives of the citizens. More so to the people of Clare who vented their anger at the Irish soldiers.

"Well bad cess to the amadan who put them bags across the road," declared a Clare man. He tried to get his stubborn ass and cart laden with a churn of milk for the Stella restaurant in the city.

"Get on you lazy hoor of an ass. Whoever done this is more stupid than you." He belted the unfortunate animal across the back with his ash plant.

Milk splashed from the top of the urn and landed on him as the ass bucked in retaliation. Some minutes later the man came upon a soldier standing in the road covered in branches.

"Are you responsible for all this?" He looked across from his cart at the soldier. The soldier waved him on. The Clare man was not to be deterred.

"Will you come out from there, you're fooling no one. Least of all me. Sure I can see you". He waved his ash plant at the soldier. The donkey approached the soldier and smelt him. Then he began to chew his camouflage. The soldier shooed the donkey away and stood at the far side of the road.

The ass refused to go through the chicane of sandbags. Shying backwards he tilted the cart and upset the churn of milk.

"I'll have the guards on the lot of you," he jumped off the cart and led the reluctant ass through the chicane.

"I will, I'll have the guards on to the lot of you. You'll see." He shouted as he dragged the reluctant ass through the chicane.

"A decent man cannot make an honest day's living without some fools making a bigger idiots of themselves than what they are already." He jumped on his straw seat and gave the ass another belt on the backside with his ash plan.

"If you lot had as much wit as you have now you'd all be half wits and in the mad house in Limerick. Gob Shites all of you and that's for sure." With this mouthful he settled back on the cart. The soldiers began to cheer the unfortunate man on his way.

"Whoa! Whoa!" He pulled the reins to stop the ass. Jumping off the cart he returned to the group of soldiers teasing him.

"And what's more, if you don't know where the mad house is I'll tell you. It's in Mulgrave Street. You'll be in good company there with your own." He returned to his cart. Again he walloped the poor ass. The ass again kicked his hind legs in protest and shook the Clare man off his seat.

"There's no use in you blaming me for them Amadans," he spoke to his donkey as he tried to calm the excited animal.

"You should listen to your donkey. At least he has an ounce of sense. More than we can say for you." The soldiers derided the poor man.

"And if soldiers like you are all that the Free State has to offer then God save Ireland." The Clare man replied in defiance.

"And if wit were shit you'd be constipated." A soldier shouted back.

Moaning to his donkey he continued his journey to Limerick.

By this time we had journeyed out past Cardavon to where we saw a convoy of lorries parked in a boreen. Apart from a few sentries the rest of the soldiers were standing about in groups in a field at the cross. Others were busy cooking a meal over turf fires. We knew that the soldiers would have chocolate. This was a scarce commodity in the city.

"Got any chocolate or sweets?" We begged of the soldiers.

"Tell you what son. You tell us where the soldiers in Limerick are and I'll let you have your bar of chocolate." Reaching into the pocket of his tunic he produced the coveted bar .Was this soldier really asking two patriotic sons of Ireland to betray their city for a bar of chocolate? He was and he knew well that we would tell him all we knew. Anyhow we knew that it was all a game.

"I suppose you boys know Limerick well?" He tapped his ruby leggings with his cane as he awaited our reply.

"Like the back of our hands, Sir. We know every nook and cranny of the place." We reached out our hands for the coveted chocolate.

"Where would you like to go? We'll show you the way." We were eager to get a ride in the army lorry.

"No place really. We would like to know where the other soldiers are in the city." He pointed to a map laid out before him.

We didn't really understand the map but we were able to tell him where we had seen the soldiers in the dug outs and pillboxes.

Oh the treachery of it all. Had we no shame? Selling our beloved city for a bar of *Frys* chocolate?

For our co-operation we were allowed to share in the meal and given the bar of chocolate and a slab of Cleeves toffee. On our way back to the city we occasionally stopped to smash the toffee against the walls. This to make it more manageable to chew. At the Union cross we stopped at the city boundary marking. This is made of cast iron with the city coat of arms and the twin towers. Finding two new stones we knocked off the stones someone else had placed there and replaced them with our own lucky stones. As we crossed the road we saw soldiers in a garden manning a machine gun.

"You'd better watch out there. The soldiers from Cork are coming to get you lot." We offered this advice to the soldiers.

"Get away from here before I give you a clout around the ear." A soldier shouted from a hole in the ground covered in branches.

"Did you know your face is all black?" I shouted at him as we left. He had camouflaged his face to suit the situation.

There was gratitude for you. We had told them about the enemy and they were in no way grateful. At least we got a feed and sweets from the others.

At the Strand we washed our hands and sticky mouths in the horses' trough. Then we took up a good viewing position on the river wall. After some time the enemy came into view. They were met by a hail of blank gunfire from the encampments.

Umpires came forward and pointed out the soldiers that had been supposedly killed. They also pointed out what advantage had been gained and lost. The battle raged all day backwards and forwards along the Ennis road.

We cheered and shouted from our vantage point. That was until an officer chased us off the wall. The enemy failed to capture Sarsfield Bridge. Finally the umpires decided that the enemy must retreat back out the Ennis road. Then came a lull, which lasted for some time. We wondered if it was all over and were ready to go home. Then it happened. Down the road came row after row of soldiers in full battle dress, each one with a rifle and fixed bayonet. In front was an officer with his revolver drawn encouraging his men to advance. From their mouths came roars the likes of which would awaken the dead in St Lawrence's cemetery. We leapt from the wall and made for the safety of the wall opposite.

The Limerick Garrison fought bravely, but were forced, by sheer weight of numbers, to retreat across the Shannon River. It was there that the manoeuvres finished.

We doubted very much if our betrayal had any impact on the result.

THE HAND OF THE LORD HAS TOUCHED ME

Swimming was one of our favourite past times. We spent every available moment of the summer learning new swimming and diving techniques.

There were no swimming pools provided by the corporation or by any other body. I presume that they were of the opinion that we had enough water around us in the mighty river Shannon. We did have a swimming baths of sorts. This consisted of a long concrete platform on the banks of the river Shannon at Kings Island Bank.

It's one advantage was that the men could dress and undress behind the concrete wall. This afforded some semblance of privacy although they were in full view to all and sundry on the *Distillery* side of the river.

Shame and privacy was of no concern to us. We had the whole river to ourselves. When the urge came we stripped off and went skinny dipping or swimming in the nude.

On free days in the Summer months we would gather at the Long pavement outside Killeely.

Once there we would cross the old railway line. This was built many years before by the Germans when they constructed the power station at Ardnacrusha. The line was abandoned after the completion of the power station. Now it lay rusting and deserted with trees and briars growing through it.

It is here that there is a sandy beach called *The Point*. Most of the boys went swimming in It's safe waters.

I and a few Stalwarts were fairly good strong swimmers. We would take to the river and swim to the lucrative orchards of the clergy and the gentry on the other side at *Corbally*.

Our first task was to retrieve our hessian sack from its hiding place. Then swim to the far bank and help ourselves to the finest apples and pears in the county.

Should we ever be discovered, and we were on more than one occasion, then all we had to do was dive into the river and escape to the far bank.

It was always worth the swim to the orchards. The fruit was so succulent that a bee could fly through an apple from the orchards in five seconds flat.

We never had any problems disposing of the fruit. Then we had the added bonus of the green houses. In them grew the luscious peaches and other tropical fruits hanging in bunches from the walls. Along the brick walls grew Damsons, Plums, Pears and Greengages. These orchards were indeed the gardens of Eden.

The full sack was easily transported across the river. We used it as a buoy and paddled back using our legs only.

The fruit we sold to the various stall holders throughout the city for the few pence we needed to gain access to the local cinema. Annie Rice had her stall at the corner of Denmark Street where she traded in fruits from the orchards and food from the seas. She would let you have a few coppers for a sack full of eating apples or pears.

On one occasion a new boy asked if he could swim across to the orchards with us.

"We're not going to-day. There's someone working in the orchards. Perhaps next time," I told him.

Some days later the same boy saw me going into the water with my sack over my shoulder.

"You're going over to day. Can I come this time please?" he begged.

"Can you swim far? It's farther than it looks if you must know. There's the current to take into consideration. That could take you well past the metal bridge." This is the iron railway bridge across the Shannon.

"I'm a real good swimmer. You ask anyone." He looked around seeking someone to confirm his story.

"Oh come on then. I have no time to look for your references." I waded into the water my sack tied round my waist. He followed.

We both swam upstream against the tide before finally reaching the shallows. I pointed to a gap in the clearing giving us clear access to the orchards.

"Oh God help me. I'm being pulled down." I looked around annoyed with his shouting and splashing.

"Will you stop your fooling about and shut up it's not funny. Someone will hear you."

"I'm drowning honest I am. Oh Good Jesus I'm truly sorry for my sins. Please help me." He floundered and splashed in the water. This was a new experience for me as I had never encountered a drowning person before. I swam across to him as he splashed and panicked in the water.

"I thought you told me that you could swim? I told you that it was a long way but no you had to prove yourself." I swam in circles around him.

"It's the long weeds, they're pulling me down," he gasped as he paddled with his hands and swallowed copious amounts of water.

"Is that what all this is about? You're just a coward. Sure they are only water Iris. They won't do you any harm." All that shouting because a couple of weeds tickled his toes.

"Come on then. You swim beside me until we reach the bank. Its not that far." I swam nearer to him.

He jumped on to my back as soon as I came within reach of him. We were like a couple of frogs mating only I was under the water more often than above it.

I must have swallowed half of the river before I came to the surface spluttering and breathless. I could not shake him off my back as he was clinging to me like a leech.

I rolled over in the water. Somehow I shook him off my back and regained my composure. He came to the surface coughing choking and crying.

"You do that again and I'll drown you myself. Come on we're nearly there." I pointed to the bank a few yards away.

"Please tell my mother I love her," he muttered to me.

"Oh tell her yourself. I don't know where she lives. You've ruined my whole day if you must know." I encouraged him to swim the last few yards to the bank where we lay down exhausted.

He lay on the grass like a corpse, his eyes were fixed on something visible to him alone. His mouth opened and closed like a fish out of water. I went over and touched him, God help him he was as cold as death. Then he recovered somewhat and clutched at a handful of grass.

"Thank God I made it. Never again I promise." Rising he knelt in prayer on the bank as a bubbly foam came out of his mouth.

"What do you mean never again? Just how do you expect to get home? " I pointed to the bank on the other side.

"What all the ways over there. Not on your Nelly you won't catch me in there again."

"Tell me then. How do you intend to get home?" I looked down at him.

"I'm going to give myself up. God gave me a second chance and I'm not going to let him down." He was adamant that God had saved his miserable hide.

"Who's bloody back were you holding on to out there. Did you think that it was St Christopher? For your information it was me in case you forgot." I pointed to my chest.

"I don't care I'm still going to give myself up," he insisted.

Normally I wouldn't bother my arse about a fellow like that. He was not going to give the game away on us.

"Look! I am not about to let you give the game away on us. Tell you what! I'll go and fill my sack and you can float back on it. That way you won't sink."

"What! Are you asking me to offend God again? After all I promised him. Are you stark raving mad or something?" He looked at me as if I were the Devil incarnate.

"Now just you look here. All your mates are over there and so are your clothes. Like it or lump it that is the only way back." As I argued with him I heard someone coming.

"Now you've done it. Someone heard us and is coming to look. Quick hide." We crouched down in the reeds.

"How are you getting along?" It was some of our mates.

"Getting on! This bloody chicken nearly blew the game away."

"Why what has he done? What's wrong with him? He looks alright to us."

"He only wants to make his confession and give up skinning orchards." I mocked.

"So what! Let him here for now. We'll fill our sacks and collect him on the way back."

"Now you wait here until we get back and whatever you do keep quiet and out of sight." I warned him. Off we went to collect the apples and pears from the orchards.

Returning some time later with our ill-gotten gains we found our friend once again on his knees praying.

"Say one for me whilst you are at it," I mocked him.

"You may mock but your day will come." He rose to his feet.

"Tell you something, your day has come." I told him.

"What do you mean?" He looked at me in disbelief.

"Oh come on one of us will swim on each side of you. You can hold on to the sacks and pray."

We had to frog March the struggling boy into the water. By the way he reacted one would have thought that he had Hydrophobia. He clung to the sacks like shite to a wet blanket all the way back and prayed.

We paddled one each side of him until we reached the point.

"Get your clothes on and never let me see you out here again." I warned him.

With our freedom intact we returned to the city where we sold our ill gotten gains for a few coppers.

We would have enough for the Thomond cinema and a Chester cake.

WAR YEARS

As the war raged on in Europe, we in Ireland, had our own war. Ours was a war of survival. With so many involved it became a matter of the survival of the fittest.

The corporation in their wisdom decided that the citizens should be given adequate protection should the war spread to Ireland. The people of the Strand barracks were notified that on a certain day gas masks would be issued to them free. If it was something for nothing then we would be there. However this advance warning caused a certain amount of panic amongst the prophets of doom.

"Did you hear Kate! We're all doomed. Jesus help us the Germans are coming and are going to gas us all." Our prophet from the next room was sending out her message of doom and gloom.

"I know what it is to be gassed Kate, it's horrible. *Old Spin Ryan* across the square was gassed by the Germans. He told me all about it."

The stories grew by the day until people were looking down the river at each and every boat that came in. There was also the rumour that this was the final message of the Blessed Virgin made to the children at *Fatima. Armageddon!* The end of the world. Nothing could save us. We should make preparation to meet our maker. In the *Peoples Park* the ghost of the hanged man was again seen. The story is told in Limerick that when a major war or disaster is about to occur a man is to be seen hanging on the railings of the park. People went in droves to the park to witness this phenomenon. Mother told us that it was well documented at the time. Signs were seen in the Heavens. The Churches were never so full. (Perhaps this is what we need today to fill them) Even old Balty Dinneen filled sandbags and placed them on his window sill. That was until one fell down one rainy night and nearly killed a passer-by. These craw thumpers had a lot to answer for by driving half the people mad. The great day came and mother assembled us in the square. We waited for the delivery of the gas masks. There we stood like Amadans, waiting for the Local Security Force to come with a lorry load of gas masks.

"The ship bringing them from England must have been sunk by the Germans. Oh! Heaven help us we are now at the mercy of the Hun." It was the prophet of doom at it again.

"I hope that the Germans don't drop any gas on us until we have got our gas masks. What say you Kate?" These words of wisdom were a great comfort to us all.

"Will you tell me Mary what are they like. Would they fit over my shawl?"

"Would what fit over your shawl, a Hun is it? You'd make better use of him inside your shawl I'm sure of that." This brought on a peal of laughter that could be heard across the Shannon. It also relieved a tense situation.

"How would I know, I never saw a gas mask. Why don't you ask one of the old soldiers? They should know." Mary's friend was not at all helpful.

"I'll go and ask old Spin Ryan. He's standing over there by the gate." Spin Ryan got his name from the way he walked. He had been shot and gassed in the war. An old war wound had crippled his leg to the extent that when he walked it spun. There were many perhaps too many disabled veterans from the first war who had different disabilities. There was no disrespect in calling them by their nicknames and none taken.

"What gives you the idea that the Germans will bomb us? What about Churchill? Dev refused to let him use our ports. He has an axe to grind with us."

"Use the bit of common sense that God gave you. How could he bomb us? Our men over there would kill the hoor if he tried."

All speculation stopped as finally an army lorry came through the gates. This must have been a very important lorry indeed. In the back were members of the Local Defence Force in uniform wearing steel helmets and carrying rifles. If the corporation were intent on putting the fear of God into the people then they were making a good job of it. The lorry was driven to the centre of the square where it stopped. The tailgate was dropped down and two members of the defence force jumped off the back and stood either side of the truck.

"God Masie. I know we have a bad reputation but we'd never think of stealing an army lorry. Would we?" Molly sniggered behind her shawl.

More soldiers came from the lorry. Small cardboard boxes were piled up on the tailgate.

"Gather round, gather round. We have to show each and everyone of you how to protect yourselves," the soldiers called. The driver and his companion joined the others.

We formed in a circle as they unloaded the cardboard boxes from the back of the lorry.

"In the event of an air raid or an invasion the various factory sirens dotted around the city will sound. He placed his thumbs in the button holes of his top pocket.

"Now before I issue you with these valuable gas masks. I will show you how to fit them and adjust them. This is most important in order to keep the gas from getting into your lungs."

He reached into the big cardboard box and from it removed a smaller box that had a string handle.

"Now you, Sir! Please step forward." He pointed to a young man standing at the front of the circle.

"Who me! There's no use in you calling me out. I'm off to England tomorrow."

"Good luck to you young man. When you get there you will see that everyone has to carry one of these." He held up the box.

"Alright Mam, would you mind?" The woman he had selected removed her shawl from her head and giggled.

"Over here now and don't be shy, it's for your own good." By this time he had the box open and was holding up the rubber facemask. The young woman stood before him as he held the mask over her face. He placed the mask against her face. With it on she looked like a monster from outer space.

"You look much improved already, keep it on Moll." A smart arse called.

"This is no time for flippancy young man, just pay attention will you please. You will notice that the straps are loose at present." He held out the white tapes at the back for all to see.

"It's of little use like this. They must be adjusted until the mask fits the face snugly. He removed the mask from her face and adjusted the straps before he once again placed it over the woman's face. As she moved her eyes she looked like a fish in a bowl.

"Now the crucial test is this." He held the cardboard box tightly against the breathing grill.

The woman in a panic began waving her arms in the air. Her eyes vanished behind a cloud of misted glass. She was trying desperately to remove the offending mask.

"This is a real good fit as you can see." The man held tightly on to her keeping the cardboard box close to the breathing grill. The poor woman was having a fit as she tried to breathe. She looked in real need of help as she slumped to her knees.

"Will you take that f****** thing off the woman. What are you trying to do, murder her?"

A hero from the crowd stepped forward and grabbing the man pushed him aside. The box fell to the ground and we could see the mask swell and deflate as she filled her lungs. The man stepped froward once again and removed the offending mask.

"How do you feel Mam? You are bound to feel a bit claustrophobic the first time. You'll soon get used to it." The woman rose unsteadily from the ground and retrieved her shawl. Regaining her composure she threw the shawl back down on the ground and taking a deep breath she landed a punch to the side of his face that would do justice to a heavy weight boxer.

"God forgive you. You brute, you fecking bastard, you tried to kill me." She staggered around the yard holding her throat and rubbing her eyes. Then falling to the ground she gasped and with her legs in the air, not becoming of a lady.

Her eyes were filled with tears as she looked up from where she lay gasping for breath and calling the curse of Jesus on the poor mans soul.

"I would rather die from the gas than in that yoke. Take it away from me. You ignorant fecking bastard, you wait until my old man gets home. He'll make mince meat of you so he will. You tried to murder me, so you did, you fecking sadist" She threw the precious gas mask across the square.

However his patience paid off. He was a real diplomat for in the end he had us all trying them on. He told us that there were air raid shelters off Nicholas Street and that we should use them in the event of any air raids.

"Would we have time to get that far before the bombs landed?" One woman wanted to know.

"You could if you could run like *The Hairy Man,*" another wit promised as she laughed out loud.

Her question was a logical one, considering that Nicholas Street was some miles away. Nobody it would seem was taking the matter seriously.

"Well no! I doubt it. Then you could always find a cellar and use that or go under the table."

"There's ten of us. I doubt very much if we'd all fit under our table. We haven't enough room to sit at it as it is." Came another excuse.

"Perhaps the fishermen would oblige and take you across in one of their boats," he further suggested.

"Perhaps pigs might fly." Came another humorous remark.

"Have you any idea as to when they might drop these bombs and what will they look like?" Came another intelligent question.

"What makes you ask such silly questions? They may never drop any. Who said the Germans would do it. What about the English?"

"Shure it doesn't matter who drops what. Does it really matter we will all be killed anyway."

"You speak for yourself, there's a fine cellar in the basement of my Nellies kitchen."

"Would there be room for us in it?"

"You'd need to ask Nelly, she has seven children of her own." As this cross conversation continued the man was getting more annoyed at their lack of concern for their safety.

"It's all right for you to get annoyed mister." We would like to be prepared to meet our maker. Is that not so?" The people agreed with the speaker.

"You all know where the air raid shelters are, don't you?" He continued.

"You should ask the young ones that question. Disgusting places, dens of iniquity. Far worse than *Paddy's Hedge* wouldn't you agree. The money wasted on them would have been better spent on houses." (Paddy's hedge was a isolated boreen used mainly by courting couples on the west side of the keepers cottage at Troy's Lock on the canal.)

"Will there be a Priest in the shelters in case he's needed?" A *Craw Thumper* asked.

"We must go now. We have more masks to issue. Take special good care of them they could save your lives." With these words of wisdom they were aboard the lorry and left the square.

We found our masks great fun. We used them as monster masks when we went out to play. We were the Clay Men attacking Flash Gordon. We tried to use them in the river but we were nearly drowned as they filled up with water. When we got into a scrap, we used them to belt each other with. Others found them handy to start the fire with.

Pill Boxes, blockhouses and air raid shelters were built at all the strategic cross roads leading into the city. These monstrosities were familiar sights around the roads leading to the power station at Ardnachrusha up to a few years ago. These were intended as defensive emplacements in the event of war. They became comfortable courting places. The couples could look out through the slits and watch for their parents or the country parish Priest on the prowl.

To the priest, they were dens of iniquity. To the courting couples, they were a Godsend.

GALILEO

Another occasion and another time we were being taught mathematics by a learned brother. He tried to instil into us the basic principles on the subject being addressed. Having spent some time writing on the large blackboard. He believed that he was making some progress. I was glad that he thought so. I for one didn't have a clue as to what he was writing down or talking about.

"Now explain in simple terms the meaning of Velocity? Turning around he threw the piece of chalk. This was his method of finding a volunteer to come to the head of the class and answer the question. On this occasion I happened to be in the line of fire. Caught unawares, to be honest I was day dreaming. I looked at the blackboard with my mouth open and then at him. I could see by his looks that he expected an intelligent answer. As I did not have one I looked pleading towards the large statue of Christ high on his pedestal for guidance. He looked down at me in sorrow. Perhaps he was in sympathy with me for I could see that he did not know the answer either. Then inspiration came to me in a flash. What was wrong with me? Of course I knew the answer.

"Well Sir. It happened like this," I addressed the class with my hands stuck in my braces. "In the 17th century an Italian mathematician by the name of Galileo took two stones of unequal weight to the top of the tower of Pisa. You know that one that is leaning. There he let them drop to the ground and so proved that all objects fall with equal Velocity." I nodded my head in complete agreement with what I had said, not that I fully understood what I was talking about or what he was doing dropping stones from a tower. There was silence for a moment. I looked around at the brother expecting some form of accolade from him. I expect that he was as puzzled as I was by my brilliant answer and needed a little time for it to register.

"So far so good we want to hear more. What do you know about him?" The good brother folded his arms and with a smile that would do justice to a crocodile he looked me straight in the eyes.

"Galileo Sir. We all know about him don't we?" I looked in trepidation at him as I racked my brain. Then *Eureka* I remembered that I read all about him in the *Encyclopaedia Britannica.* Now was my chance to reveal my learning and my conceit.

"Galileo Sir. He was a mathematician born sometime about 1660 or thereabouts. I'm not too sure of the exact date." I was enjoying myself. I continued "He was the man who discovered the planet *Jupiter* and wrote a book on the universe. He was put in gaol by the Pope, for proving the world was round. You see Sir, the Pope being infallible claimed that the world was flat and....." that was as far as I got. I was lifted some two feet off the floor, by my Cossacks (sideburns) and shook like a rabbit. Before being dropped to the floor.

"How dare you! How dare you! Get up you little sarcastic runt." The brother was standing over me with the dreaded black strap. He was like a *cobra* ready to strike if and when I moved. I felt as if my scalp had been lifted clean off my head. Like a crab I made a sideways move and rose to my feet.

They say that a little knowledge can be a very dangerous thing and on this occasion it was. What possessed me to speak in such a derisory manner about His Holiness? Galileo had to recant his findings, so why should I a schoolboy in Ireland be any exception.

"Is this the learning that you get in the gutters of Limerick? Well is it? Profaning the name of His Holiness. Put out your hand."

I swear I saw the brother grow two feet. He blessed himself with his right hand in which dreaded black strap appeared like a rabbit from a hat.

Leather hit supple flesh four times. Excruciating pain shot up my arm time and time again. Then he called for my left hand where he inflicted the same punishment.

"You will not be going for your bun and bottle of milk to day. Do you understand? Now sit down and in future keep a civil tongue in your head."

To be brutally beaten physically was one thing. To be deprived of one's source of food was a mental scar that time would not obliterate.

It was the next day when we were at break that my mates gathered round me and asked me who this Galileo was. Why had the brother got so irate about him?

"I wish to God that I'd never heard of him. See the trouble he brought on me." I had no love for the great mathematician.

"Tell us anyway. We won't tell a soul. Will we? Why did the Pope put him in jail? We did not know that the Pope had a jail." They looked to one another to confirm that the secret was safe with them. What a fool I was, not alone did I tell them what I knew but I added a bit of spice of my own making. Keeping a secret by them was like trying to capture a fart in a colander.

Now there were plenty of smart Alecs in our city and I was no exception. Inadvertently we brought a lot of punishment on ourselves. A quisling of a rat went behind our backs and reported to the brother. He told him that I was preaching sedition against his Holiness. Once again I was called before the good brother and beaten before he demanded that I should recant.

I felt like Jesus, (perhaps not) I was betrayed by my mates and scourged by Pilot. I was now handed over to Herod. In the form of the brother superior, we all knew just what to expect from him. The man was like a bull in every sense of the word. The very mention of having to appear before made many the boy wet his pants.

"So you will not be told, will you?" He kept shouting at me as he walked up and down the room. Up and down, up and down sweeping the dust from the bare boards with his long cassock. I wished he would get on with the ultimate punishment.

"Bend over the desk." I heard him say.

Panic struck me, what was he about to do? Was this why the boys dreaded being sent to him?

There was to be no escape I done as he ordered. There was a short pause and then a stinging pain.

I was lashed time and time again with a willow cane on my legs. On my bottom and on my back, the pain was far worse. If that were possible than that inflicted by the dreaded Black Strap.

"Let that be a lesson to you. Now get out of my sight." With that I was dismissed and ordered back to my classroom.

In some recess of my mind I felt grateful that he had not deprived me of my bun and bottle of milk.

That hope was soon to be shattered. When the time came for us to go to the shop and have our break. I was told to sit where I was and get on with reading the parables. I would have to forgo my daily ration of food.

I thought to myself that poor Galileo fared worse than I did. Was he not incarcerated in jail? Had the brother had been in a real spiteful mood perhaps I could have been sent to the reformatory at Glin or I could have been sent to the brother's prison at Danagan. Whatever was I thinking? I could show a brave face but my whole being felt that I was an orphan without hope.

That night I lay in my share of the single bed contemplating what my future prospects would be. I could see no light at the end of the tunnel and once again alone in the cold dark room I shed my tears of sorrow and frustration onto my pillow.

OFF THE ICE MAGGIE

During the late winter and early spring we usually got a lot of ground frost. When this occurred we would take ourselves off to the High Road leading from Thomondgate to Killeely. There with buckets of water and brushes we would make a slide of ice.

Boys and girls would come racing down the hill and onto the ice. There they would glide at speed to the bottom depending on their skills.

"Off the ice Maggie," Would come the warning cry to anyone still on the slide as others were approaching. There was many the accident when some fool tried to be clever and stop others who were travelling down at high speed.

Others would fail to stay on their feet and go down on their backsides. Tearing off what patches there were on their trousers in the process. There were more bare arses seen on a frosty night on the slides than there were stars in the sky. Mother's would have a busy night replacing the patches ready for school next day.

Girls were be in a better position with their strong linen knickers made from Rank flour sacks. Sometimes these too would come adrift, especially if the elastic broke. The girls would depart holding on to their knickers in embarrassment.

We were so proficient at the slide that we would place objects in our paths and pick them up as we raced past. It was nothing short of miraculous to witness boys in their bare feet slide down the ice. The soles of their feet must have been as hard as horses' hooves. They were an added bonus to the slide as their feet polished the surface.

Anyone with studs on the soles of his boots was immediately barred from the slide. These scratched the ice and damaged the slide. Whenever this happened it was soon repaired with a wet brush. When the guards came on the scene we would make a hasty retreat until they had passed.

When the screaming got beyond the endurance of some of the neighbours they would warn us to keep quiet or else get off home.

At the bottom of the hill a coal and coke merchant carried out his business. As it was the war years he mostly sold logs, cinders and turf. There were evenings when on his return from the city after trying to make an honest copper he would be confronted by us.

"Scuttering kids. Damn and blast it. Do you want to take the feet from under my ass?" The irate man would jump off his cart to check the asses progress around the slide.

Most times the asses feet would be covered in hessian sacking as would the wheels of the cart to prevent them sliding. When he didn't have this protection he would curse and swear at us. We would try to defend our slide.

"You can easily go round Ballynanty Mister. The road is clear there you know." We would try to be helpful and at the same time divert him away from the slide.

"I won't bother me arse going around Ballynanty if you don't mind. Indeed why should I and me a business man?" He would try to guide the donkey down the hill. The donkey being the more intelligent of the two would stubbornly refuse to budge.

"The ass has better sense than you mister," we would chide him.

"You keep a civil tongue in you head you little fart or I'll be the death of you." Letting go of the reins he would charge into the crowd only to land on his backside. When this happened that he would turn the air blue with his language.

"If you leave our slide alone, we will help you to get the cart home Mister." Would come a compromise.

"I don't know why I give in to you kids anyway. You should be home doing your homework if you must know." He would allow some of us to accompany him home round the longer route. Holding on to the cart and ass we would guide them home safely.

There were times when the gathering got too large and the shouting too noisy. It then some spoil sport would put salt on the slide. This would melt the ice and ruin our fun. Some of the parents were worse than the children, as they tried their luck on the slide.

"God Mary It's ages since I tried this. I must have a go." Down the slide would race one of the mothers. Should she reach the bottom safely she would run to her door laughing and giggling like a schoolgirl.

"I never had such fun. What if my Sean came home and saw me now? Whatever would he think"? She would giggle as she stood in the jamb of her door with the neighbours.

Others would venture on to the slide only to lose their nerve and slide ungraciously to the bottom. There was many the one in trying to hold her skirt down to protect her modesty landed with more bruises than were necessary.

The women took it all in good fun. The men would feel really embarrassed should they fall, especially if the women or their children were watching.

This was one of our many sports and harmless fun. It was enjoyed by both the young and the old of the parish.

REMEMBER THE GHOSTS OF LIMERICK

Another story as told by my Uncle Gerald.

In was on a cold day on the sixth of December in the year of 1921 that Britain created the Irish Free State. A truculent treaty was imposed on the delegation sent to Downing Street. It was so worded as to serve the interests of England. Ireland would not be free of the fetters of the crown.

The delegation sent to England had no mandate to sign any treaty. Their task was to listen to what terms the British had to offer and bring them back to Dublin for consideration of the provisional government. England was well aware of this. Yet she blatantly demanded they sign their agreement at once or face all out war.

Irishmen, women and children had suffered and died in the cause for a united and free thirty two counties Ireland. They waited in trepidation for any news that would bring peace. The treaty was supposed to give sovereign power to the Irish people over all Ireland. Those who without authorisation signed the treaty were duped by the small print.

Ireland would not be granted the same status as the other members of the commonwealth. There was one very important let out for six of the counties of Ulster. They would be allowed to opt out of a united Ireland at the end of six months if they so wished by voting to do so. England had divided Ireland with a stroke of a pen.

Then they twisted the knife by demanding an oath of allegiance to the British crown....

It read as follows....

I do solemnly swear true faith and allegiance to the constitution of the Irish Free State as established by law

Further that I will be faithful to his majesty King George the Fifth, his heirs and successors by law, in virtue of the common citizenship of Ireland.

With Great Britain, and her adherence to and membership of the group of nations forming the British Commonwealth of Nations.

Et Tu Brutae

Ireland was not being given her freedom and no true republican could swear this oath. Michael Collins who was one of the signatories remarked after he signed it *"I have signed my own death warrant"*. Britain was aware of the reception such a treaty would receive when it was disclosed to the people.

Ireland was on the verge of a bloody civil war. The country was divided between those who rejected the treaty and those who signed it. Two opposing armies faced each other.

Families were divided as brothers took sides. Irish households were in turmoil. Comrades who fought the British in the hills and streets were now sworn enemies. Catholics in the six counties who once lived peacefully beside their Protestant neighbours were hounded out of their homes. Thousands were fleeing south for protection from the 'B' specials, a murderous army created by the newly formed government of Sir James Craig. In June of 1922 Field Marshal Sir Henry Wilson a security adviser to the Unionists was shot dead in London by two members of the IRA They were captured and condemned to the gallows.

England demanded that the Free State take action. Michael Collins tried to save the lives of his former companions without success. He capitulated and executed both men. England threatened once again to invade Ireland and tear up the treaty unless the IRA were wiped out.

To appease the English, Michael Collins gave the IRA twenty minutes to surrender the Four Courts to him. When they refused he borrowed two field guns from the English and began to bombard his former comrades.

A bloody civil war took to the streets of Ireland. England had once again won the day. Most of the country was in the hands of the Irish Republican Army. The Free State army was unable to challenge them. They did not have the firepower. England came to their rescue and gave the Free State an extra ten thousand rifles and ammunition. She then stood by and watched them kill each other in a bloody and bitter civil war.

They armed the Protestants in the north with a million rifles. They were ready and willing to move south, should the republicans show signs of winning. The situation was desperate for the republicans. Collins found that he could not with all this extra firepower, take the south of Ireland by land and so with the help once again of England he invaded Cork, his native city, by sea.

Michael Collins was to die in August of that year shot by his former comrades in a gully named *Beal-na-Blath* (Mouth of the blossom) outside the town of Macroom.

In 1924 the Free State government approached the English government and asked them to ratify the treaty. England now had a problem on her hands. Should she honour the treaty to the letter and start another civil war between the Protestants in Ulster and the Catholics in the South or manipulate the wording to appease the north? Sir James Craig who was now the Prime Minister of a newly formed Northern Ireland Government refused to attend any meetings dealing with Ireland. He was not a signatory to the treaty so why should be accept it.

Large areas of Tyrone, Fermanagh, Derry, Down and Armagh wanted in accordance with the treaty, to be incorporated into the Free State. There were a few isolated areas in East Donegal and North Monaghan who wanted to go into the North. There would be no free vote by the peoples of Ireland. England was well aware what the outcome would be. A vote would favour of a United Ireland. If Ireland were allowed to go her own way there was little doubt but that the empire would follow.

The empire on which the sun never set would slowly disintegrate as other nations were bound to followed where Ireland led. This would not be allowed to happen. A newly formed commission was set up by the English government of the day. It alone would decide the fate of Ireland. It was a foregone conclusion what the outcome would be.

With a few sweeteners from the English government the Free State government of the day ratified the amended treaty. A treaty that was to sow the seeds of a bitter civil war that exists to this day in the six north eastern counties of Ireland.

Perhaps the ghosts from the violated city of Limerick now walk the streets of the six northern counties of Ireland.

Remember Limerick, the city of the violated treaty.

THE DAY I WENT TO LIMBO.

(Limbo we were taught in our religious lessons was where the souls of the saints who died before Christ were living. Also sent there were all the babies who died without receiving baptism. [Catholic babies of course] There they would remain suspended in apprehensive animation until the final judgement day.)

Seeing the cans of various sizes and shapes being gathered up. I knew that it was blackberry picking time again. Bruno my faithful dog, sat at my feet wagging his stumpy tail. That dog had more foresight that the seers of old.

Mary, my second eldest sister was in the scullery. She was scraping a licking of margarine on a few slices of bread. This would be our lunch, dinner and tea.

Mother would not accompanying us on this occasion. She had an appointment with Angelene's mother. I wanted to remain with her but not for her company. I knew that the mother hen would bring Angelene with her.

"You stay here and Mary calling? Are you serious? There's no fear of that. We know what trouble you caused last time." Mother remembered only too well, but that's another story yet to be unfolded.

"You don't need me do you Mary?" I pleaded with my sister. She would have none of it.

"You'll come whether you like it or not. You cannot be trusted on your own so get ready." She had no more understanding of my feelings than mother had.

It was one of those sultry days. A lazy day that one usually associates with late August. The sun was obliterated behind a thin veil of cloud. There was dew on the grass in the front garden of our house. I knew that the blackberry bushes would be covered in *Devil Spit* and *Fairy Shrouds. (Spider webs)* These were not at all to my liking. In parts of Ireland bushes with *Devil Spit* on them were to be avoided. It was said in hushed voices that the Devil himself had been at them. The other members of the family took no notice of this but I did. I never wanted to tempt faith. I promised myself that I would put a few with the *Devil Spit* on them in Mary's can in revenge for making me come.

Our route was to take us to the other side of the city, through Rosbrien and on to our destination at the Whitegates. Why my family insisted on travelling all that distance for a few blackberries I never understood. In the old cemetery of Killeely there were blackberries the size of plums for the taking.

"Good God! What next! Robbing the dead. I never heard the likes." Mother blessed herself and gave me that knowing look when I innocently suggested it.

I kept my thoughts to myself after that look. To suggest such a sacrilege once was tempting faith. To suggest it twice was asking for a good chastisement with the cane. I went to the threshold and began to play with a few marbles as I waited.

The door opened to the noise of rattling tin sweet cans. Bruno began to jump up and down barking in his excitement. I rose reluctantly to my feet and was given a tin can. Bruno took one look at the closed gate. Then with a well judged eye he backed off a few steps. With the speed of a gazelle he charged the gate and vaulted it like the thoroughbred that he was. I was really proud of my dog.

"Will you try for once to control that flea bitten mutt." Brendan took a swipe with his can at my dog.

Some time later we were in the boreens of county Limerick. Mary scouted around until she found a field rich in blackberries. We vaulted the gate and like a plague of locust we descended on the bushes of ripe blackberries.

Blackbirds, Thrushes, Robins and Wrens, all trying to fatten themselves in preparation for the coming winter scattered on hearing us shouting.

When I saw my sister Phyllis sneaking the odd blackberry into her mouth I wondered. Would she get the runs again as she had the day we went blackberry picking with Angelene?

I wandered down the field and walked straight into a pile of skutter recently dropped by a cow. In doing so I disturbed a flight of horseflies that were feasting on it. In their annoyance they stung Bruno and me. I looked down at my arm and saw a cheeky horsefly with his proboscis plunged deep into my arm sucking up my blood. With a swift movement I splattered him to kingdom come. He would bite no more. Going to the hedgerow I found what I was looking for, *a dog leaf.* This I rubbed on the wound to stop it itching. The juices from the leaf would neutralise the sting. This was another cure we learnt from mother. Perhaps she was a reincarnation of Asclepias, the God of healing and son of Apollo. Mother had a good cure for constipation and that was to eat the stems of dandelion flowers or suck the white sap from them. Just thought I'd mention it in case anyone was having problems.

I could not rub the dog leaf on Bruno, not with all the hair he had. He did not seem to be worried as he ran across to the stone wall and began studying something.

Crossing over to his side I noted that he had cornered a large hedgehog.

"Bruno leave him alone. He's covered in fleas." He looked up into my eyes. Then back at the hedgehog. As he could neither make head nor tail of this strange animal he trotted after me. Occasionally he looked round to see what the hedgehog was doing.

As I reached a small spinney I noted a long run of wild strawberries growing along the stone wall. These I would collect and keep secret. They would make a nice surprise and treat for Ma.

Having collected all the ripe berries I moved further down the field searching for more. Then I came across a bush of purple round berries. I was tempted by their colour and decided to try one. Not too bad I thought and continued to eat the ripest. I put some in with the wild strawberries. I knew that mother would appreciate them. Then I heard my sister calling me. It was time for lunch.

She gave us a slice of bread each and a swig of milk from the lid of the can. I spread some blackberries on my bread and began to eat them. I became dizzy and began to see large blue, black, green and yellow spots. They kept bursting before my eyes and dispersing. Only to appear and reappear over and over again. I shook my head trying to clear it without success. They began to come at me quicker and quicker. The field spun one way then the other. Faster and faster it spun taking me with it. A long black funnel came towards me and sucked me inside. What was happening to me? Then came a powerful flashing light that burst into a crescendo of sound and colour. I wanted to pray but was constantly interrupted by the flashing coloured lights and noise. My ears felt as if they were about to explode. I was floating out into space. The earth spun faster and faster below me. I felt my stomach retch and heave. Someone was calling and crying. I could not see who they were. I reached out to them. Something or someone was dragging me away from them to a place where I did not want to go. The place was dark and foreboding. Constant flashing and bursting lights hurt my eyes. I had to try and escape but I could not. I was being slowly sucked into the abyss. I knew that I was on my way to *Limbo*. Mother would not be able to get her strawberries there. Message flashed through my young mind. I struggled and fought to return to earth but the magnetic pull was too great.

I was now well and truly within the black hole. There would be no redemption until the end of time. Would mother miss me and who would take care of Bruno and Cibby Eye lashes? It was all too late now. I bid good bye to the world. All went black.

I awoke to find that a monster was grabbing my mouth and forcing it open. He was trying to steal my soul from my mortal body. I resisted but he stuck a long stick down my throat and began to probe inside my body. My soul being invisible was safe from his searching. Feeling the stick probing in my stomach my whole body convulsed and I got sick. This did not stop the demon. It only encouraged him further. He kept throwing coloured balls at my eyes to confuse me. They exploded in a rainbow of myriad coloured stars. Confusing me and causing me intense pain. My eyes were being pulled from their sockets and my ears were being beaten with drumsticks. The pain and the noise was disorienting me.

Still I resisted. He would not get my immortal soul. It was all I had left now that he had stolen my body. Slowly I floated off into space. I was now in *Limbo*. I floated around peacefully. Where were all the other boys and girls who had been sent there? I was alone, the only soul waiting judgement day. Perhaps it had passed and I was overlooked. Would God take pity on me and come back for my soul? Questions without answers raced through my troubled mind. I didn't want to be alone. I wanted to be with all the others in paradise.

The gates were flung open and the demon again attacked me. He was determined to gain my soul. I called to my dog but he was not there. Then I realised that dogs don't go to Limbo. The demon knew this and continued his attack. He was now forcing a burning liquid inside me. My whole body ached and heaved as it rejected the foul taste. It burnt my stomach, the demon laughed. Then I heard him speak in tongues to other devils. I wanted to cry out to my God that I was sorry for all my sins. I tried crying out for his help but he had deserted me.

Where was my faithful dog, Bruno? I tried to call on him for help. He must have been eaten by, the giant hedgehog. No! Not my dog! He was safely back on earth. Again I was held in a vice like grip by the monster. More foul hot liquid forced down my throat. Once again my stomach rejected it and I vomited. The monster laughed all the more. Would my agony ever end? I knew now how Christ must have felt in the garden of Gethsemane. I was being held down and a wet blindfold was being put over my eyes, I must resist. Was this how my life was to end? Trussed up like a turkey and left floating forever and ever in space. I would rather be dead. I could not die. Was not my soul immortal and could never die?

I cried to God, one last time, surely he would hear my plea. I forced my eyes open and looking up saw the blue sky.

I thanked God, he had heard my plea and been good to my soul. I reached out and felt the green grass of old Ireland. I had returned from hell and beaten the Devil himself so I had.

"Are you alright? Lie still." I looked up at a worried face above me. It was the face of an old man. Perhaps it was St Peter.

"Feeling a bit better son are you? God help you." I knew now that this could not be St Peter.

I reached up and felt my forehead and found that it was covered in a damp cloth. Had the Devil left the cloth behind him? I thought.

What had happened to me? I looked in puzzlement at the old man. Was he a fairy King who had now taken me to *Tir-na-nÓg*? No matter; I was glad to be back in the field again. I tried to rise to my feet but I was too weak.

"Lie still. You'll soon be alright Louie." My eldest sister came and looked down at me. She was crying and praying at the same time. How did she get into Limbo I thought. Perhaps God let her in to look after her little brother.

I was lifted on to a bed of clean straw in the back of an ass and cart. The old man took the drivers seat and Mary sat beside him. Soon we were back home in our own house. There I was removed from the cart and put to bed.

Although I told mother that I felt better she insisted that Doctor Holmes be sent for.

I told the doctor when he came that I felt really good. I did not know what to tell him. There was no need for he had the answer.

"You are a lucky boy to be here today. Whatever possessed you to eat them. Have you not got the sense that you were born with?" He looked down at me but he was not really cross.

"You can thank God that the farmer had the sense to see what had happened and put his fingers down your throat. Otherwise you would be lying on a slab now. The salted water was a blessing for it flushed out the poison. You owe your life to that man." He looked down at me and I saw a smile on his face. He was glad that I was alive.

"Don't you know what Deadly Night Shade is when you see it"?

"Jesus help us all. Did you say Deadly Night Shade doctor? What sort of an amadan are you anyway?" Mother interrupted and looked from me to the doctor.

"Oh no! Not you doctor! Him! It's always him and that dog of his. Drive me to an early grave they will between them." Bruno lying under my bed moved to the far side of the bed on hearing mother.

"You have more lives than that cat of yours. Someone must be watching and praying for you." I guess that she was glad after all to have me back. Bad and all as I was.

I had not been fighting a demon as I thought. In my traumatic delirium I was resisting the good Samaritan in the guise of the farmer.

Deo Volente. Things were back to normal in our household, only this time my tears on my pillow were tears of relief.

THE DROWNING AT ROSMADDA MILL

It all came about on a sultry day in mid July. My brothers and myself with our dogs and pals set out for the swimming pool at *Plassey*. On the way we were joined by *Bully Benn* a close friend.

"Never mind *Plassey*, the place will be swarming with women and children. We should go out to the Pike." He suggested.

"Ok then, the Pike it is." My brother Frank agreed on behalf of his brothers. I had no say in the matter.

Off we went down Athlunkard Street and on out Corbally. It's a long stretch of the feet from Limerick to Corbally and more so when one had to watch the dogs. The farmers had a bad habit of placing poisoned meat in the fields to protect their animals. Should the dogs eat it then that would be the end of them. Reluctantly I kept the lead on my dog. I explained to him the reason why I was forced to take these draconian measures. I'm sure he understood .

"We'll drop into the sweet shop and buy a few sweets and lemonade." The sweet shop was the old Toll house at the end of the *Pike Bridge* that was used in the past to collect the toll money to repay the cost owed to Limerick Corporation for its construction. Although the sweet shop has long since closed I believe that the *Lahiff* family who ran it still live there.

Having purchased what sweets and minerals that our meagre resources allowed we retraced our steps and went down the long stone steps leading to the banks of the river Blackwater.

"Away you go, Bruno." I released my dog. Barking and jumping he was off along the bank.

"That dog of yours has 'Rats' on the brain." Brendan remarked on seeing him searching every hole on the bank.

I had to be careful and stop him from entering the ruins of what remained of the Rosmadda Mill. This was a dangerous place for man and beast.

We found a sandy cove at Corbally near the Lax Weir. In the centre of the river lies Saint Thomas's Island and nearer to the shore but still some distance away is *The Liberty Stone,* the tip of an island that has long since sunk beneath the waves.

"This is what we were looking for. Last one in is a sissy." Bully Benn pulled his braces from his shoulders and stepped out of his trousers. Donning a pair of home made trunks he entered the river.

"Oh my God, it's freezing." He called, as he stood undecided up to his knees in the river.

"Dive in, then you'll not feel the cold." Joseph encouraged him.

Soon we were all in the river including our dogs. One was trying to outdo the other by showing off their skills.

There were a few scuttled sand cots in the river and we used these as diving boards. Bully told me that the big Pike lurked in the sand of the River Bed and would jump out and bite the toes off the swimmers. I ignored this scary remark.

We swam around in the river for some considerable time. As the day wore on the sun began sinking and a chill came over the water. It was time to pack up and make for home. We did not have towels to dry ourselves in those days. The only way to dry out was to run briskly up and down the bank.

When we reached Parteen we followed the tail race to the Point.

"I'm going in for another dip if anyone cares to come. Then I'm going to cross to the island." Bully challenged.

"If you want to freeze to death then go ahead." Frank who was wrapped up in his shirt remarked.

Bully plunged into the water and began the long swim. As he reached the metal bridge we realised that he had caught cramp. Slowly and deliberately he sank beneath the surface. He didn't make a sound. He just vanished.

"Come on get him out quick." Patrick jumped into the river and slowly but surely with the help of Frank got him to the cove.

"I think he's dead." I looked down at the blue lips and the ashen face of Bully.

"He can't be dead, he was swimming up to a minute ago." Brendan began to panic.

"He's dead alright, look at his purple lips. I saw a body like that once in the Shannon." I told them.

"What can we do now?" Panic set in as we looked down at the still body of our pal.

"We'll say the act of contrition for his soul and then carry his body home, what will his father say?" Patrick led the prayer.

"Louie, you run on along the bank and see if you can get some help." I was instructed.

It was dusk and darkness was approaching fast.

I ran on to the bank accompanied by my dog. At the stile I stopped and waited. I saw the gang coming along the bank. Patrick had Bully over his shoulder and Frank was holding his legs up.

"There's nobody about, what are we going to do. Is he really dead, can I have a look?" I asked.

"Of course he's dead. Now hurry up and get his parents will you."

Off I raced again along the bank to Bully's parents home. Once there I spluttered out the sad news that their son was being carried home dead by my brothers. At first they refused to believe me. Then in a panic they took off and I followed.

I was more than shocked to come across my brothers running along the bank screaming that they were being chased by a ghost. I looked after them wondering if the ghost of the *Long pavement* had moved from one bank to the other.

I stood for a moment longer I looking puzzled as they continued their flight along the bank. Then I saw the ghost and was off down the bank like a hare before the hounds. The ghost was catching up with me fast and I was glad to come in contact with Bully's parents coming in the opposite direction.

"Oh Benn! Benn, my son. Thank God you are safe and well." I stopped and looking around I saw the ghost embracing Bully's parents.

"Come here you little caffler, what made you tell such a wicked story." His father caught me and wrung me like a chastised dog.

"Honest Sir, we believed he was dead. He turned blue like a corpse." I tried to explain.

Bully, fair play to him came to my rescue. He explained how he fainted in the cold water and how we saved his life. He could not understand why we were running away from him as he had done nothing wrong.

The guards came on the scene, having been told that a person had drowned at the Long Pavement. Bully, explained as best he could what had happened. He could not however explain how he came to be lying on the River Bank so far from the Point.

Patrick was asked for his explanation of events leading up to the reported drowning. He told them of how we saw Bully drown and that I told him what a dead body looked like and they believed me. He was carrying the body home when he heard moaning. He dropped the body believing that Bully's ghost was leaving his body.

His parents were advised to take him to *Barrington's hospital* for a check up. It was explained to all and sundry that the dead had not risen. The cold it seemed had reduced the temperature of his blood and there was water in his lungs or something like that. With the heat from Patrick's body and the jolting on his shoulder Bully had come round.

When mother heard the story she wanted to know what fool imagined that he was dead. Worst still who told his parents such a wicked story.

"It was Louie who said he was dead and then he ran off and told his parents." They betrayed me like Judas betrayed Jesus.

"I might have known, was his dog with him? God in heaven whatever next?" Raising her hands to heaven she invoked God's help in coping with her son. Me!

THE TATTERED CAT

The sun was hopping off the stones that Saturday morning as I set out for drawing lessons at Sexton Street College. I had no dread of the Black Strap for our art teacher was never known to raise his voice in anger less alone use the Black Strap.

Some twelve months previous we were informed that an additional subject would be added to our curriculum. As there was no time available during the week we would have to attend on Saturday mornings. This I can assure the reader did not go down too well. What leisure time we had was being further curtailed. As we arrived in the classroom each pupil was given a drawing or sketchbook and a box of pencils. A young Brother entered the classroom and under his arm he carried a tattered mummified cat.

"Good morning boys, he smiled as he placed the cat on the table. We looked at the cat and then at him in that order.

"Good morning, Brother," We replied as we sniggered and nudged each other. There were no morning prayers as he set about the task in hand.

"It must be Henry Iretons cat that he found," I whispered to my mate.

('Henry Ireton {1611-1651} was an English General. In 1642 he joined the parliamentary forces and fought at Edgehill in 1642. He fought at Gainsborough in 1643 and at Nasby in 1645. He married the daughter of Oliver Cromwell in 1646.

In1650 he was sent to Ireland where he became Lord-Deputy and settled in Limerick. He had a lucky cat of which he was very possessive and proud. He considered it to be a lucky mascot. The cat died under mysterious circumstances. Some say the cat drank poison meant for him.

He had the cat buried, some say with full honours in the grounds of Saint Mary's Cathedral. That has never been confirmed. Where the cat was buried remained a mystery, that was until it turned up in our classroom, or so I claimed.)

The good Brother produced drawings and sketches from the hands of the great masters and assured us that such work was not beyond our capabilities. We could become great artists and painters with a little training and perseverance.

"My Dad is a painter, he paints the town every Saturday night when he gets the few bob," A smart arse remarked.

"Our first effort will to draw this simple cat," he patted the mangy specimen on the head. I looked out at the sunshine beckoning me to come out and play. The birds were singing in the trees, the countryside was alive. "What am I doing in this God forsaken place?" I groaned.

"Draw the body first." He drew a neat oval shape on the blackboard in white chalk, then followed the head and tail and soon he had completed the drawing of the cat.

I made the effort to draw the likeness of the cat. I drew big circles and small circles on top. Two ears and a few whiskers followed, I looked at it. Well not too bad considering!

"Don't try so hard, take a little time to think, then try again." Were my ears deceiving me? Was this a Christian Brother standing over me encouraging me to make the effort. Usually school opened with the brother sweeping into the room, taking out his beads and we coming to our feet to answer the prayers in unison. Then the Black Strap came to the fore belting the desk. This to remind us what to expect should we upset him. Not so, this gentleman, he was compassionate and we wanted to please him. He was over generous when he told me that my drawing of the cat was to say the least- "Well not too bad but requiring working on." I drew that bloody cat over and over again and always with the same result.

"You are improving, keep up the good work." He would encourage me. Weeks went into months and as the other pupils progressed I was still struggling with my cat.

Autumn came and by now I had given up all hope of drawing the cat. I sat every Saturday morning drawing an apple. He would bring an apple from the orchard for us to draw. Whoever drew the apple best was given it as a reward. I never got an apple until one day he brought in an extra one and gave it to me for my effort or was it perseverance?

I still remember the beautiful historical map of Ireland he drew and his sketches. These he would bring to the classroom and ask for our opinion.

One Saturday morning he came into the classroom and stood with his head bowed. We thought that he was saying a silent prayer. Lifting his head he studied us for some time. We could see that all was not well with him. He began to walk up and down the floor in an agitated state. He tried several times to address us but was unable to. Finally he stood beside the many articles which we were supposed to be drawing and addressed us.

"Boys, this is the last lesson I'll give to you. There will be no more drawing lessons on Saturdays, you will no doubt be glad to hear. I'm leaving for pastures new and I would like to thank you for tolerating me and for all you tried to achieve. Some of you will make it, others I fear have not got the talent." He looked at me and smiled.

"Now let us say a short prayer and then you can all go home." Taking his beads from his pocket he faced the huge statue and with tears in his eyes opened with 'The Hail Mary.'

With the prayers completed he returned to his desk and began collecting up the various objects including that bloody cat. The pupils looked at him in silence. It was all so solemn and silent, you could hear a pin drop, everyone was sad. Even the tattered cat looked miserable. This was a strange reaction, usually we would be over the moon to be told that we could go home.

No longer would I have to try and draw that stupid cat. Why could I not do it if only to please this gentleman. I was sorry that I let him down and was finding it a heavy burden to carry, he sat with his head bowed for some time. The silence was electric. I knew that many were now feeling sorry for the times that they stole his apple and I was no exception. If I had my way I would go into Limerick and buy him the biggest apple tart in the Bakers shop. Alas! I was as poor as a Church mouse and it was all but wishful pipe dreaming. In his presence I had all but forgotten about the dreaded *'Black Strap'* and my miserable days in school. We had respect for this teacher. He understood our problems. He was and always will be one of us.

As I was wondering as to how I could compensate him for all he done for me I heard him calling my name. I looked up and slowly came forward to the head of the class. I rested my hand on his desk but I did not look at him.

"Don't worry, I'm not about to scold you. I know that you tried ever so hard to draw Ireton, the cat and yes I know that it was you who christened him. I was thinking thought, would you ever let me have your sketch book"? He half smiled.

"Of course Sir, there are plenty of empty pages left." I was relieved.

"That is not the reason for me wanting it. I often watched you looking out of the window dreaming of running through the fields, no doubt. If I had my way I would have let you run free, but the decision was not mine to make. You can from now on do all the running and racing that your heart desires." With these words he dismissed me. I could not believe that a Christian Brother was actually apologising to me. Slowly but deliberately he picked up his accoutrements and again looked at us.

"God bless and hold you in his keeping, remember me in your prayers." Crossing the floor he lifted the brass latch and like a ghost vanished from us forever.

I cannot remember his name but I cherish his care and devotion to his vocation and his pupils. Why he left the college I never knew, nor will I ever know where he went to. I'll always remember the gentleman with the tattered cat and hope that when he died that they buried that blasted Tattered cat named Henry Ireton with him.

Epilogue

I have now finished writing another chapter relating to my life and adventures. I hope the reader will bear with me. I have little doubt that there will be a posthumous examination of all that I have written to date.

There are chapters that not as pellucid as one would expect and for these I crave your indulgence. It could be argued that time has obliterated some of my memories.

I would like to believe that my autobiography was in the style of Lucianus. That I fear would be too ambitious or conceited.

It is not prejudicially written and I have no doubt but the reader will appreciate this. I am narcissistic enough to think that the reader will understand what it was like growing up in a war situation. I tell the stories warts and all.

My story relates very little to the Limerick of today. The comparison between my Limerick and the Limerick I wandered through as a child is but a passage from history. The reader will be hard pressed to find any semblance to my Limerick in todays thriving city. When I was a boy a seagull could make her nest in the middle of O'Connell Street and not be disturbed. Today one takes their life in their hands when crossing the same street.

This is a great achievement and a credit to my city and its citizens. These adventures could be the adventures of thousands of children throughout Ireland.

In appreciation I humbly dedicate this my autobiography to my wife Bridget who was so tolerant and understanding throughout my research and writing.

To my five sons who helped me through times of despair and frustration with their constructive criticism and encouragement.

To Arlene Duff my niece, and her husband Michael from Canada

To my two fellow scribblers Joe Hennessy and Maureen Sparling a special thanks for all your help

To you the reader who bought my books and so made it possible for me to continue writing.

MY THANKS!

P.S. I hope you will stay with me as I continue on my journey through life.